THE LIVING LAND

AN ACCOUNT OF THE NATURAL RESOURCES OF

the living land

BRITISH COLUMBIA

RODERICK HAIG-BROWN

PRODUCED BY
THE BRITISH COLUMBIA
NATURAL RESOURCES CONFERENCE

PUBLISHED BY
THE MACMILLAN COMPANY OF CANADA LIMITED
TORONTO
1961

This book has been designed by Robert R. Reid and printed and bound in its entirety by Evergreen Press Limited, Vancouver. The text, set in Intertype Cornell, is printed on paper made especially for the book by Island Paper Mills, and is the first book to be printed on paper made in British Columbia.

PRINTED IN CANADA

preface

THE British Columbia Natural Resources Conference is the producer of this volume, which was originated, written, illustrated and printed in British Columbia. The book is intended to stimulate the thinking of British Columbians about the proper use of their rich inheritance of natural resources. It is hoped, also, that the book will serve to advance the cause and the philosophy of conservation among the peoples of the world.

The British Columbia Natural Resources Conference, now completing its fourteenth year, is an independent, non-profit organization devoted to objective study of the natural resources of British Columbia. Both the Executive Council and the membership of the Conference are drawn from university, government at all levels, and industry, both labour and management.

Each year the papers and discussions offered at the annual Conference sessions are edited, printed and distributed as Transactions. In the dozen volumes published to date can be found comprehensive and authoritative data on the natural resources of the province; inventory of resources, status, problems, administration, management and research are covered with varying emphasis each year, according to the Conference theme. In 1956 the *British Columbia Atlas of Resources* was printed and sold – the first such comprehensive natural resources atlas ever published for a province or state.

Because the *British Columbia Atlas of Resources* was eagerly accepted by the public the Conference decided to produce a book as a companion volume. It was believed that a non-technical account of the past, present and provident future uses of the natural resources of British Columbia would serve several purposes – complement the *Atlas*, provide an easily read account of British Columbia's natural resources, and in some measure provide a "geography" of the province to place beside books on the "literature" and history of the province published in 1958 during the province's centennial year.

In 1959, the Executive of the British Columbia Natural Resources Conference commissioned Roderick L. Haig-Brown, author, naturalist and magistrate, Campbell River, B.C., to write the book, based on the findings of the Conference over the past twelve years. This, *The Living Land,* is his book, in the interpretive style of a professional author. His editorializing makes for provocative reading which should kindle, among all men and women of to-day and tomorrow, a lively and serious interest in the care and management of their most precious possession – the earth with the natural resources in, on, and about it.

The designer of the volume, Robert R. Reid, Vancouver, was also commissioned by the Executive. It was his function, so to speak, to compose the music for the lyrics of the author. Mr. Reid's chief assistants in the artistic production of the volume were Thomas Brayshaw, Hope, B.C., and Keith C. Smith, Haney, B.C. As with the author, Mr. Reid was given a free hand and so, in design and typography, this is his book.

In the preparation of the book, the Executive Members of the British Columbia Natural Resources Conference, both present and past, have been freely consulted by both author and designer.

BRITISH COLUMBIA
NATURAL RESOURCES CONFERENCE

author's foreword

IT GOES WITHOUT SAYING that a book of this scope is beyond the competence of one man working alone. I have been constantly dependent upon the advice and assistance of the standing committees for the various resources set up under the B.C. Natural Resources Conference. Their advice and assistance has been rendered not merely generously and conscientiously, but with the utmost regard for my own responsibilities as sole author. I have been further guided, helped and encouraged at all stages of the work by Dr. D. B. Turner, secretary and founder of the Conference.

My purpose has been to produce a popular account of the natural resources of British Columbia and their management, so far as possible within the ideals and concepts that have been gradually developed through the years of the Conference's activities. To some extent this has restrained my strong predilection for sharp comment, broad generalizations and contentious ideas, but the reader will find that I have not always been restrained. I am happy to take full responsibility for the book as it stands, for the ideas expressed in it and values assessed; wherever my voluntary restraint has tempered my judgements I am satisfied that it has placed them in sounder accord with the available facts.

Because the book is designed as a popular account I have avoided footnotes and precise references. The book is designed to be read rather than studied and its purpose is to give the ordinary man and woman a clear idea of the resources themselves, their interrelationships and the difficulties and responsibilities that proper use and management entail. My chief references have been the B.C. Natural Resources Conference *Atlas* (1956) and the twelve volumes of *Transactions* that have been published to date, especially Volume IX (the *Inventory*, 1956) and the three volumes following it. Other major references have been the *B.C. Continuous Forest*

Inventory (1937) and *Geology and Economic Minerals of Canada* edited by C. H. Stockwell (1957).

This book is dedicated to British Columbia, the people who live there now and those who will come after. I hope it also expresses my respect and admiration for the devotion and intellectual integrity of the many men and women who have contributed to the B.C. Resources Conference over the years, as well as my feelings of companionship with them and friendship for them. I believe that the Conference's unique combination of government, university, industry and labour, its emphasis on inquiry and mutual education, on the examination of problems and the posing of questions rather than attempting hasty solutions, is a useful and constructive pattern of human relationship that has application in many other fields.

R. H. B.

November 1960

contents

illustrations in colour

PART I. THE FRAME OF THE LAND

a brief history to begin   CHAPTER 1

IMMENSE NATURAL RESOURCES – vast natural wealth – inexhaustible natural resources – these phrases and many others like them have been used about practically every geographical and political division in North America. They have long been the treasured toys of promoters and boomers and boosters, the happy playthings of politicians, the sad and doubtful comfort of struggling settlers and ordinary working people. Like other good phrases, excessively used and abused, they have become fogged in meaning, remote from reality, suggesting only some vague form of future wealth that may be realized if certain things happen; something that ought to be looked after and probably is not being; something that ought to benefit everyone and probably will benefit few.

Just over a hundred years ago, Queen Victoria referred to her new colony of British Columbia as "certain wild and unoccupied Territories on the Northwest coast of North America". Only a few years later Dr. Helmcken was in Ottawa telling the Fathers of Confederation of "our mineral resources–gold, silver, lumber, coal" and "of the myriads of salmon – that they could be thrown on shore by hand in many places." This makes him one of the first important boosters of the province's natural resources and he met with a fairly standard reaction: "They were polite enough to listen. But ever after when I said anything remarkable to them about B.C. they would say: Oh! Here is another of Helmcken's great fish stories." But "one called B.C. New Canada and supposed it would one day become a most important province." Sir George Cartier, then acting head of the government, went still further: "Lower Canada and British Columbia will be the most important parts of Canada. British Columbia has a great commercial future."

Since that time British Columbia's resources have been developed, exploited, depleted and, in some instances, built back; some are still under-developed, some have not yet been developed at all. This also has been a standard pattern in most areas of

The first resource to be trapped, fur, resulted in the near extinction of the sea otter. Subsequently protected from hunters, it is now making a slow recovery in the Aleutian Islands.

North America and calls for a short examination. Natural resources do not have an absolute value, like gold in the bank, callable at any time. They have different values at different times and under different conditions of accessibility and markets. The first settler finds the forest an enemy against which he must struggle to win a few acres of ground for his agriculture; he may even burn it away to make grazing land for his beasts. To the later settler that same forest would have had a value many times greater than all the farm yield of the land. Yet its destruction was an inevitable stage in development. Without the first settler's beach-head of agriculture, the second settler would never have survived to realize the value of forests still untouched.

The first resources used in British Columbia by white people were fur and people – the fur of the sea otter and the native peoples to hunt them. It was a rewarding trade, with ready markets in China, and developed rapidly during the last fifteen years of the eighteenth century. During that time the long coastline was opened and explored. A few years later the sea otter was practically extinct and the trade was finished. It was the perfect example of how not to use a resource – utterly uncontrolled exploitation to the point of destruction. Yet without the inducement of the sea otter, the coast would certainly have remained for many more years unsurveyed and little known.

The fur trade also built the first settlements of the interior of the province. It was beaver this time, an utterly ruthless exploitation of them at first by the North West Company, then by the Hudson's Bay Company. In a hundred and fifty years and the width of a continent, the Hudson's Bay Company had not developed any conception of managing its great fur-producing lands to maintain a safe and steady yield. It simply pushed farther and farther into them and constantly urged its clerks and traders and factors to ship more and more bundles. Even in the 1830's the great John McLoughlin could take pride in his policy of sending Peter Skene Ogden to trap out all the beaver of the Snake River country and so prevent American traders from finding a return there.

As the demand for beaver fell off and prices dropped, the Hudson's Company began to look at other resources. Salmon of the Columbia and the Fraser could be salted and shipped in barrels to the Hawaiian Islands. Lumber could be cut and shipped to the growing city of San Francisco. But the means were still primitive, the markets still distant and uncertain. Coal discoveries at Nanaimo were more promising – coal at tidewater shipped easily, would not spoil and found ready markets. But even with this, settlement was still slow in coming and nothing more than the fur trails and the fur-traders' river routes suggested ways into the inland parts of the province.

It was those routes that led the way to the next resource – gold. And it was a golden key that first unlocked the province to independent settlement. Gold, it would seem, is the ideal resource for such a purpose. Of high value and small bulk, readily transportable, always in demand, it attracts men unfailingly and urges them on through every difficulty and danger. Further, it is a resource that cannot be damaged by over-exploitation – man digs it up or sifts it out, makes use of it and that is the end of it. Yet the gold that brought population to British Columbia was probably just as expensive to the natural wealth of the province as the wildest of land-clearing fires. The miners worked the river bars for their gold, sorting and sifting the gravel, sluicing it and washing it, piling it in great heaps along the river banks. In doing so they effectively destroyed salmon runs whose value over the years since then would have exceeded by many times the value of all the gold they found. The immediate gain was necessary – gold brought money and people to the province, salmon at that time did not and could not – and made sense in the knowledge of the times. To-day it would be common sense to leave the gold in the gravel unless ways could be found of taking it out without damage to the fish.

The gold did not last, but settlers remained to raise cattle, cut lumber, catch salmon and clear farm land. In time the prospectors found other valuable metals – silver, lead, zinc and copper. The transcontinental railway brought more settlers, as well as a new means of reaching markets, and it also set a precedent for a new means of developing natural resources – the policy of railroad charters and land grants.

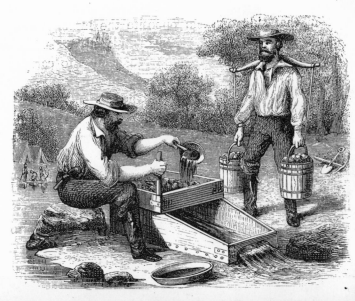

The second resource was gold. This engraving is from an 1883 issue of a magazine entitled *The Resources of British Columbia* and was captioned "The Modern Rocker — one of the most simple and useful machines used in placer mining". Courtesy of the Provincial Archives.

To-day the public looks back on the railroad land grants as mismanagement and stupidity, if not worse. Yet in their time they made at least as much sense as the burning of forests for grazing lands and the destruction of spawning gravel in the frantic search for gold. If the province was to be opened up for use and settlement, railroads seemed to be the only answer. Railroads cost a great deal of money and were a heavy risk to the investor. There was plenty of land, in fact land was all the government could offer the investor as some security for his risk. It was only with great difficulty that Robert Dunsmuir was persuaded to undertake the building of the Esquimalt-Nanaimo Railway on Vancouver Island; he had made several million dollars from his coal mines and presumably saw little point in risking them for a railroad that was unlikely to pay its way for many years. Even the grant of twenty miles of land along the right of way, including some of the finest timber stands in the province, probably did not look very good to him in 1882.

By the turn of the century seventy-three railroad companies had been incorporated in the province, nearly half of them planning to serve the mining districts of the Kootenays. Nearly all of them had been promised extensive land grants instead of or in addition to cash subsidies. It seems altogether fortunate that of the seventy-three companies only eleven finished their lines and were able to claim the grants. Yet without those that were built it is quite unlikely that the great mineral yields which played so large a part in the economy of the province from 1890 to the First World War could have been realized nearly so soon as they were.

After 1900 it was the turn of the forests. Were they not inexhaustible, covering nearly the whole face of the province? There were ready markets for the fine Douglas fir timber of the Coast. Steam-power had come to replace oxen and horses; it could move giant logs as though they were match sticks and even a small locomotive could haul more timber over far greater distances in far less time than oxen and horses. In 1900 the sawmills produced just over a quarter of a billion board feet. By 1910 the annual cut passed a billion feet; by 1920, two billion; by 1928, three billion. Lumber had replaced fur, gold and base metals as the mainstay of the province.

It was rankest exploitation, without any attempt at management or thought for the future. Hundreds of square miles of the finest timberland in the province, mainly on Vancouver Island and the Lower Mainland, were stripped of trees and burned over. The heavy rains channelled and eroded the torn earth, soil was washed from ridges into gullies and flats, and from there into the streams and rivers. The province grew on it, but the land would never be as good again for growing timber. And all too often, with the destruction of the timber, salmon streams had been damaged or destroyed, recreational values had been impaired, whole watersheds had been modified in character and value. It was development, but like the gold of the Quesnel River, it was expensive in terms of the province's future.

This short sketch of early and destructive development is by no means exhaustive, nor is it unique; it could be roughly matched in almost any area of North

America. It cannot be said to have represented any deliberate or consistent policy; it was rather a large-scale opportunism, haphazard and uninformed, designed solely to open up the province, caring nothing for the true nature of the resources involved and taking no thought for the future. Such philosophy as there may have been behind it probably reflected the warning given James Douglas by Lord Grey from the Colonial Office as the Colony of Vancouver Island was founded: "It is obvious, when an eligible territory is left waste, unsubdued to the use of man, it is impossible to prevent persons from taking irregular possession of the land." Memory of the loss of all the territory north of the Columbia to the forty-ninth parallel was still fresh at the time and fear of further American encroachments has remained a factor in provincial thinking almost to this day.

But even in those times the province had a minority of thinking people who recognized the waste and injury and felt it should be checked. I remember ordinary working loggers in the twenties who found time to pause on the job, look out over the devastation and say: "This can't last." They were thinking of hemlock logs left

to rot on the ground because it didn't pay to haul them to market, and of timber cruisers' reports of how little was left of the old-growth fir stands. I remember ordinary working fishermen who counted off the creeks that no longer had significant runs of salmon and remembered an abundance that had long since faded.

Boom times are not good times for conservation talk – everybody is too busy making money out of exploitation. But in the thirties there was both time and reason for such thought and the public mood was receptive. Whatever had been done in the past was not well done. The theory of a society mounting ever higher and higher up the scale of good living on the husks of its resources no longer looked so bright; a measure of stability, even at the cost of some atonement for past sins, seemed infinitely desirable. For the first time British Columbians began to consider their resources as something to be studied and used wisely. The bright dream of a steadily sustained yield from soil and water, from forests and fisheries and farms, from grazing lands and game herds, even from the superabundant mountains themselves, seemed within the realm of practical politics.

There were strong voices speaking. The work of the Pacific Biological Station at Departure Bay was becoming known and for the first time it seemed that some of the mysteries of the Pacific salmon runs might be revealed. F. D. Mulholland published his report on the forest resources of the province and an aggressive Chief Forester, E. C. Manning, began the task of educating public and legislature. In 1925-6 the widely copied system of registered traplines had been introduced in the province. Some relief work went into improvement of parks and small measures of reforestation. The International Fisheries Commission had begun restoration of the seriously depleted halibut banks. The great Vancouver Island fire of 1938 gave final warning that any hope of natural forest regeneration must depend on planning, effort and protection.

Salmon in Gordon Creek, near Yale. A description of spawning salmon which accompanied this engraving illustrates the pioneer attitude towards natural resources: "This source of wealth needs but to be gathered — no tilling of the soil, manuring, provision against late frosts, drought or other ills. . . . It may almost be considered nature's bounty to man, bestowed with a lavish hand, and for which no recompense is demanded." From an 1883 issue of *The Natural Resources of British Columbia*, courtesy of the Provincial Archives.

War is one of the mortal enemies of wise use of natural resources, but the war of 1939-45 was only an interruption to the new thinking that had begun to stir British Columbians. Plenty of ambitious young men came back from the war, to complete their education and move out into the fields of resource management. No one knew just what to expect – boom or depression. There were precedents for both. But, as always after wars, there was hope that a new and better world had been made, that old mistakes would now be repaired and new ideas would find their place.

In this favourable climate Dr. D. B. Turner, Director of Conservation in the provincial Department of Lands and Forests, conceived the idea of a yearly conference on natural resources, with delegates from government, university and industry. It was a new idea, untried elsewhere and only partly formed, but it reflected the thought that had been stirring among British Columbians through the previous twenty years.

The first conference, held in 1948 with about a hundred delegates, was an immediate success. The post-war boom had already started. Men working in and with the resources were already aware that they were facing heavy responsibilities and most difficult problems. It was becoming clearer than ever before in the history of the province that resource uses were often conflicting – could lumbering co-exist with mining and recreation, hydro-electric power with fisheries, agriculture with industrial and residential building, wildlife with grazing rights and crop spraying, clean rivers with industrial and domestic wastes? The Annual Resources Conferences soon became a clearing-house for conflicting needs and conflicting points of view. Men who were dealing daily with research, administration or operations in the various resources set forth their knowledge and their difficulties, listened to each other with surprising degrees of sympathy and patience, left with broader knowledge and a clearer understanding of the welfare of the province as a whole.

The first conference dealt with four main resources – agriculture, forestry, mining and fisheries. It was soon evident that this foundation was not broad enough and the Conference today recognizes ten main divisions, all as "natural resources", People, Soil, Water, the three basic resources, with Agriculture, Fisheries, Forestry, Mining, Power and Energy, Recreation and Wildlife as the main resource uses.

It is not my concern here to give a detailed history of the conferences. There have been twelve at this writing, each dedicated to a specific theme. Each has produced a thick volume of transactions, heavy with graphs, tables and statistics, of vital importance to the specialists concerned, but often difficult and obscure to the lay public. Each conference grows larger, more intensive, better informed and more productive. The twelve volumes of conference transactions, available in school and public libraries throughout the province, as well as in government, university and business offices, now make the authoritative reference work on the natural resources of British Columbia.

The Conference has never considered itself an "action body". That is to say, it makes no attempt to press its conclusions or findings on authority of any kind. Its purpose is rather education and information through thorough exploration of all problems in resource management. To this end it collects and co-ordinates the best possible sources of information, often bringing specialists from other provinces and other countries, though depending mainly on the local sources – government, industry, university and private interests – because these are closest to the matters involved. Through this simple and entirely voluntary machinery it aims to encourage the highest possible degree of co-operation among those responsible for the management and use of the provincial natural resources. This might well be called self-education; when trained and intelligent men, used to the disciplines of scientific objectivity, listen to each other's points of view, some good is bound to come of it. And there is not the slightest doubt that nearly all problems of resource use are now discussed throughout the province far more intelligently and with much better mutual understanding than was the case before the Conference started.

But the originators of the Conference had still another purpose – that of interesting the general public in the nature and use of the resources on which the province depends. This purpose may have been slighted at times by the intricate technical detail of many of the discussions, but the Conference Executive has never lost sight of it. Both press and radio have always been encouraged to attend and have given excellent coverage. In 1953, the Conference published a picture relief map of the province, emphasizing physical features and transportation routes, which was a great success. Encouraged by this, it brought out in 1956 a "Resources Atlas", the first of its kind ever produced. Some forty-eight pages of maps in full colour are used to show the distribution, quantity and quality of the known resources, from soil and climate to wildlife and fisheries, from hydro-electric power and minerals to population and public parks.

A detailed text to match this publication obviously exists in the twelve volumes of transactions that have been published by the Conference. But it is by no means an easy text to use, except for special reference, and it is neither simple nor popular in scope – most of the papers submitted are quite technical and detailed, and comparatively few deal directly with the over-all philosophy of use and conservation in natural resources that the Conference has developed.

The purpose of this book is to provide a text that will in some measure express the thoughts and ideas that have been developed through the years of the Conference, to define the scope and nature of the province's resources and to be a useful companion to the Atlas.

conservation defined CHAPTER 2

AN EASY DEFINITION of the word conservation is "proper use of natural resources". But this still leaves a difficult and wide-open question: What is "proper use"?

This is as it should be because conservation is a dynamic, not a static, conception. It does not mean simply hanging on to things, like a miser to his gold. It means putting them to use, seeking a valuable return from them and at the same time ensuring future yields of at least equal value. It means having enough faith in the future to respect the future and the needs of future people; it means accepting moral and practical restraints that limit immediate self-interest; it means finding a measure of wisdom and understanding of natural things that few peoples have attained; ultimately, though we no longer see it in this way, it is a religious concept – the most universal and fundamental of all such concepts, the worship of fertility to which man has dedicated himself in every civilization since his race began. We may well believe now that an intellectual and scientific approach is more likely to succeed than a mystical one. But without moral concepts and without a sense of responsibility for the future of the human race, the idea of conservation could have little meaning. Since it deals for the future as well as for the present, it must always be as much an act of faith as an intellectual exercise.

The basic resources of any country are soil and water and, largely depending on these, climate. All three can be damaged by misuse, utterly destroyed by persistent misuse – and when they are so destroyed the civilizations that grew upon them, however great and powerful, are utterly destroyed with them. The Sahara Desert, the arid lands of the eastern Mediterranean and the Euphrates Valley all supported civilizations that were supreme in their time, wise in their time and secure in their time. But the wisdom of the time was not enough; the water failed, the soil eroded and blew away and desert sands blew in to bury the wonderful cities whose wealth the land had once supported.

Soil and water and climate are the permanent resources; together they make habitat, the set of conditions that favours the growth of timber, wildlife, fish, cattle and farm crops. Used within proper limits they are renewable and perpetual resources. Used without regard for those limits they deteriorate steadily and may quickly pass beyond the stage where the knowledge and effort of man can restore them.

Soil builds slowly, over thousands, sometimes millions, of years, by the persistent forces of ice and water and wind on rock, by the growth and decay of vegetable and animal matter, by the action of bacteria. Man has learned to use it for the growth of crops and domestic animals, he has learned to drain it and irrigate it, to increase its yield and keep it in good heart by the use of chemicals and by mixing in borrowed humus. Agriculture is intensive use of the soil, the oldest deliberate use, and it is an ancient science; but it remains an inexact science, haphazardly applied. Many modern agricultural practices, including techniques of drainage and irrigation and fertilization, ultimately deplete and destroy soil. Soil cannot renew itself fast enough to keep up with abuse or misuse.

Soil also makes natural grazing land for both wild and domestic creatures. It grows every stick of timber that goes to the sawmills and pulp mills. It grows the natural ground-cover that is needed everywhere to hold up the rainfall and feed it gently to the watercourses. To a great extent soil also fertilizes the lakes and streams on which the main fisheries of the province depend. These are uses of soil that have been all too little studied. Man has generally taken them and their yield for granted; more often than not his use has been without regard for the limited knowledge he has and therefore seriously destructive.

It would seem then that a simple first rule of conservation should be: "Take care of soil and water and the rest will take care of itself." Essentially, this is so; but it is too simple. In the use of natural resources many factors enter – human, economic, social, political, provincial, national and international. And it is necessary to examine each resource both separately and in its interrelationships with other resources before these influences can be understood and valued.

I have suggested that soil, water and climate are interdependent. If the water fails, the soil will fail; if the soil is damaged, the water will be lost; if soil and water values change, climate will change; if climate changes, the values of soil and water must change with it. It is well to think of these as the fundamental and paramount resources, to set them somewhat apart and grant them extreme respect, to test all resource uses in terms of their effect on them. It is important to realize that soil and water can fail and vanish quite quickly beyond the point of man's power to restore or replace them.

Having established this, it is tempting, and probably not altogether inaccurate, to think of all the other resources – farm crops, timber, fisheries and so on – as secondary resources, or even as merely "resource uses". But this would be unnecessarily confusing, since all these things have long ago been accepted as natural resources, and it would be misleading since nearly all of them are concerned with essential and irreplaceable phases of life that convert soil and water into value and meaning.

At this point still another question must be considered. What is a resource? A resource is something existing or growing naturally in a country which can be put to effective use by man, now or in the foreseeable future. Within this definition, resources are of several types. Physical geography is a resource, for instance, in that it modifies climate and provides transportation routes. Man himself is a resource in that he serves himself and his fellow men by the labour of his brain and muscles. Scenery is a resource in that it provides inspiration and recreation and even attracts wealth from citizens of other countries. To develop any comprehensive plan and philosophy of wise resource use, all these must be considered. They have been considered, measured and examined at most of the annual Resources Conferences held in British Columbia.

The more commonly recognized resources are of two main types, renewable and non-renewable. The non-renewable resources are the minerals – valuable or useful metals and energy sources such as coal, oil, natural gas –, and other substances that can be put to industrial or domestic use. At first consideration it might seem that conservation has little meaning in terms of these resources – they are discovered, worked, used and that is the end of them. It is important here to go back to the definition of conservation as "wise or proper use of a natural resource". Mineral resources are among the most important and valuable a nation can have. They are usually hard to find. They are often difficult to assess both as to quality and quantity when found. They may be difficult to work or process. They depend on transportation. Their use and development may affect other resources, and other resource uses may help or hinder their development.

All scientific advances in prospecting and exploratory work mean better use of mineral resources. New smelting and separating processes can bring old mines back to life. Ready access to road, railroad or other transportation can transform an uneconomic prospect into a productive mine. Cheap power close at hand may make the difference between profitable and unprofitable operation. Mine tailings or mine effluents may damage other resources, such as fisheries and forest or agricultural land. Limitation of access by some other use may restrict prospecting. Legislative control on the export or import of minerals may be wisely or unwisely conceived. All these points and others like them call for continuous research and examination if discovery and use of the province's mineral resources are to continue.

The renewable natural resources, timber, fish, wildlife, agricultural and recreational land, are the ones most commonly thought of in terms of conservation. Not so very long ago it was believed that preservation was the essential rule for protecting these resources; the hunter must be limited in his hunting, the fisherman in his fishing, the lumberman in his tree-cutting, and all would be well. Man looked, for instance, at heavy fishing and declining salmon runs, and thought he saw cause and effect. While it is true that there was overfishing in many areas, this was only one of many causes for the decline in the runs. Stream obstruction, pollution, damage to spawning areas, reduced stream flows were all contributing to the decline. Almost unnoticed, it was the *habitat* of the fish, the water conditions essential to their reproduction and survival, that were being affected, largely by the use of other resources.

In the forests it was not only the destruction of young growth incidental to the harvest of mature trees that was causing damage to future crops; injury to soil by burning and erosion was a far more serious and permanent threat. In the field of wildlife much the same was true. There had been some excessive and wasteful destruction for market and other purposes, but the draining of swamps and marshes that destroyed the feeding and breeding grounds of wildfowl and the competition of domestic herds on the open ranges produced losses far greater than all the efforts of the hunters. At the same time, whenever conditions were improved by intensive agriculture or by the stripping away of mature climax forests, wildlife increased and multiplied.

These simple instances emphasize the first principle of conservation to-day – the protection or improvement of habitat, that whole set of natural conditions and circumstances that contributes to the successful propagation and development of the renewable resource. A very important part of this protection and improvement may be in harvesting the resource adequately and at the right time. If timber, for instance, grows rapidly for a hundred years but only slowly for the next two or three hundred, it may be wiser to take a succession of hundred-year crops than to wait for mature growth. Herds of game animals reproduce better if their numbers are kept within the safe capacity of their winter range and the range itself will be protected from permanent damage by overgrazing. An excessive escapement of spawning salmon may mean damage to the nests of early-running races by the late runners and result in a double loss – reduction of the commercial yield of that year and reduction of the yield of early runners in the next cycle.

I have written so far as though each resource were separate in its own compartment and its users in complete control of all its affairs. This is not so at all. Nearly all resource uses conflict in some measure, some to the point of mutual intolerance. Salmon runs and hydro-electric power are an outstanding example of such conflicts; logging practices may conflict with stream flow for both power and fisheries, or with recreational uses or with flood control; timber spraying, and even orchard and crop spraying, can cause serious damage to fish and wildlife; recreational lands such as wilderness areas are completely intolerant of other resource uses and parks are only slightly less so. Drainage of agricultural land may be destructive of wildlife and may affect the value of other land nearby. Irrigation may conflict with other water uses, such as fisheries and hydro-power. Excessive cattle grazing may conflict with forestry and may reduce or wipe out big game herds.

These and many other problems like them have been discussed each year in the Resources Conferences and out of the discussions has developed a theory that may be generally phrased as "multiple use with priorities". It is an ideal, a sort of guiding philosophy that cannot always be realized but which clearly points the way to wise management of natural resources. It puts emphasis on co-operation rather than competition, and by so doing constantly suggests new and profitable areas of research and leads to discoveries that might not otherwise have been reached.

Encouragingly often uses that seem to conflict are found on examination to work in quite well together. The hunter, for instance, can take a hundred annual crops from forest land while one crop of trees is growing. His use of the land entails a minor fire hazard in some seasons, but at the same time he controls wildlife whose browsing would seriously damage regrowth. A flood-control dam may be of value to both fisheries and agriculture, yet produce electric power as well. But even when special interests conflict it is often possible by planning and understanding to find room for both without serious detriment to either, and with proportionately greater benefit to the province as a whole. The clearing of shorelines around lakes behind storage dams, for instance, preserves recreational values that would otherwise be completely lost. A watershed may be managed to provide electric power, fisheries, irrigation, recreation in various forms, clean water supplies and even disposal for moderate quantities of industrial wastes; one or other of these uses may demand priority of consideration throughout the system or in parts of it, but under proper control and planning all can contribute a maximum of value without damage to the others.

I have said already that dealing properly with resources is dealing with the future. This presents a problem that can never be perfectly solved. The arts of prophecy remain uncertain – perhaps were never more so than in this age of extraordinary technological progress. What is a resource today may be a drug on the market tomorrow; today's slag heap may yield tomorrow's most precious mineral. Improved transportation, increased population, increased leisure, changes in public fancy – all these factors have worked, and may still work, to create values scarcely suspected a generation earlier.

For many years controlled burning of logged-over lands was encouraged as wise forest practice, since it tended to encourage regrowth of Douglas fir rather than hemlock. Since that time hemlock has become a desirable timber for pulp and cellulose and there is every reason to suppose it will become more and more desirable as technology advances. It is abundantly clear now that the risks of controlled burning were unwisely taken, especially since the "control" so often failed. And it may well prove in years to come that where the method succeeded in producing fir instead of hemlock stands the total is loss rather than gain.

Fifty years ago coal reserves were the measure of a nation's greatness. It seemed logical and wise to men of that day to take account of a seam of coal one foot wide buried five thousand feet underground and to reckon it as a future resource, even in

British Columbia. Today a seam three times that thickness and less than half the distance underground seems scarcely worth the trouble of inventory. In 1913 British Columbia's probable coal reserves were estimated at eighty-four billion tons, in the belief that every ton would sooner or later be needed. Today the estimate is five or six billion tons, and no one can see just how or when they will be used. But it is altogether probable that they will one day be used, perhaps when other energy sources become more expensive and new ways are found of developing energy from coal, or perhaps when science or technology develops a wholly new range of products from the material. The second of these possibilities may well be discounted for practical purposes at present, but the first most certainly cannot be and should not be.

This is a particularly good example of the problems of anticipation in resource management, but there are hundreds of others much like it, some of them far more immediate. How soon will ordinary thermal and nuclear plants become cheaper sources of energy than water? Should water-power be developed cautiously with this in view, or is it wiser to push ahead with all possible speed before it is outdated, as coal has been? How far dare British Columbia go in her present practice of converting her limited first-rate agricultural land into real estate for domestic or industrial use? What will be the future value of protein food resources such as the salmon runs as world population increases, living standards improve and Far Eastern markets open up?

All these are questions to which different answers are given by different authorities. Yet all are questions that must be met and answered in practical ways almost daily by those responsible for resource use and management. They have been examined and re-examined in past Resources Conferences and they will be examined again many times in future conferences. Little by little the answers change and adjust to new thinking, new information and new circumstances. They go to the very heart of this matter of conservation, the wise and proper use of natural resources. Because they have no set and ready answers, they also go to the very heart and root of man – his integrity. How great is his integrity and honesty of purpose? How far will he choose to be guided by his wisdom and power of reasoning and sense of morality, how far by short-term self-interest?

Because the future is unknown and changes in many unforeseen ways from its obvious probabilities, he can only try the matter out. But there is no excuse for not trying. It is a matter of puzzling a way among the conflicting ideas and advices and opinions, and reaching decisions as honestly as may be.

physical features CHAPTER 3

BRITISH COLUMBIA is the third largest province in Canada. Like the other western provinces it is bounded on the south by the forty-ninth parallel, on the north by the sixtieth parallel. Its western boundary is the Pacific Ocean; its eastern boundary is the divide of the Rocky Mountains, except in the northern half, where the line turns from the general north-westerly direction of the mountains to due north and takes in a great section of the Peace River watershed. The total area of the province is 336,255 square miles. Outside the Peace River area its main physical features are the Rocky Mountains, the Coast Mountains and a great interior plateau between them which is broken by lesser but still formidable mountain ranges.

Geologically it is a young country. The Pre-Cambrian Shield, which covers much of Canada, is upwards of two and a half billion years old, the rocky roots of mountains long worn away by the action of wind and rain and snow and ice. Mountain building is said to have begun at the coast and worked eastward, thrusting up sedimentary rocks formed in Paleozoic times, 200 to 500 million years ago. In the Coast Mountains there was much volcanic action, from the earliest times until Tertiary or "recent" geological times, the forces of molten rock pushing up through fissures and crevices and the weaker caps of the sedimentary rocks, to burst out and spread into the mighty granitic shapes that are only partially worn down to-day. In the Rockies there was little volcanic action, so that the stratification of the sedimentary rocks still shows quite plainly and the older rocks of the first up-thrust still make the mountain shapes.

The Cordilleran system, the great chain of mountains that runs almost unbroken through the Americas from Cape Horn to Point Barrow, extends from the Alberta foothills to the Pacific and so includes the whole of British Columbia. The Eastern Cordilleran region is made up of the Rocky Mountains and their foothills, westward to the Rocky Mountain Trench. The Western region is divided into the Inter-

ior System, which includes the Interior Plateau and the many mountain ranges between the Rockies and the Coast Range, and the Western System, which includes
the whole of the Coast Range, the Coastal Trench and the off-shore islands.

The geological map of British Columbia shows a tremendous complication of
rock formations of widely varying ages and types, particularly in the southern interior where many important ore bodies have been found, and in the north-western
and central parts. All these variations have had their influence in shaping the face
of the country, but glacial geology has had more immediate and practical effects
and almost every human activity in the province reflects these.

Since the mountains were established, the whole of British Columbia has been
covered at least twice, probably several times, by tremendous ice sheets. The last of
these withdrew or melted about ten or eleven thousand years ago, leaving behind it
something very much like the bare shape of the land as it is to-day. Behind the
retreating ice the present sites of Vancouver, Victoria, New Westminster, Powell
River, and much of the east coast of Vancouver Island slowly rose from several
hundred feet under the sea. The gravelly, well-drained soils began to grow timber,
and great glacial streams continued to build up their delta lands. Lakes drew down
into their present shapes as the huge ice dams burst and released their floods. Much
of the original rock was buried under new overburdens of sand and gravel and clay;
canyons and dry valleys and river channels were cut by the melt waters; gigantic
boulders, known to geologists as "erratics", were left scattered here and there over
the face of the land and along the shores of lakes and salt water where the retreating ice had dropped them.

With the warmer temperatures animal life returned. The salmon pressed against
the faces of the retreating glaciers, a few reaching further with each stage of withdrawal to establish the individual races that make the runs of to-day. Caribou,
elk, deer and the fur-bearers moved in. Waterfowl found food and nesting sites in
sedges and rushes that grew in the clays of the marsh edges. And very quickly man
came back; eight thousand years ago, probably no more than two or three thousand
years behind the retreat of the ice, he was catching salmon and eating wild cherries
in the Fraser Canyon above Yale.

In the years since that time the normal processes of erosion by rain and wind
and temperature changes have worked to break down the rocks still further, to
lessen the mass of the heights and fill the valleys. Forests have grown and died to
nourish new forests. River channels have shifted and silted and changed again; the
remaining glaciers have shrunk away to the highest land and vegetation has crept
up the mountain-sides behind them.

Considered over the ages, the face of the earth is a changing, impermanent thing.
Considered in terms of a man's span or that of a civilization, it is solid, permanent,
immutable, because the constant change is so slow as to be almost imperceptible. To
twentieth-century man the face of British Columbia breaks down into four main
components: 118 million acres, nearly sixty per cent of the total area, is forest land;

twenty million acres, about five per cent of the total, is farm or grazing land; four and a half million acres, almost two per cent of the area, is fresh water in lakes or streams; and the remaining 85 million acres, about one third of the total, is classed as "rock and barren", including snow-fields and glaciers and alpine tundra. In addition there are the coastal seas, the long, narrow inlets, the passages among the hundreds of islands, large and small, and the shallow waters of the continental shelf that extends for an average distance of thirty or thirty-five miles offshore before dropping away for ten or twelve thousand feet to the ocean floor.

Within this frame, on or under its surface and in the atmosphere above it, are the province's natural resources, the basic wealth that the effort and intelligence of the inhabitants must convert into usefulness. The effect of the *cordillera* is expressed in the one-third of the land area that is classified as rocky and barren. It is expressed again in the fact that more than seventy-five per cent of the land area is three thousand feet or more above sea level – above the limits of practical agriculture in these latitudes, useful only under favourable circumstances for the summer grazing of cattle. British Columbia is mountain country. Only in the Peace River district are there extensive areas of flat land.

Because the province is mountainous, the valleys are tremendously important, not only as the main areas of settlement, but as the only practical routes of overland travel. The province has three main river systems, the Peace-Parsnip-Finlay in the north, the Fraser-Thompson-Nechako, which drains almost the whole central part, and the Columbia-Kootenay-Okanagan, which reaches into the south-east corner and a section of the south central part. In addition to these, there are the Skeena, Nass, Iskut, Taku and Stikine which lead out to the northern part of the coastline, several lesser systems that provide possible outlets on the more southerly inlets, and the Liard system which drains the extreme north-east of the province into the Arctic.

Of the three great river systems, only the Fraser is wholly within the province. It rises from the Rockies near Yellowhead Pass, swings north-westward along the Rocky Mountain Trench, then curves westward and southward to be joined by the Nechako at Prince George. From Prince George its course is almost due south for

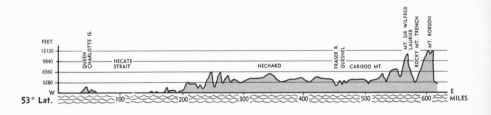

more than three hundred miles to Hope, then due west through the Lower Fraser Valley to enter the Strait of Georgia at Vancouver. It drains practically the whole of the main interior plateau and the Cariboo Mountains as well as the eastern slope of the Coast Range. South of Prince George two major tributaries, the Quesnel and the Chilcotin, come in from east and west respectively; and at Lytton the strong clear flow of the Thompson River comes down from the Monashee Mountains beyond Kamloops and from Albreda Pass behind the Cariboo Range, only a short distance from the source of the Fraser itself.

Like the Fraser, the Columbia at first follows the north-westward line of the Rocky Mountain Trench, gathering to itself the flow of the Columbia ice-fields and the Selkirk glaciers, then makes its great bend round the northern end of the Selkirk Range and turns south through Revelstoke and the Arrow Lakes. The Kootenay rises in the mountains east of Golden, flows almost parallel to the Columbia but in exactly the opposite direction, to Canal Flats, just beyond the head of Columbia Lake, whence it follows the Trench across the international boundary. In Montana it bends round to run north again and re-enter Canada south of Creston, flow through Kootenay Lake and join the Columbia at Castlegar. From there the Columbia continues southward into Washington State.

The Peace River also gathers its strength along the Rocky Mountain Trench but, unlike the Fraser and the Columbia, it cuts eastward through the Rockies to the great Canadian plain and so to the Arctic. The Finlay comes down the Trench from the north, draining the eastern slope of the Omineca Mountains, while the Parsnip comes from the south to meet it at Finlay Forks. From there the united rivers pour through the great canyon of the Peace, past Hudson Hope and Fort St. John to the Alberta boundary.

In the northern half of the province the Omineca, Skeena and Cassiar mountains make the effective divide, rather than the Rockies or the Coast Range. North of the Peace the Liard also cuts through towards the east, while the western slopes are drained to the coast by the Skeena, Nass, Stikine and other streams that reach through to the heads of the long inlets. South of these the Coast Range is an effective barrier and short-run streams come directly down from glaciers and mountain slopes to the southern inlets.

Because of its broken terrain and extensive recent glaciation the province has a tremendous number of lakes. The great majority are small, from a few acres to a few square miles in area, but they are important for the water they store, for their great recreational values and very frequently as nursing waters for young salmon. The larger lakes are all long and narrow, confined by the typically deep and narrow valleys between the mountain ranges in all parts of the province. Atlin and Teslin, two of the largest, are in the north-west corner of the province and extend into Yukon Territory. Babine, Stuart, Shuswap, Quesnel and François, varying from ninety to nearly two hundred square miles in area, are important salmon-raising lakes – Babine for the Skeena watershed, the others on the Fraser-Thompson watershed. The Arrow Lakes are really an expansion of the Columbia River's channel and one day will make storage for the Columbia hydro-electric projects. Kootenay Lake already provides valuable water storage for a succession of hydro-electric plants on the Kootenay River. Nechako Reservoir, which was once a circular chain of smaller lakes with little variation in altitude, is now the largest body of fresh water in the province and provides storage for the Alcan hydro-electric plant at Kemano.

British Columbia is not an easy province for the mind to grasp and understand – the mountains divide it and twist it into complex topographical patterns. There is a long ocean shoreline, a Coastal Trench roughly paralleling the Rocky Mountain Trench in the east, and a great maze of islands. And many of the topographical patterns complete themselves south of the forty-ninth parallel or north of the sixtieth, beyond the limits of the province.

It is possible and useful to think of the southern part of the province as a series of valleys lying south of the line of the Thompson River and the Big Bend of the Columbia, and in practice this is what British Columbians do. There is Vancouver Island in the extreme west, then the Strait of Georgia lying like a huge lake between the island mountains and the Coast Range. After this the lower Fraser Valley or, as it is sometimes called, the Lower Mainland. Across the Cascade Range is the fruit-growing Okanagan, then the West Kootenay and the East Kootenay, the last extending to the foot of the Rockies.

North of the junction of the Thompson and the Fraser are the Cariboo country and the Chilcotin country, both part of the interior plateau, which extends beyond Prince George, about half-way up the province. West of Prince George are the Bulkley and Skeena valleys, extending to salt water at Prince Rupert. To the east the Fraser curves around the Cariboo Mountains to find the Rocky Mountain Trench.

Only a few miles north of Prince George, still less than half-way up the province, the Arctic watershed begins. The Coast Range is narrower and more broken here, so that several streams cut back through the Alaskan Panhandle to drain the Stikine Plateau and the western slope of the Cassiar Mountains, but the main drainage is to the Arctic, first by the Peace and its tributaries, then by the Liard and its tributaries, and the flow of both these rivers eventually reaches the Mackenzie. The drainage of Atlin and Teslin lakes in the north-west corner of the province is to the Yukon River. In broad terms, matching the Cariboo and the Chilcotin in the centre of the province and the valleys of the south, the three divisions of the north are the Stikine, the Cassiar and the Peace River "countries".

British Columbia is between four and five hundred miles wide, from east to west, and nearly eight hundred miles long from north to south. It is fenced by mountain ranges and built upon mountain ranges and its main communication with the rest of Canada and the western world in general is still by the Rocky Mountain passes. But it has nearly forty-five hundred miles of sheltered coastline looking out over the North Pacific. This in itself is practically a resource – the asset of geographical position that has made many states and nations great in their time. While the present political, economic and social obstacles continue to block proper trade and interchange between east and west, it may be a sleeping asset. But no intelligent appraisal of the province's future development can fail to take account of it.

soil resources   CHAPTER 4

GEOLOGY AND PHYSICAL GEOGRAPHY make and describe the bare bones, the frame-work, of a country. Soil and climate, rainfall and stream flow, vegetation and animal life are its flesh and character.

Soil is the yield of the original geological materials of an area after they have been worked upon by various agents – climate, living organisms, topography and time. Over ninety per cent of the dry substance of most soils is mineral matter, weathered or worn from the original rock. The bases of nearly all British Columbia soils are the deposits left behind by the last ice age. Because the country is so broken and varied, these themselves differ widely. Different climates, different elevations and different ground-covers have worked over the past ten thousand years to produce still greater variations and complications. In a single ranching and grazing area near Kamloops, for instance, no less than six types of soil have been classified over a five-thousand-foot range in elevation.

The study and classification of soils is a difficult and complicated affair, still in process of development, and thoroughgoing soil surveys are slow and costly. Modern soil science makes large use of at least four other sciences - geology, chemistry, physics and bacteriology. It concerns itself not only with agricultural soils, but with grazing, forest and alpine soils, and even with the use of soils for such purposes as dam-building and as foundations for roads and buildings. It is closely concerned with water storage, water tables and water use, as well as the study of climate.

Soil classification is based not merely on the surface or topsoil that directly interests the farmer or the gardener, but on the several layers of material that lie above the more or less unchanged original deposit, usually to a depth of three or four feet. These layers or "horizons" nearly always differ widely in character from the surface soil, but may very materially affect it by their mineral content, acidity or alkalinity, capacity for holding or draining water, texture and other qualities. A good forest soil, for instance, may have a layer of partly decomposed vegetable matter, another of dark mineral soil with good humus and biological activity, another of brown mineral soil with accumulations of clay or iron and finally the original glacial deposit. A good farm soil may be a simple series of alluvial deposits to a depth of several feet, all of them rich and active, or may grade through a foot or so of good black soil, to a leached layer of grey or white clay, to mineral soil with clay or iron, to mineral soil high in calcium. Certain standards of classification of this broad kind have been arrived at and are being applied in soil surveys throughout Canada.

In British Columbia some ten million acres have been studied and classified during the past thirty years. This represents less than five per cent of the total area of the province, but since almost sixty-five per cent of the area is classed as barren or capable of very limited production, and since surveys have been directed towards the more productive areas, the figure is significant. It is a continuing survey and in time will probably cover the whole thirty-six per cent of the province that has productive soils; meanwhile an informed projection of the results already obtained can be made to give a broad idea of the type and extent of the province's useful soils.

About five million acres of the land so far surveyed is classified as suitable for agricultural crops, and it is estimated that this figure represents three-quarters of the total agricultural area of the province; a considerable proportion of this land would need heavy capital expenditure in clearing, draining or irrigation before it could become productive, but since food from the land is one of the prime needs of man there is little doubt that the necessary improvements will be economically practicable within the reasonably near future. It seems sound, therefore, to consider and protect these soils as part of the agricultural potential, even though their use to-day may be limited to timber-growing or water storage or cattle grazing. At present less than 1.2 million of an estimated 6.6 million acres of arable land in British Columbia are being farmed, and most of the rest is under forest.

Because of the province's complex geological history there are no extensive areas of individual soil types sufficiently uniform in development to be called Soil Zones, as are the great Black Earth areas of the U.S.S.R. and the North American plains. But soil experts have been able to recognize "soil areas" which they feel are roughly equivalent to zones except that they are relatively small in size and rather more complex – several groups of soil typically and closely associated in intricate patterns.

The most important soil areas of the province are scattered among the valleys of the south, the plateaus of the interior, the plains of the north, and the great gaps in the mountain ranges. These correspond closely to the physical features described in Chapter 3 – across the south, the Rocky Mountain Trench, the Kootenay, Columbian and Okanagan Trenches, the Fraser Gap and the Coastal Trench; in the interior, the Plateau system; along the Coast Range, north from the Fraser Gap, are the Bella Coola Gap, the Skeena Gap and the Stikine Gap; among the northern interior mountains are the Dease Gap, the Rocky Mountain Trench again, the Liard Gap and the Peace Gap, and finally the Tramontane Plains of the north-east.

There are only two broad groupings of soils in British Columbia: Grassland and Forest. The Grassland soils roughly correspond to the Black Earth soils, grading through Brown, Dark-brown, Black, Degraded Black and Prairie-like. The last two of these are also grouped with the Forest soils, which include also Brown Wooded, Grey Wooded, Reddish-brown and Podzol. Other classifications, developed under either grassland or forest conditions, are the alluvial, organic and mountain soils. Alluvial soils are recent deposits from glaciers, glacial lakes or rivers. Organic soils are of vegetable origin under varying stages of decomposition, from peat moss to muck. Mountain soils are in pockets, sometimes organic, sometimes approaching podzols, but most commonly rock fragments incompletely weathered.

GRASSLAND SOILS

There are about two million acres of Grassland soils in the southern interior parts of the province, including the Okanagan, Similkameen, Thompson and Fraser valleys, the Grand Forks and Princeton-Merritt areas. These soils are mainly Brown, Dark-brown and Black. About 600,000 acres are suitable for fruit farming, grain growing, fodder crops or general farming, and the remainder for grazing. The area as a whole varies from dry to very dry – the rainfall of the Brown soil areas averages about six to ten inches a year, that of the Black soils about fifteen to twenty inches – so irrigation is essential. Under irrigation small farms intensively used are highly productive.

The Degraded Black soils are estimated to cover just under a million acres in the Central Interior and Tramontane plains. The Bulkley Valley area has about 600,000 acres, Dawson Creek and Fort St. John about 350,000. In the Central Interior these soils are mainly used for general farming, forage crops and grazing. In the plains they grow valuable grain and mixed farm crops. There are serious problems of water erosion which call for careful farming, with mulching, manuring and contour plowing, since these soils are naturally declining towards podzolic or forest profiles; heavy summer thunderstorms characteristic of the area accelerate the decline, and erosion of open, unprotected soils is very rapid. By the same token, good management, especially under mixed farming, can make for improvement and much greater stability.

FOREST SOILS

The Forest or Podzolic soils cover about 67 million acres of the province. The term "podzol" means literally "ash-like" and defines a soil with an organic surface mat over a thin grey layer leached of its organic and mineral values. This is the combined result of wet climate and a heavy growth of coniferous forest which limits evaporation, causing the moisture to wash down into the ground and carry or leach out the minerals and organic components with it. Such soils are generally acid and of limited agricultural value although they, like the Grassland soils, have widely varying profiles. As already noted, some of the Degraded Black and Prairie-like soils are grouped with Forest soils by the experts. The range continues through at least three types known as Grey Wooded soils to the Reddish-brown Concretionaries and typical Podzol with its sharply defined subsurface layer of greyish-white material, heavily oxidized and very low in humus.

Small areas of Dark-brown Prairie-like soils, altogether about 80,000 acres, are found along the south-east coast of Vancouver Island, especially on the Saanich peninsula and near Duncan, Nanaimo, Qualicum and Comox. These limited areas of good soil at low elevation, with mild temperatures and a long growing season, are highly valued for specialized crops such as small fruits, bulbs, and seed growing.

Brown Wooded soils occur extensively along the Rocky Mountain Trench, over 4½ million acres in the northern parts and in the Liard and Omineca valleys, rather under a million acres in the southern parts and the Kootenay Valley. About 400,000 acres are classed as arable and the remainder is grazing or forest land. These soils are generally immature and alkaline and have developed on subsoils that are heavy in lime. Only the finer textures support agriculture.

The three types of Grey Wooded soils account for about 32 million acres. A little less than two million of these are Brown Podzolic-Grey Wooded soils and are found mainly on the forested hillsides of the southern valleys. Podzol-Grey Wooded soils are found mainly along the Hart Highway north of Prince George, in the Rocky Mountain Trench and the Peace River area. Their estimated total is rather over five million acres, which is mainly of value for growing timber, though 1½ million acres will support some grazing. These also are coarse-textured soils and only 50,000 acres are considered arable.

Nearly 25 million acres of typical Grey Wooded soils are found in the Central Interior (18 million acres) and in the Peace River (5 million acres) and Fort Nelson (one million acres) districts. These are primarily timber-growing soils, with aspen, spruce and lodgepole pine on the upland sites, black spruce, willow and larch where drainage is poor; the more open areas are used for "timber grazing". They are mildly acid soils, deficient in organic matter, nitrogen and phosphorus. The better types can be built up into fairly productive agricultural soils by the use of fertilizers and mulch crops.

Nearly four million acres of Concretionary Reddish-brown soils are found along the south-east coast of Vancouver Island and in the uplands of the Lower Fraser Valley. About a million acres of this is considered arable and the rest grows good timber. This type of soil is developed under warm summers and cool winters of fairly high rainfall. The upper layers are thin and porous while the lower layers are often dense and cemented so that the water runs off laterally, leaving them very dry in summer and quite wet in winter. They are low in nitrogen, organic matter and phosphorus, but respond well to lime and fertilization. Where they are not too rough and stony and clearing expenses are not too high they are useful for dairying, small fruits and mixed farming.

The typical Podzol soils are found in the wettest areas of the province – on the slopes of the island mountains, along the Coastal Trench and the Coast Range, and in the high-rainfall areas of the Columbia Valley and the Rocky Mountains. Their total acreage is more than twenty million, of which less than half a million can be considered arable. With their typically long, cool, moist growing season and high winter rainfall these soils support the principal stands of rain-forest timber – Douglas fir, western hemlock, true firs, western red cedar and spruce. Properly managed they can support rapid regrowth and large forest crops.

RECENT ALLUVIAL SOILS

The recent alluvial soils are among the most valuable in the province. They are built by water-borne deposits in the deltas and flood plains of rivers, so are found in widely scattered areas. The most important are those of the Lower Fraser and Pemberton valleys, the Bella Coola Valley and the Creston area. The total is about three-quarters of a million acres of which nearly half a million are considered arable. Even though these soils commonly need dyking and draining and heavy clearing, their value fully justifies the expenditure. The non-arable areas are magnificently productive forest sites for the western red cedar, grand fir, maidenhair fern association.

ORGANIC SOILS

Organic soils are produced where organic matter is formed more rapidly than it decomposes. The most readily recognizable are the peat soils, where the plants are compressed rather than decomposed; but the gradations of decomposition vary all the way to the state known as muck – a sufficiently descriptive term. The mucks are intensively used for market gardening and berry growing, but the less decomposed soils are likely to require draining, clearing, liming, manuring and fertilizing at excessive cost for to-day's demands. There are some 4½ million acres of organic soils in the province, mainly in the Fraser Valley, the Tramontane plains and alpine areas. Only about a hundred thousand acres are considered arable.

MOUNTAIN SOILS (UNDIFFERENTIATED)

The province has 161 million acres of mountains which are largely bare rock, snow-fields and glaciers. But mountains are the source of soil and even in the mountains pockets of soil are scattered almost everywhere. Some, which grow fair stands of timber, are immature types probably approaching Podzol. Others are Lithosols, rock fragments still undergoing the weathering processes that will convert them into true soils. The alpine meadows usually are organic, cold and poorly drained and based on permafrost at the higher altitudes. Below timberline the mountain soils grow some valuable timber though it is often difficult of access. Above timberline their value is chiefly as summering-grounds for big game herds, the growing of alpine flora and the retention of moisture. The open alpine slopes and meadows have great recreational values that will be increasingly used.

SOIL CONSERVATION

It is not too much to say that ninety per cent of the economy of the province is based directly or indirectly upon soil. The whole of agriculture, livestock raising, forestry and wood manufacturing, which together account for well over half the annual yield of wealth, are directly dependent upon soil. Fisheries and hydro-electric energy are dependent on soil as the greatest of all water reservoirs, without which there would be no balanced run-off at all. Only mining and production of the fossil fuels might be considered relatively independent, and without soil they would find themselves looking out to distant markets from an empty land.

In agriculture, British Columbia seems to be one of the have-not provinces. Less than 1.2 million acres of the 6.6 million estimated as potentially arable are at present improved and under cultivation; much of the rest is under forest crops and likely to remain so for a long while to come. This area of improved land represents less than one acre per head of population, compared with a figure of 2½ acres per head that is considered necessary to provide minimum food requirements. The province can, and of course does, economically import large quantities of agricultural produce from other provinces, but it is far from self-supporting in agriculture and with a steadily increasing population it is bound to go farther and farther behind. In time the need to import may become a very serious liability.

This, together with the facts of rapidly increasing world population and at least proportionately increasing food shortages, makes it clear that sooner or later it will become not merely economically sound but absolutely essential to develop all the arable land in the province. Such a statement may seem remote and speculative to some people, and there have been no less speculative suggestions that synthetic foods, artificially raised planktons and other such innovations will relieve the shortages. But the fact remains that vast shortages already exist, and have existed for a long while; only economic difficulties stand between these shortages and North American surpluses. Moral considerations long ago made it plain that the economic difficulties must be overcome and political considerations are daily emphasizing the point. In time the problem is certain to be solved and in the meanwhile all arable lands must be considered a resource of paramount importance, worthy of fullest protection, even though they may not be immediately developed.

It has been pointed out that the average cash yields of arable lands in British Columbia, because of intensive use and a favourable growing climate, are something like three and a half times the Canadian average. From this it is argued that the farmlands themselves are capable of supporting a population of *farming people* up to 3½ times the Canadian average for equivalent acreage. This does not mean a yield 3½ times greater in food value and it seems questionable that the figures would hold for the undeveloped arable lands of the province, since large acreages are in the Bulkley River and Peace River areas, where bigger farm units are essential; but it certainly emphasizes the quality and productivity of the arable lands so far developed.

There is no possible doubt that well planned irrigation could bring many thousands of valuable acres into high production, especially in such places as the Thompson Valley, where soil is good but rainfall negligible. The yield of some areas that are already improved and highly productive, such as the lower Fraser Valley, can also be markedly increased by irrigation. The water is available. It is simply a matter of finding the economic demand and ensuring, by the use of proper techniques, that leaching is avoided and water tables are preserved.

Most soil experts consider that a large proportion of the province's four and a half million acres of organic soils could be drained and converted into profitable farmlands. But present information suggests that these lands have greater value as water reservoirs and that extensive draining might seriously affect the value of nearby farms and other resources. It is clear that nothing of the sort should be done without a great deal of careful study, but it is more than likely that proper survey and assessment would show that some recovery could be made with safety.

While the relatively small acreage of arable soil is intensely valuable for the province's future, the large areas of grazing and forest lands are in some ways even more important to the over-all economy. Some grazing lands have soils that could be converted to arable use by irrigation, while the carrying capacity of others could be increased by irrigation or other improvement. The chief danger to these lands is overgrazing, which can lead to very rapid soil deterioration and serious erosion. Damage of this sort immediately affects other resources – water storage is reduced, excessive silting may damage stream beds and destroy salmon spawn, flood control is made more difficult, game animals are starved out, recreational values are reduced or destroyed, and forest cover and reproduction may be set back. Because of the very large areas of the province involved, carefully calculated grazing controls are essential to the proper use of all grazing and "timber grazing" soils.

Forest soils, which cover the largest area and are by far the most important in the economy of the province, have suffered greater damage than any others through mismanagement, especially in the coastal areas of high rainfall. Clear logging, followed by drastic burns, has exposed the already weak soils. Thin soil covering the rocky ridge tops has been swept away into the gullies, leaving many formerly productive ridges completely barren. The rains have swept through the unprotected hillsides, further leaching the weak soils, often carrying them away to pockets or into the streams and rivers. Skid-roads planned only for logging purposes have packed the soil in some places and increased gullying in others.

Since all these soils had already suffered the damage of growing a full crop of climax coniferous forest, with its high demand, slow evaporation and extensive leaching, the natural process of restoration takes over in the re-seeding of pioneer types of deciduous trees such as alder, maple, poplar and willow. In the normal course these would restore the soil deficiencies and in time permit the climax coniferous forest to take over again. This is a long, slow process which foresters have tried to shorten by replanting coniferous stands. The process is often successful, but it raises the very important question of how much damage may be done to the soil by production of successive coniferous crops on damaged soil. The wiser course may very well be to allow the deciduous crops to develop and do their work of restoration while technological research is put to work to find economic uses for them.

It is clear that no significant quantities of soil are going to be built up during the lifetime of this civilization and that all existing soils will be needed for survival. Some may be improved, some may be converted to more productive uses. But the tendency under any highly developed civilization is always towards loss of soil.

Erosion and exhaustion through misuse are the commonest causes of loss, in British Columbia as elsewhere. But in a country whose arable lands are as limited as those of British Columbia urbanization or "city-spread" can be a major cause of loss. In the lower Fraser Valley industrial and residential subdivisions are swallowing up some of the most productive land in the province and there is no doubt that protective measures are long overdue. There is plenty of room for building sites of all kinds on the less productive hillsides, and while these may be more costly to develop there is no possible doubt that the long-term economy of the province would gain enormously.

Further significant soil losses are to be expected also from large and small hydro-electric projects which flood the already limited valley floors of the province. These losses may not be felt as immediately as are the losses of arable lands to urbanization, because they occur in remote areas, where only limited development or utilization has been undertaken. But in any long-term view they are soil losses that reduce the potential yield of the province just as seriously as erosion or urbanization or any other cause. The only difference is that they may be expected to lead to a compensating yield of a different type. Power lines and highways also remove large areas of soil from production.

Soil, and the use of soil, affects all the resources and all their uses. In return it is directly affected by these uses. Soil does not look after itself. It cannot restore itself at anything approaching the speed with which human use can damage it, and all damage from misuse is progressive. Scientific understanding of soils and their uses has advanced steadily throughout the twentieth century and some good work has been done in British Columbia. But there is room for a great deal more and, because soil is fundamental, the proper care and use of the other resources cannot be undertaken without it. Unfortunately most soil research is in the realm of pure science, which does not show immediate cash returns for expenditure, so money is not easily found for it. But as government and industry advance into planning for long-term use instead of short-term exploitation, the need for understanding soil is bound to become so obvious that money will be found.

Photographs of the soil profiles taken by Peter Parsons of the Photographic Branch of the Department of Recreation and Conservation. The other colour photographs are by Dr. C. A. Rowles of the Department of Soil Science, University of British Columbia. The profiles themselves were loaned by the Soil department.

...luvial soils of recent origin are widely distri-
...ted along many British Columbia rivers. Such
...ls are often potentially very productive but are
...metimes subject to flooding and may require
dyking and drainage. In the profile of the typical
alluvial soil shown at the right, note the three
successive surface soil layers that have been buried
by fresh deposits.

ALLUVIAL

The soil landscape (below) and profile (right) are typical of Black (Chernozemic) soils. These soils are found in Southern and Central British Columbia and in the Peace River region. Chernozemic soils are usually neutral to slightly basic in reaction and quite fertile, though insufficient soil moisture during midsummer often limit crop yields unless irrigated. Black soils are very valuable for ranching, mixed farming and grain growing.

BLACK

Gray wooded soils are very widely distributed in Central and North Eastern British Columbia. The surface mineral horizons of these soils are distinctly gray, (see profile at left) and when cultivated they impart a similar gray colour to the cultivated fields (see soil landscape below). Gray wooded soils are valuable for forestry, the principal natural species being spruce, pine and poplar, and for mixed farming, the most suitable crops being legumes, grasses and coarse grasses.

GRAY WOODED

REDDISH BROWN
(CONCRETIONARY)

PODZOL

BROWN WOODED

DARK GRAY
GLEIZOLIC

ALL WATER comes from the oceans in the form of rain, fog, hail or snow. It falls upon the earth and is carried back to the sea, to be raised again by the sun's heat and returned yet again to the land.

This is a simple statement of what scientists call the hydrologic cycle. British Columbia's ocean and source of water is the North Pacific and so long as the earth forms remain unchanged and the power of the sun remains constant, it is an inexhaustible source; moisture will be drawn up and clouds will form over the ocean, to be driven landward by the prevailing onshore winds. There the mountains will force them up to colder altitudes and rain or snow will fall.

Roughly one-fifth of the water that falls over land drains directly back into the ocean through the rivers. The rest is held temporarily in the snow and ice of glaciers and snow-fields or finds its way into underground reservoirs and rivers through clefts and fissures in bed-rock; or it is absorbed by soil and surface rock and taken up by plants and trees. From snow-fields and surface rock and soil it is drawn up again by evaporation, and the plants and trees breathe it out in fine vapour – an acre of corn will breathe out 3500 tons of water in its growing season. The clouds so formed may spill their moisture yet again upon the land, so that water originally drawn from the ocean may serve the land several times at several different places before it is returned to the sea again. But in the end it will return to one ocean or another and so complete the cycle. Nor is there any escape from the cycle, for all moisture is held within the ceiling of the earth's surrounding atmosphere.

In British Columbia the high mountains stand directly against the ocean all along the coast. Behind them stand successive ranges all the way to the final barrier of the Rockies in the east. Each mountain range exacts its toll of precipitation as the clouds form against it, a heavy toll on the western or windward slopes, a

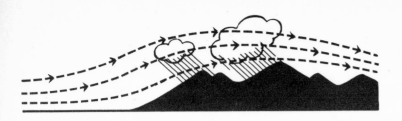

lesser toll on the leeward slopes. The plateaus and valleys immediately behind the mountains draw little precipitation and are said to be in "rain-shadow". And this, in large measure, sets the patterns of climate throughout the province. These patterns, naturally, are just as varied and complicated as are the province's physical features.

Along the west coast of Vancouver Island the rainfall is nearly everywhere in excess of a hundred inches a year. On the western slope of the high mountains in the centre of the island it is over 150 inches. From there it drops off to between sixty and a hundred inches on the eastern slopes of the mountains and finally to something between thirty and sixty inches along the eastern shore of the Island and throughout the Strait of Georgia. On the lower slopes of the mainland it increases again to over sixty inches, then to over a hundred inches and finally to a hundred and fifty inches or more on the highest levels.

Once the mass of Coast Range is passed, precipitation falls off quite rapidly to the twenty- or thirty-inch average of the interior plateau and the extreme dryness of the sheltered valleys – ten to fifteen inches along much of the Fraser's valley, in the Okanagan and in the grazing lands south of Kamloops, five to ten inches annually in the Thompson Valley, the lower Chilcotin Valley and around the Osoyoos fruit lands. It rises again to fifty and sixty inches and even more on the western slopes of the Selkirks and the Purcells, drops away to ten or twenty inches in the Rocky Mountain Trench, rises once more to between thirty and sixty inches on the faces of the Rockies themselves. The air has become steadily drier as it passes eastward over the land, but there is still enough moisture for this.

North of Vancouver Island the pattern is varied only by the physical variations of the country. Across Queen Charlotte Sound the sea winds have clear access to the slopes of the mainland mountains and precipitation between Namu and Prince Rupert is as heavy as along the western slopes of the Vancouver Island mountains – averaging generally from a hundred to a hundred and fifty inches, occasionally exceeding two hundred inches. Beyond the eastern slopes it decreases to the ten- to twenty-inch average of the interior plateau, increasing again at Prince George and on the slopes of the northern Rockies. North of Prince Rupert the clouds find a way back through the Nass and Skeena gaps to make a twenty- to thirty-inch average through much of the north; this falls off to less than twenty inches along the line of the Finlay River in the Rocky Mountain Trench, increases again to as much as forty inches in the mountains and levels off to the internal continental average of fifteen to twenty inches over the Peace River country and the transmontane part of the province generally.

This, in broad outline, is how water comes to the province – from the ocean, massively and abundantly, yet with very uneven distribution, although the patterns are recognizable and easily understood. If this water were evenly distributed over the whole surface of the province it would amount to a little over forty inches a year, a very pleasant and satisfactory amount indeed for almost every purpose, if it also happened to fall at just the right seasons. The broken nature of the land produces instead what are probably the widest variations of precipitation to be found anywhere in Canada – all the way from a fourteen-year average of 264 inches at Henderson Lake on the west coast of Vancouver Island to a low of some seven inches annually at Ashcroft in the central interior. And to complicate matters still further, seasonal variations are such that some parts of the province have dry summers and wet winters, some dry winters and wet summers, some dry springs with wet winters, some dry springs with wet summers.

Largely because of these variations, proper use of the province's abundant water presents very real and complicated problems as soon as intensive use of any of the other resources is attempted. Farmers need water for irrigation, especially in the summer-dry areas; hydro engineers need even flows along the river systems throughout the year; foresters need abundant water to grow their trees and reduce their fire hazard; industries need water, cities and people need water; water is needed for transportation, sanitation, recreation, for wildlife, range cattle and fisheries. Finally, there must be protection from excessive water in the form of floods. All these aspects of water use and water control are lively issues in the province to-day and will be for many years to come. It is safe to say that decisions made over the next fifty years as to the proper uses of water will have more influence on the future of the province than any others.

It must be accepted, I think, that comparatively little can be done to achieve better distribution of the air-borne water. Rain-making devices have been used in British Columbia, chiefly in attempts to increase hydro-electric storages during dry seasons, but no one has been able to show satisfactorily just what effect has been achieved. It seems reasonable to concede that the present theories have at least some practical value – after all, hard-headed business men have put out real money to give them a chance – and to conclude from this that further advances will be made. It may well become possible, for instance, to precipitate the contents of a cloud above a storage dam rather than below it or in some other watershed, or to bring down rain on the parched crowns of a growing forest rather than on the barren slopes of a mountain top. But it is wholly improbable that any economical way will be found of precipitating moisture where it is thinly diffused through the atmosphere rather than concentrated into cloud forms. Since moisture is so diffused over the drier areas at the times they most need it, other ways of bringing water to them will have to be found, and these are likely to be variations of the time-honoured methods of irrigation by surface water or underground water.

Water control and water management are two of the most important tools of

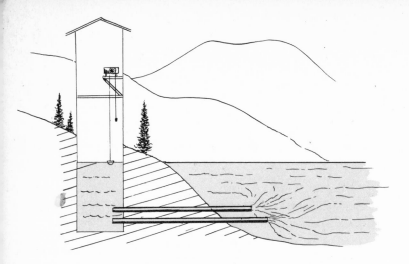

A hydrometric station measures both the height of the water in a river or stream and the rate at which it is flowing or "discharging". At left is a typical height-gauging installation and at bottom right is an illustration showing the measuring of stream discharge.

good resource management. The first prerequisite of water management is knowledge – knowledge of stream flows, of climatic conditions, of snowfall, of ground storage. The province has between two and three hundred active meteorological stations and about the same number of active hydrometric stations, which measure stream discharges. It also measures the depth and water content of snow on between seventy and one hundred snow courses, carefully selected to be representative of specific areas. Most of these stations are in the southern part of the province, on the Fraser and Columbia watersheds, but more will be established in the north as the country opens up.

The chief means of water control is storage. British Columbia, with its steep mountain slopes, narrow valleys and swift-flowing rivers, is not the easiest place to store water artificially. The natural storage of glaciers and "permanent" or seasonal snow-fields, of lakes and swamps and peat bogs, of soil and forest and other ground-cover, is, therefore, of very high value. Most qualified observers believe that drainage anywhere in the province should only be undertaken after most careful investigation, and then cautiously. Similarly, foresters are paying much closer attention to cutting systems that will retain snowfall for a maximum period. They are beginning to look with a doubtful eye on hauling methods that pack the soil excessively or tend to groove it into watercourses that speed run-off and lead to gullying.

Irrigation dams are the simplest and oldest form of man-made storage on a considerable scale. Their purpose is simply to hold the water of a wet period and feed it to the land in dry periods. Water may also be pumped from rivers and lakes and from underground for the same purpose, though usually at greater cost.

Most communities in British Columbia depend on storage dams for domestic water. Hydro-electric dams store vast quantities of water with the prime purpose of evening stream flow by holding back water from winter rains or spring and summer snow-melt; they may or may not conserve water for other purposes as well. The diversionary hydro-electric dams that turn water back from its natural flow through the interior of the province to spill it down the slopes of the Coast Range by the shortest route to salt water, actually reduce water storage, though it will probably be many years before the province is sufficiently developed to need the water that is lost in this way.

Of all man-made storage devices, flood-control dams on headwater streams are probably the most nearly ideal, since they can exert real control at comparatively low cost and in so doing serve all the other resources that depend on water with damage to none of them. Flood-control dams have been little used in British Columbia so far, though an important plan for such storage has been worked out on the Fraser system. It seems likely that they will eventually have a place on nearly all watersheds in the province, no matter what the priority use of the watershed; fisheries, forestry, hydro-power, agriculture, recreation and settlement all benefit from intelligent stream control and in due time intensive use of one or other of the resources or a combination of several will justify the expenditure.

The quality and abundance of British Columbia's water undoubtedly make it her most valuable single asset. Salmon fisheries, agriculture and forest growth depend absolutely upon it. Harnessed in the rivers, it produces vast quantities of electrical energy. Much recreation and a good part of the province's attraction for tourists, including the valuable sport fishery, depend upon water; scenery in large measure is water – water in glaciers and snow-capped mountains, water in lakes and falls and streams and forest growth. At this stage of development, perhaps it is dangerous to talk about a surplus of water. At least 400,000 acres of potentially good crop land still need water to make them productive. The majority of salmon and steelhead spawning streams could produce more fish given increased flows at low periods. Much of the good forest land could produce quicker and heavier crops with well-maintained water-tables – it is seldom realized that most of Vancouver Island, part of the Fraser Valley and a good section of the Lower Mainland suffer from summer drought affecting both farming and forestry. Modern industry uses vast quantities of water for cooling purposes and for waste disposal. Much water is needed for all these purposes, but it seems fairly certain that when all has been done that can be done to make full use of available water, many parts of the province will be left with seasonal flows that return largely unused to the ocean.

With water shortages already acute in parts of California and Arizona and bound

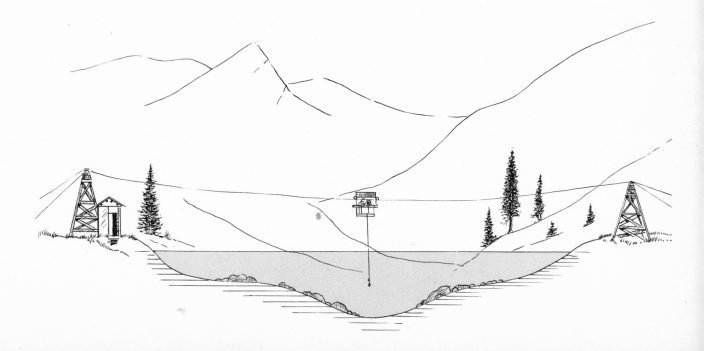

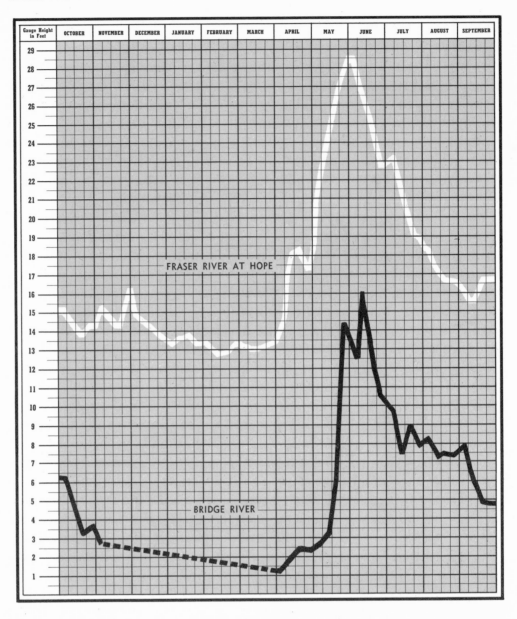

Above is a graphic illustration of the yearly fluctuation in gauge height of two rivers. The broken line in the Bridge River graph represents the winter frozen period. This Bridge River graph is based on figures obtained by a Dominion Government hydrometric station before the B.C. Electric dam system went in. Since then, the fluctuation has been reduced almost to nothing from the sixteen to one ratio shown here.

to become more acute throughout the Pacific states as population increases, it has been suggested that British Columbia's surplus water may one day become an exportable commodity and a highly valuable one. Since the only alternative is recovery of fresh water from the ocean, an extremely expensive process, there is not much doubt that this is so. At first sight it seems merely an extension of the principle of exportable water for hydro-electric purposes that will shortly be put into effect on the Columbia watershed. But there are important differences. The water in the Columbia is already leaving the country and has already been committed to important uses below the border; what will be exported is stored and regulated water, and the return for this will not be cash or credit, but a proportion of the power realized through regulation of the river flows. Direct export of water would be, as direct power exports have proved in the past, permanent and irrevocable. Populations would be built on it and could not later be destroyed by its withdrawal. Before exporting water, British Columbians would have to be very certain that it was a true surplus which could never be needed or used within the province.

The chief problem in management of the freshwater resources is that of retaining them in the land and in the watercourses until the greatest possible use has been made of them. They may, it is true, be damaged or wasted in other ways than by quick run-off – by silting and pollution, to name two – but these are matters for other chapters. So also is the salt-water resource itself in direct form, the water of the coastline and the continental shelf that does so much to shape the character of the province.

Precipitation of airborne water is a powerful factor in climate, but it is not the whole story. Climate is the sum of several things, the chief among them, after precipitation, being temperature, wind, humidity and sunshine. It is not a simple sum, but a total of averages and extremes measured through the months of the year. As everyone knows, climate is not constant or predictable; it can vary widely from year to year, and it is powerfully affected by pressure changes and large-scale movement of air masses. But it is constant and predictable within certain limits; we can be fairly certain, for instance, that winter temperatures in Victoria will not fall below zero, and we can be equally certain that winter temperatures at Fort Nelson will fall below zero.

For most people, the only useful way of expressing climate is by direct comparison with some place known to them. A man from Prince Rupert will know what to expect of Bergen in Norway when he is told that its climate is very similar to Prince Rupert's. If he were merely told that Bergen had a mean annual temperature of 44°F., with the low months averaging about 35°F. and the high months about 58°F., and an annual precipitation of over eighty inches, lower in the summer months but well distributed through the year, he would be considerably less certain of what to expect. Climate is an abstract thing and does not readily take shape from measurements. But it remains true that many of its important aspects can be expressed in terms of measurements.

Climatologists, who have to do something with the problem, express themselves in both ways. The south-east coast of Vancouver Island and the Gulf Islands have a climate formally classed as Cool Summer Mediterranean; much of the interior of the province and the transmontane section has a climate called Humid Continental with Cool or Cool, Short Summers; the Okanagan Valley and a good part of the Thompson Valley are Middle Latitude Steppe; the higher elevations of the mountains throughout the province are considered Polar, though this classification naturally applies at lower elevations in the far north than in the south.

These classifications have fairly precise meaning for the scientist and at the same time they carry a roughly suggestive message for the layman. Certain types of measurement permit similar useful generalizations. The total of frost-free days, for instance, gives a useful idea of the length of the growing season; mean daily temperatures for January and July give a fair idea of the normal extremes; a fourth measurement is of accumulated heat, expressed in the number of days in the year the temperature is above a certain figure, multiplied by the average number of degrees by which it exceeds this figure. Taken with the number of frost-free days, this gives some idea of the intensity of the growing season.

Climate is influenced by latitude and also by elevation, but these influences are fairly slight – a degree or two of mean temperature variation for each degree of latitude and perhaps three or four degrees for each thousand feet of altitude. The really large variations are caused by the movement of great atmospheric air masses; these movements are created by the atmospheric winds and usually limited by the protective mountain ranges. Very broadly, it could be said that the province is a rather unequal battleground for the generally mild air masses from the Pacific and the harsher Continental air masses. For the most part Maritime air prevails west of the Rockies and Continental air on the east, but at times either one may invade the whole province, and at most times some Continental influence is felt west of the Rockies.

Both the Maritime and Continental air masses are of northern origin and so are called Polar Maritime and Polar Continental. The Polar Maritime air usually comes to the Pacific Coast by a long, circuitous route from north-east Asia, first southward, then swinging eastward and finally north-westward along the coastline, bringing abundant moisture and relatively high temperatures to the south-east winds that are typical of winter weather along the coast. Its summer travel tends to be more direct and the summer north-westerlies are characteristically drier and cooler. Coastal temperature ranges are therefore kept at a minimum, with a January mean of 32°-40°F., a July mean of 55°-60°F. and an average of something over 200 frost-free days.

Much of this Pacific air passes over or between the Coast Mountains but throughout most of the interior of the province it is soon modified by the Polar Continental air coming down from the Yukon and Alaska or from east of the Rockies. Only in the southern interior is the Maritime air usually dominant and here its effect shows up most plainly in the sheltered valleys. The Fraser, Thompson and Okanagan valleys and the West Kootenays have January means of 20°-32°F. and July means of 65° to 70°F., and the first three of these have between 150 and 200 frost-free days – about the same number as can be expected along most of the south-east coast of Vancouver Island.

This effect reaches over as far as the southern part of the Rocky Mountain Trench and up the Fraser as far as Quesnel, where the average number of frost-free days is between 100 and 150. But from there north it falls off sharply in the face of the Arctic air masses. At Prince George the number of frost-free days is between 50 and 100. A few miles north, at the sources of the Parsnip, it drops to less than 50 and except where the Skeena Gap reaches in, this holds throughout the entire northern part of the province lying west of the Rockies. East of the Rockies Continental air pushes in to give much of the grain-growing Peace River Country a frost-free period of over a hundred days.

These, then, are the major atmospheric influences on the climate of the province. They are subject to extremely sharp local variations; a temperature of 74° below zero at Smith River in the northern part of the province is believed to be the lowest ever recorded on the continent, while summer temperatures of well over 100°F. are common in the Thompson Valley and along a short section of the Fraser. The large lakes of the interior valleys have an important local effect in modifying winter climate and these same valleys may feel the summer effect of Tropical Continental air masses pushing up through the dry interior of Washington State. Along the coastline the heads of the major inlets have January mean temperatures ten to twenty degrees lower than those of the outer coast and cold interior winds from the mountain passes can produce below-zero temperatures at sea level. Victoria averages 2193 hours of sunshine yearly, one of the highest recordings in Canada, while Prince Rupert has only 989 hours, the lowest recording in Canada. Altitude everywhere has sharp local effects upon climate, not merely because of elevation but because of the shadowing effect of the mountains themselves; a southern slope will be exposed to many more hours of winter sun than a northern slope and a high ridge may provide important protection from prevailing winds.

Climate plays an obvious major part in the use of agricultural resources – to a great extent it controls what crops can be grown; it may influence irrigation, fertilization, manuring and pest control. It is equally important in almost every aspect of forestry, from fire control to the selection of strains and species for reforestation. Climate powerfully influences water storage and stream flows, and so is of concern to both fisheries and hydro-electric engineers. It is a tremendous factor in flood control. It affects transportation of all kinds and has important bearing on recreation and tourist values. In the far north and at high altitudes, cold winters may limit the working days and affect the costs of mining, construction work and other projects.

Up to this point in history, man has been able to influence climate only involuntarily and nearly always for the worse; by wholesale cutting of forests, by draining of swamp lands and by exhausting soils, he has all too often created deserts. He is able now at least to give serious consideration to such formidable projects as the Russian proposal to dam Bering Strait and pump warmer Pacific waters into the Arctic Ocean. Whether he is also able to predict accurately and control closely the effects of such projects seems much more doubtful. Fortunately the international and political aspects of such undertakings are sure to prove much more difficult to solve than mere engineering problems, so there is likely to be a healthy delay while a good deal more knowledge of climatic conditions and effects is developed – enough, perhaps, to make the projects themselves look far less attractive.

Meanwhile, man will have to go on learning how to use natural climate, how to live in it and work with it – a task in which he has so far proved outstandingly successful. The extremes and variations of climate in British Columbia, which are greater than those of any similarly placed area in the world, present many problems. But steadily-improving knowledge and increasing understanding are certain to reveal more and better ways of living in the country and of using its resources safely and fully.

the forests CHAPTER 6

HAVING SET the broad physical features and conditions of British Columbia, it is natural to go on to the forests. The province has some 118 million acres of forest land, nearly sixty per cent of its total area. Since over thirty per cent of the total area is classified as alpine and barren, it is easy to understand that forest land represents the overwhelming proportion of the province that is used, lived in and familiar to the people. Forest crops and the manufacture of wood products account for some forty cents of every dollar earned in the province. Forests are by far the most valuable of the province's directly realizable resources.

In all the expansive talk of industrial development, oil and natural gas, hydro-electric power and other such spectacular affairs, this fact is sometimes obscured. It can be forgotten quite readily in city life and is seldom honoured as it should be in politics. But the public feels it and remembers it sharply enough when there is a prolonged strike or shut-down in the woods, and again when a particularly disastrous fire season calls attention to the inadequacy of its means of protecting the forests. This awareness fades away rapidly in normal times, but it should not, because there is nothing so far to suggest that the forests may one day be replaced by some other major source of income. So far as anyone can judge at the present time, the prosperity of future generations of British Columbians will depend just as heavily upon the good condition of the forests as does that of the present generation.

The province's forests vary with climate and rainfall and altitude. Their character and pattern of distribution strongly reflect the rainfall patterns already described – that is to say, the heavier and more luxuriant forests grow on the western slopes of the mountains, where the rainfall is heaviest, while lighter and sparser forests grow on the eastern slopes. Working eastward into drier climate, the forests grow steadily lighter and the trees smaller, except in the Columbia Mountains where rainfall rises well above the interior averages. The deep valleys of the south are often treeless on their floors and lower slopes, either grassland or semi-desert. Considerable areas in the north at fairly high altitude are alpine and treeless, as are smaller areas in the south at still higher altitudes.

Of the 118 million acres of forest land in the province, 56 million acres support mature forest, and the remaining 62 million are younger forests in various stages of growth, or land that has been logged or burned, or both logged and burned but is considered suitable for the production of commercial forest. The most important and valuable timber lands are those of the coastal area: Vancouver Island and the Queen Charlotte Islands, most of the smaller islands and the whole of the mainland coast from Vancouver to Prince Rupert, including the long inlets and the valleys at their heads. Naturally the quantity and quality of the timber varies greatly over this vast area, but it is all of the same coastal, rain-forest type, thickly crowded, drawn to great height and massive crowns that exclude almost all sunlight from the forest floor. Fire is not a serious hazard except in the south, and then usually on logged-over land. Except behind fires, regeneration is good and regrowth is fairly rapid, but the brown podzolic soils common to most of the area and the cool climate do not produce a growth rate nearly as rapid as that of Washington State and some of the other more favoured forest areas of the world. In other words, this is the best forest land in British Columbia or in Canada, good by any standards, but by no means the best in the world, as British Columbians sometimes like to think.

The southern two-thirds of Vancouver Island, and a roughly corresponding area along the mainland coast, is within the Douglas fir belt and the timber here is, or was, superb. Below the 2000-foot level, Douglas fir is the predominating species, sometimes making up as much as seventy per cent of the stand, with western red cedar, western hemlock and true or silver fir accounting for the rest. The trees are large individually, sometimes up to six feet and more on the stump and rising well over a hundred feet to the lowest limb. In the best stands they are closely spaced and individual acres have yielded as much as 100,000 cubic feet in stands averaging 60,000 cubic feet to the acre; 10,000 cubic feet to the acre is a fairly common yield, though an average of 15,000 or more to the acre was considered first-class timber even in the early logging days.*

Most of this prime Douglas fir area has now been logged, much of it by devastating high-lead and clear-cutting methods, followed by serious fires which destroyed regrowth and caused a good deal of erosion. In some areas the regeneration has been good and regrowth fairly rapid. But very large areas are only slowly coming back and some are not restocked at all.

Over much of the rest of the coast cedar is the predominant species, with a supporting mixture of hemlock, silver fir and spruce; in the south, at elevations of over 2000 feet, hemlock and silver fir are often predominant. On the Queen Charlotte Islands spruce and hemlock are predominant in roughly equal proportions. Both

*All timber volume figures are here given in cubic feet to conform with present official practice in the province. For conversion purposes 1 cubic foot = 6 board feet (approximately).

ARBUTUS　　DOGWOOD　　RED ALDER　　CASCARA　　GARRY OAK

these types of forest, the cedar-hemlock and spruce-hemlock, reflect the heavier rainfall of the mountain slopes and the open coastline. Because they are less accessible they have not been so heavily logged; the damp climate keeps fires at a minimum and regeneration is generally good except where rapid growth of deciduous brush tends to choke out the conifers.

These coastal types of forest persist in the valleys and on the lower slopes of the Coast Mountains as far as the Fraser Valley, over a hundred miles inland, in the south, and almost to Hazelton on the Skeena watershed in the north. But the timber falls off in size and quality on the eastern slopes of the mountains, and soon changes character altogether.

The floors of the dry valleys – upper Fraser, Thompson, Okanagan, Similkameen and southern Rocky Mountain Trench – may be grassland or sage-brush desert or parkland. Dry-forest timber starts on the mountain slopes, at elevations of two or three thousand feet, and is at first yellow pine with Douglas fir in open stands, then fir, yellow pine, larch and lodgepole pine. Finally at elevations above 3500 feet, where rainfall is fairly heavy, it becomes Subalpine forest of spruce, lodgepole pine and alpine fir. The open stands of yellow pine and Douglas fir, which have been heavily logged, usually average only one or two thousand cubic feet to the acre; the Subalpine forest is much denser, but the trees are small and large areas have been burned over by lightning fires. Yellow pine reproduces poorly after logging and is usually replaced by fir and lodgepole pine. Lodgepole pine is also the dominant regeneration behind the major fires at the higher altitudes and the interior has large stands of almost pure lodgepole that are still immature.

LODGEPOLE PINE   PONDEROSA PINE   TAMARAC LARCH   HEMLOCK   ENGELMANN SPRUCE   RED CEDAR

Where rainfall becomes heavier again, in the Monashee and Selkirk ranges, on the western slope of the Purcells and at higher elevations on both sides of the southern Rocky Mountain Trench, rain-forest types grow strongly in what is known as Columbia Forest. These heavy forests are mainly cedar, hemlock and spruce, though white pine, larch, Douglas fir and alpine fir are mixed in with the predominant species. Some stands carry as much as ten thousand cubic feet to the acre and are comparable to good coast timber. From an altitude of about four thousand feet in the Columbia Mountains and six thousand feet in the Rockies the subalpine types take over again.

North of Clinton on the Fraser watershed and throughout most of the interior plateau as far as Prince George there is much open grassland, with scattered stands of Douglas fir, lodgepole pine and alpine fir. The trees are small and the stands low in volume, usually less than 3500 cubic feet to the acre, though occasionally up to 6000 in such areas as Quesnel Lake and the Bowron River, where local rainfall is higher. This is the forest of the Cariboo Parklands, primarily grazing land, but with considerable commercial forest value.

North of Prince George, through most of the Peace River drainage, the Liard River drainage and the northern Rocky Mountain Trench, there is a forest of white and black spruce, alpine fir, lodgepole pine and Alaska birch, known as northern or Boreal Forest. This also is a low-volume forest of smallish trees, the stands averaging less than 3500 cubic feet to the acre, but it is generally cheaply accessible and is so extensive that good use can be made of it.

This is by no means an exhaustive description of the forest types of the province,

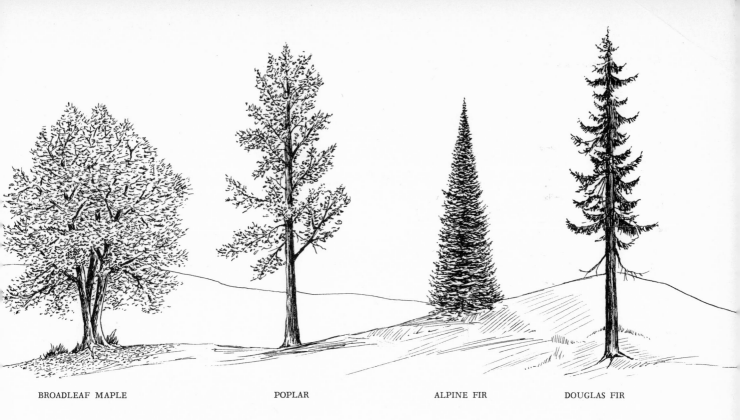

BROADLEAF MAPLE   POPLAR   ALPINE FIR   DOUGLAS FIR

but it serves to give a fairly clear idea of the range of variation and some suggestion of the complicated problems of protection, use and management. Essentially there are two great divisions, Coastal and Interior. Both are softwood or coniferous forests, evolved to their climax stage – that is to say, they have developed behind the retreating ice of ten thousand years ago through changing types of vegetable ground-cover to their present state, which is exactly matched to soil, altitude and climate and so, under natural conditions, is capable of reproducing itself indefinitely. Use and misuse by man can change or modify these conditions so that reproduction and regrowth are affected, usually adversely. This creates a whole range of technical problems, from the biological and mechanical questions of reforestation to industrial questions such as the use and marketing of species that temporarily replace the climax forests – in large sections of the coastal area, for instance, a deciduous forest of alder, maple and some poplar has become firmly established on land that formerly grew the very finest Douglas fir stands.

Beyond and above all these technical, economic, mechanical and biological problems is the one really critical problem – that of balancing the annual forest cut accurately against the annual regrowth, or increment as foresters call it. Under proper planning this should control and direct most of the other problems of management, though it often does not. It is itself a complex problem, involving all the others, because cut must balance regrowth not merely on a province-wide basis, but locally, in all the forest types and in all the key areas, if the balancing is to have proper effect. At present the Coast Forest, except on managed units, is overcut and over-committed, while Interior Forests are undercut and under-committed. Some of the difficulties of adjusting this serious imbalance will become apparent in the more detailed examination of the use of forest resources which follows.

OWNERSHIP OF FOREST LANDS

When the province was first settled, timber had very little value. Great trees were available everywhere and could be put to little use. They were an encumbrance rather than an asset to settlers who were looking for clear land that would grow agricultural crops. Early governments accordingly sold much good forest outright, simply as land rather than forest land, and made huge land grants to railroad companies without taking the timber on the land into account. Land so alienated is now known as "Crown Grant" land and use of the timber on it is not subject to government control.

A system of leasing land to sawmill operators for the cutting of timber was started in 1870 and continued with various changes in the terms of the leases until 1905. This system was abolished in 1905, but holders of leases in good standing continued to hold them under new provisions, and some leases are still held to-day.

A somewhat similar system of licensing sawmill operators to cut timber on certain acreages was begun in 1888. The operator did not have to have a sawmill of a specific capacity to justify his acreage, but he was limited to a thousand acres (later 640 acres), the licence was not transferable, it had to be renewed each year, and a royalty of fifty cents per thousand board feet was payable on all timber harvested. In 1905 licences were made renewable for twenty-one years and became for the first time transferable. Royalty was to be paid at rates prevailing when the timber was cut. This naturally produced an orgy of timber-staking and much speculative buying of timber licences. In 1907 the government stopped the practice of licensing, but by that time 15,000 square miles of the best timber land in the province had been alienated. Because this huge area could not be properly logged in twenty-one years without disrupting markets, the licences were made indefinitely renewable in 1909.

Licensing was not intended to have this effect. More than ten years earlier, in 1896, the Legislature had begun to recognize the true value of timber lands and had prohibited their sale – anything over 8000 board feet (1350 cubic feet) to the acre west of the Coast Mountains and anything over 5000 (850 cubic feet) in the interior being classed as timberland. Licences and leases were intended to permit cutting by private interests while the ownership of the real resource, the timberland itself, remained in the Crown. Many licences have, in fact, reverted to the Crown, but a total of nearly 2½ million acres of licences and leases is still in force, carrying about 13.7 billion cubic feet of timber. The 5½ million acres of privately held, Crown-granted timberlands carry about 17½ billion cubic feet of timber.

Colour photographs taken by the Photographic Branch of the Public Information Division of the B.C. Forest Service.

MOUNTAIN AND WESTERN HEMLOCK
showing difference in cones and leaves

MOUNTAIN HEMLOCK
showing female flowers above, male flowers below

WESTERN HEMLOCK OR ALASKA PINE
showing male flowers

YELLOW CEDAR
showing last year's cone and male flowers

RED CEDAR
male and female flowers and last year's cones

WESTERN WHITE PINE
showing male and female flowers

LODGEPOLE PINE
new and old cones and flowers

PONDEROSA PINE
male flowers, needles and cones

EUROPEAN LARCH
new and old cones and new growth

WESTERN LARCH
in flowering stage

SITKA SPRUCE
male and female flowers, new growth, last year's cone

DOUGLAS FIR AND WESTERN HEMLOCK
showing mature cones on both

ALPINE FIR
female flowers and new growth

ALPINE FIR
male and female flowers

DOUGLAS FIR
showing the flowers just turning up

DOUGLAS FIR, INTERIOR SPECIES
showing female flowers

DOUGLAS FIR
male and female flowers, terminal buds, new growth and ripe cone

BALSAM FIR OR AMABILIS FIR
male flowers and foliage

INSIDE THE DRYING KILN

DOUGLAS FIR SEED

DUNCAN NURSERY — 2 YEAR STOCK IN FOREGROUND

PLANTING CREW

A YOUNG PLANTATION — MOHUN LAKE AREA

OLDER PLANTATION NEAR CAMPBELL RIVER

As against these figures of private ownership the Crown holds some 110 million acres of forest land, carrying over 340 billion cubic feet of sound wood. The significance of this vast acreage and tremendous volume falls into proper proportion when it is realized that the figures represent an average of about 3000 cubic feet to the acre compared to an average of about 3200 cubic feet on Crown Grant lands and 5500 cubic feet to the acre on licences and leases. In other words, the great proportion of government-owned timberland is in the Interior Forests, where yields are low, or in the poorer and less accessible parts of the Coast Forest.

Since the government in British Columbia does not cut timber or manufacture wood products, government ownership of timberlands is not in itself important. But government control of the use of timberlands is all-important if sustained yield and sound forest management are to be ensured. This was recognized by the Sloan Report of 1946, which recommended a system of forest-management licences and public working circles on which sustained-yield management – by balancing cut to increment over ten-year periods – would be practised.

Forest-management licences, now known as Tree Farm licences, were designed primarily for timber owners who had manufacturing plants – sawmills, pulp mills or whatever they might be – to supply, or who planned to build them. In return for submitting his existing holdings to the government management policy, a plant owner would be granted, in perpetuity, enough additional Crown acreage to take care of the needs of his plant. This had the effect of encouraging the establishment of long-term industry and at the same time brought a significant area of alienated forest land back under government control. The holder of a forest-management licence has no ownership of the licensed land, only of the timber crop from the land – and his ownership of this is conditional upon his proper management of it. There are twenty-eight forest-management licences in the province, totalling about three million acres, with a timber volume of about 15 billion cubic feet. No others are to be granted for at least five years, pending re-examination of their effect.

Public working circles are blocks of Crown timber planned as units that can be cropped under sustained-yield management. The whole ownership, control and management of these areas remains in the hands of the government through the B.C. Forest Service. The B.C. Forest Service simply lets contracts for the cropping of various parts of the area at the proper times. The intention in this was to make a supply of timber available to small operators who could not take on the responsibilities of perpetual sustained-yield management. Thirty-two public working circles have been established in the province, providing an annual yield for small operators of rather more than 190 million cubic feet from a little over two million acres.*

*Twenty-two sustained-yield units have been added to this total since 1957. They comprise 13 million acres of forest land bearing 21 billion cubic feet of mature timber.

The colour photographs illustrate the reforestation work being carried out by the B.C. Forest Service.

Two other forms of timber holding are provided for, the farm wood-lot licence and the tree farm. A *bona fide* farmer may apply for up to 640 acres of Crown forest land provided he will manage this with any other forest land he may own on a sustained-yield basis. A tree farm involves no Crown land, but provides taxation relief for any small owner of forest land who undertakes to manage his holdings as a tree farm – that is, for the production of continuous forest crops.

The general effect of these new developments has been to bring about one-third of the province's annual timber cut of one billion cubic feet under sustained-yield management, mainly through the forest-management licences and the public working circles. This, plainly, is a very large step towards proper use of the forest resource. A secondary effect has been to speed up the concentration of timber holdings in the hands of a few large operators. To some extent this may be inevitable; modern operations designed to make the fullest possible use of timber call for large capital investment and diversified markets. The large operator either supplies his own markets in his own diversified plants or is able to fill specialized markets year in, year out. From his large holdings he is also better able to meet whatever markets are currently favourable. A large operator can balance losses against gains, while a small operator has only gains or losses. And there can be little question that a large holding of timberland lends itself much better to sustained-yield planning and practice than a small one.

Many small operators do not wish to become simply contractors, working for the large operators or bidding on the annual cut of the public working circles, and in this they have a good deal of public sympathy. It has long been part of the social philosophy of the province that natural resources are public property and that a direct share in them should be open to small investors as well as large. Small operators have served the province well throughout its history in mining, fisheries and agriculture, as well as lumbering, and it would seem that they have a part to play in sustained-yield operation.

Of the twenty-eight forest-management licences already granted in the province so far, only one is smaller than 15,000 acres. From this it appears that a smaller unit under somewhat different terms is needed for the small operators. To meet this need a system of "Tree Farm Licences" was suggested at the Ninth Resources Conference. Some of the details proposed for this form of licence were that it should not exceed 3000 acres, capable of an annual cut of half a million board feet; that it should be transferable to another owner only if his total holdings would still be less than three thousand acres; that rental and forest-protection tax would be the same as for a forest-management licence; and, of course, that there must be a specific working plan for the harvest of the timber, a cut balanced to regrowth over each ten years, reforestation where needed and proper access roads and water supplies for fire control.

Whether the small logger would survive on this basis is, perhaps, debatable, but it seems clear that he should be given a chance not merely to survive but to grow, if only because a system of this sort gives far better control of the use of forest land than do timber sales. But the small logger is more important than this. He is still essential to efficient harvesting in the interior forests, and his independence and ingenuity are needed throughout the industry to provide new thought and new blood.

The important changes that have come about since the Sloan Report of 1946 promise well for the forest lands of the province, but so long as two-thirds of the annual cut comes from land that is not fully controlled, there is still much to be done. There is no doubt that the sustained-yield concept has developed a whole new appreciation of the value and importance of forest land and has influenced the use of lands not directly subject to its control. But it is only a first step, one that roughly fits the exigencies of the moment. These will change and further changes will come as they do. At present it can be said that the broad principle of treating forests as a soil crop, of constantly balancing cut to regrowth, has been recognized. But a real management system must go far beyond this, into the infinity of details that make forest land less or more productive, into the proper balancing of cut by areas and species and the planning of regrowth to meet specific needs. How the present systems of tenure will fit into the intensive managment that is bound to come remains to be seen. But it is important that no system should be so permanent and inexorable as to stand in the way of the best possible management practices.

CHAPTER 7 *harvesting and using wood*

THE HISTORY OF LOGGING PRACTICE in the Pacific North-west is told in eras of power. Eastern logging methods of winter hauling and spring river drives have never fitted western conditions. The western logger was faced with mild climate, gigantic trees and short-run, rapid rivers. He had to have power, and power in massive quantities.

The first power era was that of horses and oxen hauling in six- and eight-yoke teams over skid-roads cunningly built and carefully greased, on flat land within a short distance of salt water. It served for a time and cleared the forest from the edge of the water. But more power was needed to reach farther back and into the hills. It had to be power that could haul all day without tiring and cover ten or twenty miles for one covered by the bulls and horses. It had to be flexible power that would gradually take up a tremendous strain without breaking rigging. It had to work on side-hills and across canyons and gullies.

The only type of power that would do all this was steam-power, and by 1900 the era of steam had begun in the woods. The first steam donkeys dragged logs straight along the ground and used horses to take the line back into the woods. But within a few years spar-trees, standing a hundred to two hundred feet high, were being used to lift the front end of the logs off the ground by a main-line running through a block rigged near the top; a second drum on the donkey pulled the line back into the woods through a system of blocks rigged at ground level. Railroads ran back ten, twenty, even fifty miles from salt water. As fast as the donkey engines yarded the logs to the side of the tracks other machines loaded them and still others hauled them away on steel wheels over steel to the booming grounds.

The era of steam-power lasted some forty years and stripped away the great stands of Douglas fir from Oregon, Washington and British Columbia. By 1940 it was beginning to yield to the era of the internal combustion engine and the rubber tire. Where the skidders and high-lead machines had roared and their rigging had clattered, caterpillar tractors were snaking out logs on the lift of high arches instead of spar-trees. Where Shay and Climax and Baldwin locomotives had hauled over steel, the muttering many-tired diesel trucks hauled over smooth-packed gravel. No longer bound by the limits of two per cent adverse grades, the roads reached farther and farther out into the hills.

The logger of to-day has power, power to burn, power beyond the wildest dreams of the old-time bull-puncher. But there has always been another logger's dream – the sky hook. A sky hook is just that, a fine big hook, infinitely strong, firmly anchored in the sky. From this the logger would hang his blocks and rig his lines to lift or haul anything at all to anywhere at all; he would be able at last to "get his logs up off the ground". Lacking sky hooks, but always dreaming of them, he has had to rig his blocks from spar-trees, gin-poles, back-trees, A-frames and tractor arches. It has helped, as have the steel wheels of flat cars and skeleton cars and the rubber tires of the diesel trucks. But it seems possible that the next era of power may really be the era of the sky hook or something very like it – the helicopter. With this kind of power a whole world of new possibilities would open up. The word "inaccessible" would disappear from the forester's dictionary, or take on some altogether new meaning. Damage to soil and young growth would be negligible. Selection and thinning of timber would become an economy, not only for the future, but immediately. Expensive road-building would be cut to a minimum. Perhaps the helicopter as such may not achieve all these things, but a hovering machine capable of vertical lift and horizontal flight is a reality; given adequate power it would be the logger's sky hook with something added.

This brief sketch of logging conditions and methods applies mainly to the heavy timber of the coastal area. The year's cut in the province was about 50 million cubic feet in 1900. By 1909 it was over 100 million. By 1912 it was nearly 250 million, by 1920 over 350 million, in 1928 and 1929, 530 and 570 million respectively. The early depression years reduced the cut to something under 350 million in 1931-3, but by 1936 it was again in excess of 500 million. In the years since World War II it has gradually climbed to the present level of over one billion cubic feet

TRACTOR ARCH

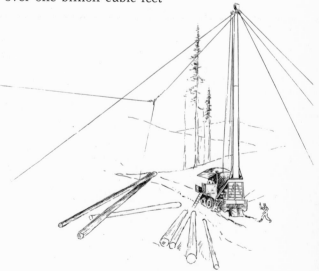

PORTABLE SPAR

annually. Until 1943 the interior log cut only once exceeded 85 million cubic feet and usually was far below this figure, so coast timber normally accounted for five-sixths of the cut through the first forty years of the century.

The tremendous increase in cut between 1900 and 1928, and especially between 1910 and 1928, reflects the growth of steam power. It was nearly all from the coast and mostly Douglas fir. It was clear logging – that is to say, everything was flattened and what was not worth taking out at the current market values was left to rot. It was usually followed by destructive fires. Little or no attempt was made at reforestation. No attention at all was paid to watershed values or soil protection. No serious attempt was made to leave seed trees. It sounds like an easy time, but as I remember it, it was not. It was a great, busting, exciting, highball time, but log prices were never high and a "haywire" show could go broke as easily as it can to-day. Too high a percentage of hemlock and silver fir in a stand was enough to make the difference between profit and loss. Even western red cedar was a liability much of the time.

The legacy of this era is damaged soil and damaged watersheds. It is also in thousands upon thousands of acres that are not properly reforested and in the lost years of growth on many thousands of acres that are now growing trees again. It is in thousands of acres that are now growing alder and maple and willow instead of the climax forest of Douglas fir and hemlock that would have reproduced itself if given half a chance. None of this is disaster, but it is all serious loss and it makes some very difficult and complicated problems.

One obvious result of these losses is that Douglas fir logging is not on a sustained-yield basis and will not be for many years to come. Douglas fir on the coast is being cut at the rate of 300 million cubic feet a year, against mature exploitable stands of under 2½ billion cubic feet – in other words there are about eight years of logging left in mature timber at the present rate of cut, and it takes at least sixty years to grow Douglas firs to merchantable size under coast conditions. Though a good deal of second-growth fir will come in to bridge the gap, it is perfectly clear that there will be a significant period during which coast Douglas fir will be in very limited

DIESEL LOGGING TRUCK

CHERRY PICKER LOADER

supply. On the same basis, mature stands of Douglas fir in the interior will last for about 24 years; coast red cedar stands about thirteen years, interior stands forty-three years; coast hemlock stands twenty-nine years, interior hemlock stands 202 years. The whole exploitable coast supply of mature trees, twelve inches or more in diameter, will be used up in about twenty-three years at the present rate of depletion.

Thirty years ago this would have meant impending economic disaster. To-day it is still a very serious matter, especially in coastal areas, but it is not a hopeless or disastrous situation. Methods of using wood have improved steadily over the past thirty years to the point where the operator can look forward to replacing much of the Douglas fir cut by cut of other species without losing his markets. Logging methods and equipment have also improved since the great days of steam to the point at which many new forest areas have become or are likely to become economically accessible. And the forester, as opposed to the logger, is able to look upon the approaching end of fully mature timber stands with positive enthusiasm. To him timber on the verge of over-maturity and decadence is timber in very poor storage. Instead of putting on a nice healthy annual growth, it is growing slowly and sometimes not at all. Insects and diseases may attack it and actually reduce the total volume. Depletion in coast forests from fire, disease and insects is rated at 202 million cubic feet a year. Fire is a serious risk especially in the interior, and blow-down may sweep through a fine tall stand on the coast. The forester wants none of this. He wants the land free to grow young trees that will keep healthy and put on volume at a rate of sixty or a hundred cubic feet to the acre each year, with good access for fire control and management. When his land has all this he knows he has a chance of keeping pace with the cut.

The biggest factor in adapting to the inevitable changes in tree species and log sizes that overcutting on the coast is bringing about is what the lumberman calls utilization – that is to say, putting whatever wood is available to him to its best possible use. In the long history of British Columbia as a forest province, the main use of wood has been in the production of lumber by sawmill operation. Until

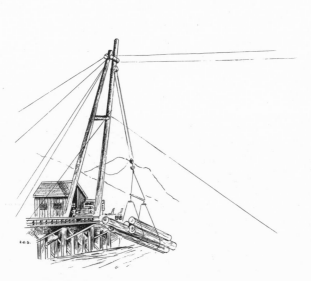

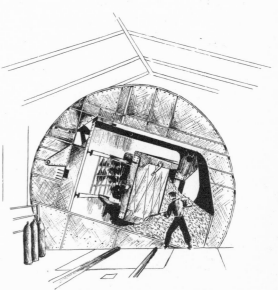

A-FRAME   RAILROAD CAR DUMPER – WOOD CHIPS

1910 this was practically the only use. In 1912 some 25,000 tons of wood-pulp were produced, but the total log cut of 235 million cubic feet yielded about 220 million cubic feet of lumber, so lumber was still the only significant production. Since that time pulp production has increased almost every year and is now in excess of 1½ million tons, using the equivalent of the entire 1912 log cut. Throughout this time both log cut and lumber cut have continued to increase, so that pulp still only uses about one-fifth of the annual log cut of one billion cubic feet, while veneer and plywood plants account for a further one-twentieth. But this change, which has been brought about by many factors, is immensely important and sets the pattern of future development. Economists believe that by 1975 the province's annual log cut must increase to 1¾ billion cubic feet, of which 1¼ billion will be cut into lumber, 1/3 billion (with probably half as much again in recovered waste) will make pulp, and the remainder plywood. The dramatic forecast of heavily increased production in the face of what at first seems a seriously depleted resource can be understood only by considering the forest resources of the province as a whole, not merely those of the coast. In theory, the forests of the province could maintain an annual cut of 3 billion cubic feet, or three times the present cut; this is the amount of new growth that the forests put on each year. In fact, such a cut is out of the question and will be for many years to come; much of the timber is economically inaccessible, much of it is of type, size and quality that could not at present be manufactured to compete on world markets. But it is within this general frame that all hope of future expansion must be considered.

From 1912 almost to the end of World War II the log cut from the interior forests of the province held at a figure of one-fifth or less of the total cut. Yet the interior forests cover seven times the area of the coast forests and contain over seventy per cent of the total sound wood volume. In the years since World War II the interior cut has been steadily increasing from its general level of 100 million cubic feet or less to more than 200 million in 1951 and more than 360 million in 1955; in 1958, it finally passed 500 million and exceeded the coast cut. This trend is expected to continue so that the interior forests will be yielding by far the greater part of the increased cut that is hoped for in the next fifteen years. It is unlikely that the coast lumber cut will increase at all, though there will be some increase in pulp production and in total log cut.

There are many reasons why to-day's log cut nearly doubles the pre-war cut but they are all contained in the lumberman's general word "utilization". The same word gives some sort of sanction to the optimistic forecast for 1975. But it would be foolish to suggest that the adjustments that must be made to achieve this forecast will be painless or easy. They will call for extensive research of a high order, skilful planning and aggressive marketing. They will also call for heavy capital investment intelligently directed.

Utilization begins with markets. Throughout the years since World War II there has been heavy demand and, in spite of minor fluctuations, a high price for wood products of all kinds. This has had several effects, the first of which begins in the woods. Timber stands that had been economically inaccessible or too low in quality or density to permit successful operation became accessible and merchantable. Money was available to convert steam and railroad operations to more flexible and more efficient diesel and truck shows. There was money also to build necessary access roads and open new areas, and the new security of tenure offered by the forest management licences gave further encouragement to long-term planning and the construction of advanced wood-using plants.

This is the second stage of utilization, which also reflects back into the first stage by making possible the recovery of tree species, sizes and qualities that were formerly left on the ground as logging waste. Before the war there were pulp and paper mills at Ocean Falls, Powell River, Port Alberni, Woodfibre, Port Alice and New Westminster. Since the war large mills have been built at Harmac, Duncan Bay and Crofton on Vancouver Island, and at Port Edward near Prince Rupert. Additional mills are under consideration for the West Kootenay area, in the Quesnel area, on the northern coast, and at Tahsis on the west coast of Vancouver Island.

The pulp mills make newsprint, high-grade bleached papers for many purposes, kraft pulp for paper sacks and cardboard containers, cellulose and other fibres for special uses. In most, if not all, cases they are able to make use of wood that could not profitably be sawed into lumber, and even to convert sawmill wastes. Usually they are combined with sawmills and plywood plants owned by the same firm so that an integrated operation can be planned from the beginning, in the woods, right through to the final product.

At present some twenty per cent of the sound wood volume of a mature forest is left behind as logging waste; up to forty per cent of young second-growth forest also becomes waste. In other words, one tree in five of a mature forest and two trees in five of young forest are lost. This loss is in the shape of small trees up to twelve inches in diameter, broken saw logs, broken chunks, inferior logs and trees, and high stumps. The loss in small trees alone is estimated to amount to ten per cent of the total annual depletion for the whole province.

To a limited extent logging practice can reduce this type of loss – unskilled and irresponsible falling crews contribute to it by causing breakage, green yarding crews pass up sound logs and may cause more breakage, inflexible and outdated machinery is unable to reach out as it should or pay its way with inferior timber. But no one, with any type of skill or machinery, can afford to bring out material that is not wanted or which commands a lower price than his operating costs.

In an efficient operation that is properly tied in to the various markets, a great deal of logging waste can be recovered by pre-logging – that is, by selecting the smaller and more breakable timber and bringing it out before the main operation; by relogging after the main operation and by care in the main operation itself. Where the operation is a fully integrated one – timber holdings and logging opera-

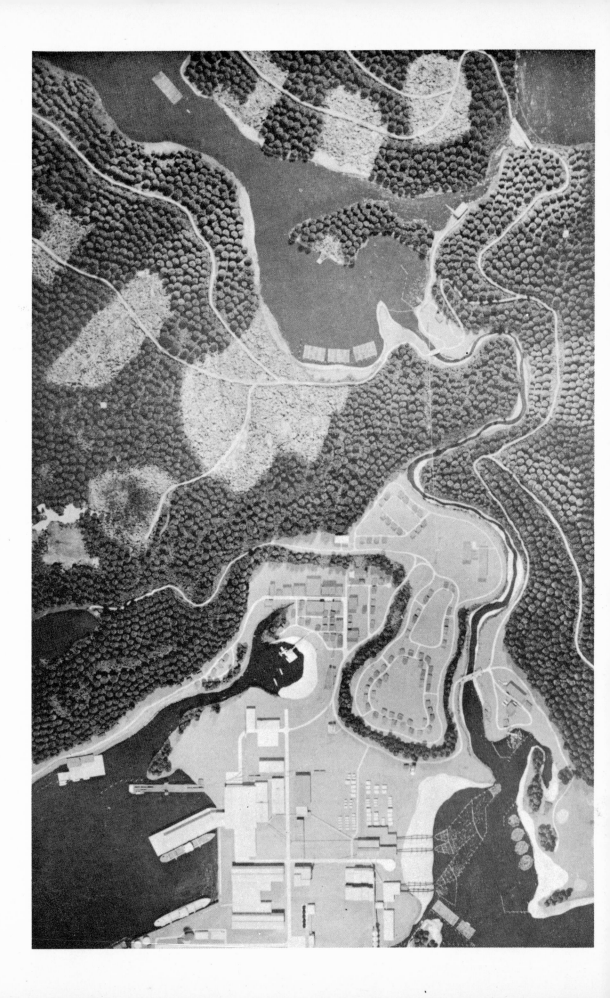

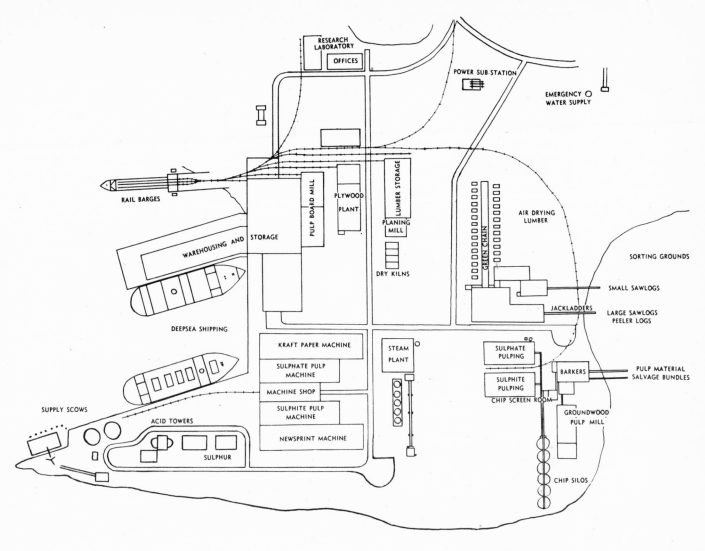

RESEARCH LABORATORY

OFFICES

POWER SUB-STATION

EMERGENCY WATER SUPPLY

RAIL BARGES

PULP BOARD MILL

PLYWOOD PLANT

LUMBER STORAGE

AIR DRYING LUMBER

GREEN CHAIN

SORTING GROUNDS

WAREHOUSING AND STORAGE

PLANING MILL

SMALL SAWLOGS

DRY KILNS

JACKLADDERS

LARGE SAWLOGS PEELER LOGS

DEEPSEA SHIPPING

KRAFT PAPER MACHINE

STEAM PLANT

SULPHATE PULPING

SULPHATE PULP MACHINE

SULPHITE PULPING

BARKERS

PULP MATERIAL SALVAGE BUNDLES

MACHINE SHOP

CHIP SCREEN ROOM

SUPPLY SCOWS

SULPHITE PULP MACHINE

GROUNDWOOD PULP MILL

ACID TOWERS

NEWSPRINT MACHINE

SULPHUR

CHIP SILOS

To use all the wood in the forest a variety of products must be manufactured. The diagram above gives some idea of the types and organization of the various industries shown in the lower part of the model.

At left is an "aerial view" of a model illustrating an ideally integrated forest industry operation. It was built for the Pulp and Paper Industry to demonstrate some of the planning and organization involved in the perpetuation of the forest and the complete utilization of its crop.

The top part of the model illustrates good forest management, and includes patch logging for maximum fire protection and rapid reseeding from nearby timber. Notice also that a minimum of wood remains on the logged-off areas.

tions are combined with sawmills, pulp plants and plywood plants under one ownership – planning and efficiency can attain a maximum within the limits of the ultimate consumer market. Recovery of residues or wastes becomes possible and profitable at each and every stage. Small and broken timber can be salvaged from the woods. Chips for pulp mills can be made from sawmill wastes; even bark is sometimes recovered and useful substances are extracted from it. High-grade peeler logs are sorted out for the plywood plants and the small cores left over from the peeling process go back to the sawmills to be cut into 2 x 4 lumber. Steadily improving processes of gluing and patching have increased the salvage of inferior veneers which can be built into useful grades of plywood. And a degree of continuity can be maintained in all this even in the face of temporary weakness in one or more of the ultimate markets, since the more profitable phases of operation can carry some losses, at least for a period.

While the fully integrated operation is probably the ideal of efficiency from the point of view of making fullest use of timber resources, the mere existence of diversified plants is or should be of benefit to the whole industry. The logging operator who has no manufacturing plants of his own is able to sell material he would once have left in the woods. The small sawmill operator can install a chipper and sell his wastes to a pulp mill. Interchange between all the various stages of operation should be possible and there is not the slightest doubt that better planning and co-operation can be used to make still greater savings.

Improvements of this sort in the uses of raw wood over the past fifteen years have resulted in the recovery of about 150 million cubic feet per year of what was formerly waste – about 65 million cubic feet of this is recovered in woods operations, about 85 million in manufacturing operations. The total recovery represents nearly one-sixth of the total annual cut and a value of at least ninety million dollars. As mature timber stands become exhausted and loggers are forced to second growth with nearly double the potential waste, it is clear that advances must continue at an even faster rate if there is to be any hope of maintaining production levels, especially on the coast.

It is scarcely an over-simplification to say that transportation is the main key to better use of the forests. Water transportation along the protected and indented coastline has been the chief factor in the early and excessive exploitation of the coast forests – a haul of more than fifty or sixty miles to salt water is a rare thing anywhere on the coast even to-day, though increasing difficulty of terrain as operations are forced back into the mountains disproportionately multiplies costs; only 0.3 per cent of coastal forest is at present considered beyond reach from a major transportation route. In the interior limited water transportation is available on some of the lakes and the Fraser River has recently been put to effective use for the movement of log-bundles, which are allowed to find their own way through the canyons and then rounded up in the quieter waters below. But nearly 36 per cent of the interior forest is beyond reach from major transportation routes. It is accessible in the sense that the terrain would permit profitable logging, but effectively in-accessible because the yield could find no way out to profitable markets. Much of this area is in the far north and many qualified observers believe it may remain be-yond effective reach for a long while to come – perhaps as long as a hundred years.

If interior forests are to continue to take over the major burden of the cut, as it is clear that they must if there is to be any major expansion in the industry, steady improvement in existing transportation will be equally essential all the way from the tree stump in the forest to the main access route itself, whether that be water or rail or road. It is, in fact, the main key to more efficient use of the available timber crop. Improvement is going on all the time, mainly in the development of smaller, lighter, more flexible equipment – rubber-tired yarders and loaders, self-loading trucks and many devices especially designed to meet particular situations are constantly proving their value. Further advances are to be expected at this stage, especially as the trees become smaller and more uniform in size; advances are to be expected also in pre-logging and re-logging techniques. But no one can seriously suppose that improvement of logging methods alone can solve the whole problem. The final answer must come at the manufacturing stage.

At the present time full recovery of logging and sawmill residues would quickly flood the existing market for pulp chips; recovery of a year's logging waste in hem-lock alone would be enough to supply one of the coast pulp mills for two full years, and total pulp mill consumption is less than the total of logging and sawmill waste. This means that in spite of all the pulp expansion that has taken place since the war, the province still hasn't enough pulp mills to match its sawmill production and provide proper integration.

If the lumber market is to be maintained as old-growth timber fades from the picture, the sawmills themselves will have to change in character to make proper use of small logs of inferior grade. Finnish sawmills are said to be able to turn out "lumber of small, sound, tight-knotted type so smoothly and accurately sawn as to make planing unnecessary" from trees that are mostly under twelve inches in di-ameter. Further advances can probably be expected in the manufacture of ve-neers and hardboards and laminated construction units such as beams and arches. Whether conservative improvements of this type will be enough to enable the prov-ince to increase or even maintain its share in world markets seems questionable, in spite of the optimistic forecasts. Sawn lumber is certainly a most useful and valu-able construction material, but it is not ideal for all the uses it is put to, especially when made from inferior timber. It is also heavy, bulky and costly to transport. Kiln drying reduces weight and improves the quality of some woods, though it also increases cost. Impregnation with bakelite or resins has been used on a small scale; these processes add strength and by sealing the wood from air make it weather-proof, with great resistance to rot and deterioration. Part of the future may be in improved treatments of this sort.

It seems certain that the most important future lies in wood chemistry – in breaking wood down by heating and chemical processes and either building it back into a useful product or extracting useful products from it. The present-day pulp mills are in the initial stages of this but they, like the woods operations and the sawmills, are relatively wasteful and inefficient. Bark from the logs is still used mainly for fuel, though such substances as wax, tannin and several forms of soil conditioner are known to be available from it. One British Columbia plant is already making a drilling lubricant from hemlock bark. The chemistry of wood itself offers an infinity of possibilities that go far beyond the present recovery of rayon and other cellulose fibres. Lignin, the main component of wood, is now largely wasted in pulp processes, but many observers seem confident that recovery of its valuable components will soon become possible. Recovery of alcohol from sulphite waste and direct distillation from wood is already possible, as are the recovery and manufacture of wood flour and plastic moulding powder and plasticized wood from other wastes.

These various possibilities will not all become realities at once. They are part of a steady process of technological development that is going on all over the world, and the speed at which they are fitted into the forest industries of British Columbia must depend largely upon the persistence, effort and ingenuity of the people working in those industries, upon the quality and persistence of government, university and private research and finally upon the demands of markets that are already in existence or can be created. It is certain only that the use of wood by pulp and other plants must increase rapidly in proportion to sawmill use if the forests are to be soundly handled, with a minimum of waste and with proper development of regrowth for the future.

It is perfectly clear that logging operations are going to be forced back into more difficult and more remote terrain, and into smaller and inferior timber. This means that under present standards of utilization, logging wastes will become steadily larger in proportion to the total cut, which in turn means a steadily reduced efficiency in the use of forest land. By increasing the proportion of pulp and other manufacturing plants to sawmills, these excessive wastes can be put to good use. Portable barking and chipping plants must be developed to move out into the woods and convert logging residues into chips and perhaps other more concentrated forms that can be cheaply hauled to the finishing plants. In all probability smaller pulp mills can be efficiently developed to reduce hauling distances. Even portable pulping plants are not beyond the bounds of possibility. These could be set up alongside temporary sawmills and portable chippers and barkers to make a closely integrated operation practically at the logging site. Once this stage is reached the harvesting of the forest crop will be efficient and even thrifty. But proper use of forest land begins long before the harvest, in planning the crop, in effective seeding and in the promotion of fast, healthy growth. The province has already lost from twenty-five to fifty years of growth on many of its finest forest sites. It is necessary to examine what is being done and what can be done to stop this loss and prevent further losses of the same kind.

managing the forests

IT HAS BEEN generally agreed at successive Resources Conferences that an essential first step towards proper resource use is the preparation of a satisfactory inventory of the resource. This sounds a simple enough assignment at first, but in a province as large and varied as British Columbia, it never is. In forestry it is particularly difficult not only because the forests themselves are so enormous and so widely spread over the face of the land, but because forest land has many uses and forest users have widely different requirements. It is difficult, too, because forests are not static. A tree grows slowly, but millions of trees all growing at the same time put on a lot of growth in a short period. Trees die both fast and slowly – fire may kill a million trees in a day; old age kills very slowly, but just as surely.

A further difficulty in making an inventory is in determining its purpose. Is it for the present or for the future? Clearly it must serve both in so far as it can, but this calls for something like prophetic vision. Who can know what future demands will be or what technological progress may make possible? The only thing the forester can do is assess and estimate the whole timber resource of the province and then break it down into its many aspects and degrees of usefulness or potential usefulness. He must check its growth and balance this against natural losses. He must examine the productive capacity of each area and determine whether the present crop is making good or bad use of the land. He must weigh and put together so many variables that his inventory will be in large measure a matter of judgment, open to different interpretation by other experts and misinterpretation by the unscrupulous.

Forest inventory reports were made in British Columbia in the years 1910, 1918 and 1937. Each was good in its time, a useful appraisal of the forest resources upon which policy could be based. Since forests grow and are cut each year and are sometimes destroyed by fire, insects or disease, no forest inventory can hold its accuracy for long, even in regard to the simplest totals. Because markets change and the standards and technology of use change, because new lines of major transportation are periodically developed, a forest inventory is bound to date even more rapidly in its classifications.

To meet this, British Columbia has now opened a "continuous forest inventory", the initial phase of which was completed in 1957, after seven years of field work, and published in 1958. It is a massive volume, nearly five inches thick, full of tables and diagrams that examine every possible aspect of the forests. It will be kept open and constantly up-to-date and no doubt from time to time, as conditions change and new information comes in, some of its assessments will be revised or modified. But its basic statements should remain unchanged for some considerable time.

The *Inventory* is concerned with forests of every possible type and accordingly classifies a very high proportion of the province, over 136 million acres, as forest land, compared with the 1954 figure of 90 million acres given in the *Resources Atlas*. This wide discrepancy is at once reduced by 18 million acres which are classified as non-commercial forest, and a further 8 million classified as low-quality site, which leaves 110 million acres of productive forest land. Seven million acres of this are classed as "protection forest", needed for erosion and flood control, stream management or snow control, and therefore exploitable only to a limited extent, if at all. Three million acres are grazing land with open or semi-open forest and four million acres are potentially arable and so classified in the *Atlas*. This leaves a total of 96 million acres of priority forest land and brings the two figures within some sort of reach of one another. The remaining discrepancy of six million acres added in the space of three years reflects the intensity of the inventory survey and the technological improvements that have made this possible. At least this extent of land, mainly in the far north, was formerly considered barren but has now been reclassified as productive forest.

The *Inventory* is a difficult volume to quote accurately because of its very precise definitions which are planned for the forest user rather than the citizen observer; but a few figures from it help to give a broad impression of the nature and extent of the province's forest wealth. The 118 million acres of productive forest land support a total of 306 million cubic feet of sound wood; 145 million cubic feet of this is mature forest, 86 per cent of which is accessible in terms of current logging practice. At this point it is necessary to consider another classification – "operability". This means forest which could be exploited under present economic conditions from existing main routes of transportation. 58.4 per cent of the provincial forests are considered operable within these terms, 35.8 per cent only potentially operable. Because of ready access to water routes, nearly 90 per cent of coast forest is operable at present as against only 54 per cent of interior forest. Interior forests cover seven times the area of coast forests and contain 80 per cent of the usable sound wood volume.

One important conclusion of the *Inventory* is that the province has an abundance of timber and good forest land. If all the land were producing as it should, if every forest area were accessible and if all the different types of forest that make up the resource could be economically worked, the safe annual cut would be three billion cubic feet, approximately three times the present yield. This encouraging figure supposes a yield of almost a billion cubic feet from the coast forests and over two billion from the interior. It assumes continuing progress in the development of logging techniques, in methods of manufacturing and using wood and in the management of regrowth; it also presupposes successful competition in a constantly expanding world market. But the *Inventory* properly does not attempt to forecast how long it may take before all these developments reach the stage where such a cut can be realized, though it suggests it certainly will not be until some time in the twenty-first century. Most authorities believe it will take at least a hundred years, perhaps considerably longer.

Except in a very remote sense, this figure of potential cut has no significance in present management. It simply suggests, in a broad way, the general direction management must take, and if used in any other way it is misleading and dangerous. The really significant figures are those of the present annual cut and the allowable cut on a sustained-yield basis. These are, respectively, 1,234 million cubic feet and 967 million cubic feet, which suggest an annual overcut of about 250 million cubic feet. But these figures have no real meaning until they are broken down by districts. The annual cut in the coast forests is 867 million cubic feet against an allowable cut of 298 million cubic feet, while the interior cut is 367 million cubic feet against an allowable cut of 669 million cubic feet; of the coast cut, 238 million cubic feet is left in the woods as logging waste and of the interior cut 37 million cubic feet is logging waste.

The above are 1957 figures, using 1952-6 averages for the coast and interior cuts; adjustment of a sort has already begun, with a sharp increase in the interior cut and some reduction on the coast; but the coast cut continues to be excessive. It seems perfectly clear that operators in the coastal forests are heading towards a very difficult period indeed, which can only be partly cushioned by better recovery of the 238 million cubic feet of logging residues and better use of inferior timber species. It is probably true that this adjustment period can be postponed by transferring the overcut to immature second-growth stands, with almost double the present rate of logging waste. But if this alternative is chosen it can only serve to produce a still more desperate situation within a few decades.

This is not new information. The Royal Commission of 1910 saw plainly that steps had to be taken to ensure regeneration of Douglas fir on the coast and made many important recommendations, which were largely disregarded. The Mulholland Report of 1937 was much more specific, and clearly sketched out the situation that has to be faced to-day. But the decision always went against the coast forests. They have been used, not as forests should be, to provide a continuous crop, but simply for a quick cash return that would help to open up the rest of the province.

This may or may not have been sound policy over-all; it certainly was and is bad resource use.

Proper use of forest land entails putting money back into it, just as certainly as does proper use of farm land. British Columbia has never returned an adequate proportion of forest revenue to the forests. In 1910, while the province of Ontario was returning 9 per cent of forest revenue to forest lands, British Columbia was returning less than 2 per cent. In the years from 1927 to 1937, while forest revenues averaged over 3¼ million dollars, the return was less than a million dollars annually; the average cash yield of the crop in those years was 63 million dollars. Today, with an annual cash yield of over 600 million dollars and direct forest revenue of 30 million dollars, government is returning only 11.7 million dollars to the forests. It should be emphasized that the thirty million dollars referred to is stumpage, royalty and special forest tax. Total tax revenue from forest industries, according to the Sloan Report of 1956, is 85 million dollars.

The forests of British Columbia are administered by the B.C. Forest Service and for this purpose are divided into five districts. The service has over 1500 permanent employees and hires seasonal employees for such work as planting and fire suppression. It maintains hundreds of miles of access road for planting and fire-fighting, is responsible for the continuous inventory and related studies, and conducts a limited amount of forest research. Some research is also done by the federal government and by private industry.

While this may sound a fairly imposing management force, it must be remembered that the province owns 93 per cent of the accessible mature forest, 91 per cent of the total commercial forest volume and 94.4 per cent of all forest land in the province. Only 16 per cent of the forest land, containing 27 per cent of the currently exploitable wood volume, is under sustained-yield operation. These percentages are constantly increasing as new working circles are blocked out and new tree-farm licences are granted but it is evident that the major percentage of forest land cannot be brought under full control and regulation for many years to come. It is equally evident that fuller management must call for steadily increasing staff and much more ambitious programmes of assessment and pure research.

In reading through the transactions of the Resources Conferences, it is disturbing to realize how often the foresters admit: "We do not know", especially in such matters as regrowth, re-seeding and replanting. Only quite broad and tentative work has been done so far in the classification of forest land by potential yield, or towards determining the proper treatment of growing forests and the best age at which to begin cutting various types of second growth. Little seems to be known of the possibilities of planting or encouraging specific tree crops for specific purposes. Yet a thorough understanding of all these points and many others is essential to sound forest management.

The continuous inventory contains figures for growth, based on sampling, which give a general idea of how important close study of growth is to management. The

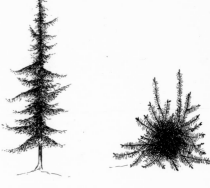

GOOD PHENOTYPE AND ITS PROGENY   POOR PHENOTYPE AND ITS PROGENY

net annual growth in commercial forests is estimated at 2.3 billion cubic feet against an annual depletion of 2.2 billion cubic feet. Immature forests have a growth rate nearly 24 times as fast as mature forest and in mature forest the annual loss through decay is greater than the annual growth. Although the growth rate in immature coastal forests is twice as fast as the comparable rate in the interior, the total annual growth of the interior forests is seven times that of the coast forests and the total immature growth is fifteen times as great. This partly reflects the much larger area of the interior forests, but it reflects also the higher proportion of healthy immature forest in the interior and the 2½ million coastal acres that are either inadequately restocked or carrying non-commercial cover. Under full management, with every acre producing as it should, it is estimated that the coast forests could produce three times their present annual yield or over one billion cubic feet a year. But it will take at least fifty to a hundred years of informed and careful management to achieve this. The interior forests are producing an annual increment within twenty per cent of their capacity by the same standards.

Quite clearly this immense task of management is one that can only be undertaken gradually, but it is equally certain that research must be forced ahead as rapidly as possible. The foresters' ideal of reforestation is natural regeneration, yet in this field alone there is an infinity of unanswered questions. Is it possible to ensure regeneration of the most desired species? How can logging wastes best be disposed of to ensure regeneration? Which logging practices promote regeneration? Which are most likely to slow it or prevent it? There are opinions on all these matters, but little real information. Clear cutting over large areas, for instance, has worked against satisfactory regeneration. Leaving selected seed trees in such areas is an improvement; patch-logging gives much better results; but still greater improvement and control will be possible when a thorough study has been made of the effect of different sizes and shapes of plots under varying conditions of climate, altitude and species requirement.

Where re-seeding or replanting is necessary, there is much still to be learned of the adaptability and suitability of both seeds and seedlings. It is already known that seeds must come from approximately the same altitude to be successful. Exotic

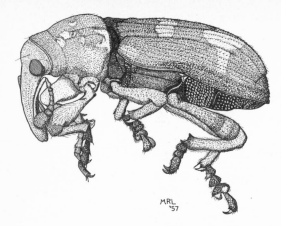

INSECTS INJURIOUS TO TERMINALS
Adult Sitka Spruce Weevil. The weevil is an important limiting factor in sitka spruce development along the east coast of Vancouver Island and the lower Fraser Valley. When abundant, it not only spoils spruce as a commercial species but also converts it to spawling forest weeds hindering full utilization of forest lands by other species.

MRL
'57

tree species generally have not done as well as natives in British Columbia. Poorly selected seed can produce a forest of inferior value or even of no commercial value at all. Douglas fir is particularly reluctant in setting seed and it may well be possible to find ways of stimulating the set. As yet foresters have not even been able to find accurate ways of judging the ripeness of the cones and the best time for collecting seed, though this is recognized as a matter of utmost importance.

Once the young trees are in the ground, there is still a great deal to be learned about protecting them from disease, insects and even fire. Disease and decay cause an annual loss of 680 million cubic feet in the forests of the province, but only about one-seventh of this is in immature forests; insects, mainly bark beetles, cause a loss of ten million cubic feet; fire accounts for between forty and fifty million cubic feet. The effect of fire in very young forests, of twenty years and under, is particularly disastrous because it can sweep through a large area with great rapidity and will almost certainly leave behind a seedless soil, without prospect of natural regeneration, since the trees have not had time to drop seed. It can be restored only by replanting and every year's delay in this means a year of growth lost, in addition to those destroyed by the fire.

As the young trees grow, sound management can improve and increase the crop in many ways. It is known that pruning and limbing will speed growth and improve quality by reducing knots in the mature trees. Thinning is essential if maximum growth is to be attained and maximum yield realized. But little is yet known of the ideal times and methods for such practices or whether they can be made economically practicable in British Columbia forests.

Sweden and Norway offer what is probably the outstanding example in the world of full forest management. These two countries together have approximately the same area of forest land as British Columbia, but the land is generally of much lower productive quality. Under full management the two countries are cutting annually about 2 billion cubic feet, twice the present B.C. cut, on a sustained-yield basis. They are much closer to the important European markets and have other advantages of long research and experience. But their achievement makes it clear that British Columbia has not begun to use the full potential of its forest lands.

Since forest lands make up over 60 per cent of the area of the province and over 90 per cent of the land that is not barren or swamp or otherwise unproductive, it is obvious that forest lands must serve not one use but many. It is almost equally obvious that forestry cannot long continue to be a priority use on such an overwhelming proportion of the province's useful land area.

Some four million acres of land suitable for agriculture must one day grow their last crops of trees and be turned over to a higher use. Several million acres of good grazing land may or may not be permitted to return to growing trees after present crops have been removed. The seven million acres of protection forest has high value in its present uses for water storage and erosion control, and it may well be found that additional large areas should be so classified. On the other hand, there are a good many acres of marginal agricultural land in the province that might better be allowed to grow trees.

The province has some 8 million acres of parkland, a significant proportion of which is forest land. Class A parks have absolute priority and no logging is permitted. Logging operations are allowed in Class B parks only if they do not interfere with the priority use.

Mining operations may claim priority use of forest lands, but over limited areas only, and their claims are never likely to be significant. Water storage projects have always been granted priority, not only in the use of forest land, but in the use of park lands. Valuable park timberlands were flooded by the Strathcona development on Vancouver Island and the Kitimat-Kemano development in Tweedsmuir Park. Something like half a million acres of forest land will be flooded by the proposed Peace River development and at least a similar acreage by the various projects planned for the upper Columbia.

Significant areas are permanently removed from production each year by power-line, pipeline and highway construction, and also by the establishment of logging roads. There is every reason to believe that these uses will continue to increase very rapidly and that sooner or later a closer control will be necessary; careful planning of permanent logging roads is already an important factor in good forest management. Bad planning not only impairs logging efficiency and removes valuable acres from production; it may also cause excessive water run-off and serious soil losses.

These are the main uses that generally take priority over timber growing on forest land when the need for them arises. A major hidden use of all forest land is

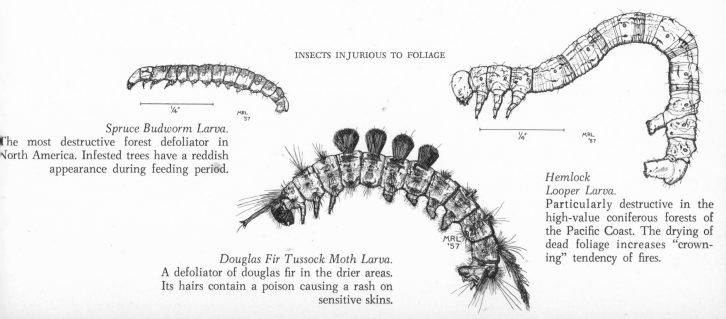

INSECTS INJURIOUS TO FOLIAGE

Spruce Budworm Larva.
The most destructive forest defoliator in North America. Infested trees have a reddish appearance during feeding period.

Hemlock Looper Larva.
Particularly destructive in the high-value coniferous forests of the Pacific Coast. The drying of dead foliage increases "crowning" tendency of fires.

Douglas Fir Tussock Moth Larva.
A defoliator of douglas fir in the drier areas. Its hairs contain a poison causing a rash on sensitive skins.

water control and while this use has priority only in the protective forests, it merits serious consideration everywhere. Fortunately good water control is every bit as important to forest management as it is to other resources. But bad management, which persists in some privately held lands, can have very serious effects on fisheries, agriculture and other resource uses.

Public recreation and the production of wildlife, including fur-bearing animals, are tremendously important subsidiary uses of forest land. Forest land can yield a hundred crops of wildlife and a hundred years of recreation while it is growing one crop of trees. In general these uses do not conflict directly with the priority use. Activities of beaver colonies may affect regrowth in some areas, but in all probability they more than compensate by conserving water. Browsing animals such as deer, elk and moose cause some losses, especially in very young growth, and black bears have killed or damaged older trees on the Olympic Peninsula, but losses of this type have not yet been assessed in B.C. In the United States and Alaska it has been estimated that weather, wildlife and "miscellaneous losses" excluding fire, disease and insects, account for less than ten per cent of the total depletion of growing stock.

Recreational uses such as hunting, fishing, camping and hiking inevitably increase fire hazard. This risk is limited by forest closures in really bad fire weather and has been greatly reduced by public education. In further compensation, there is no doubt that some fires are seen and reported earlier than would otherwise have been the case by people using the woods for recreation. A more difficult point of conflict is in the matter of access, since the most convenient access to many forested areas is by private logging road. Various problems arise in this, which are probably better discussed under the heading of Recreation.

Insect control by the use of chemical sprays can be a very serious threat to other resource uses. Some sprays are lethal to all forms of wildlife and even the simplest have caused very serious losses to fisheries and lasting damage to streams. Chemical spraying is difficult to control and it is random in action rather than selective, so many competent observers believe that biological controls offer much greater prom-

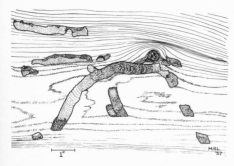

Western Cedar Borer Mines. This beetle causes structural defects in red cedar, the tunnels being excavated up to 20 feet in length by the larvae.

Adult Sawyer Beetle (RIGHT). Destructive to the wood of dying, recently killed, and felled trees.

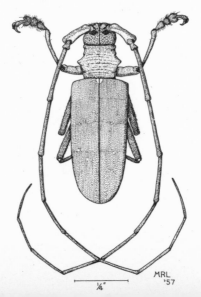

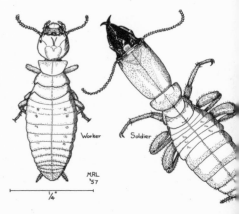

Adult Damp Wood Termites. Destroy wooden structures in contact with moisture – usually foundations – but Douglas fir and red cedar products are also affected.

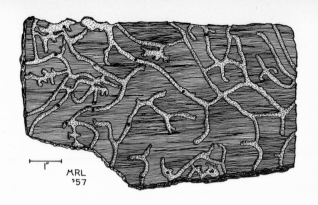

INSECTS INJURIOUS TO BARK
Western Pine Beetle Galleries.
The most important insect enemy of Ponderosa Pine, it causes heavy losses in the Nicola-Princeton area. The winding egg galleries are constructed by the adult beetles.

ise of useful effect. This is one more of the many points on which research has so far been entirely inadequate.

It has often been pointed out at Resources Conferences that conservative estimates of forest resources or pessimistic views of their condition may inhibit legitimate expansion of the forest industries. It is equally true that over-optimistic views can lead to over-expansion and serious damage to the resource, at least locally. It is important that British Columbians should recognize the damage that has been done by overcutting and bad management in the coast forest, and equally important that they should understand the possibilities of expansion in the interior.

It is obvious that the province's forest industries will continue to face strong competition in world markets. The Scandinavian countries operate at high efficiency and have important geographical advantages. Russia has tremendous forest resources and will compete more and more strongly. Both the Pacific Coast states and the Southern States of the Union have a head start in management and regrowth and probably a better productive capacity in terms of rate of regrowth and inventory turnover. They will continue to supply a high proportion of the United States' domestic market. New Zealand and parts of Australia have exceptional regrowth rates and the former is already exporting timber products. Even countries like Britain, though they will always remain lumber importers, are producing more of their own needs. The province's great trading future is undoubtedly with the Orient, and it is only when Oriental markets are fully opened that there can be any hope of realizing the full forest potential.

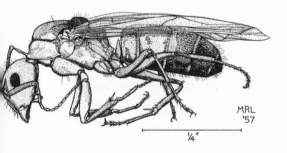

INSECTS INJURIOUS TO WOOD

Winged Female Carpenter Ant. In destructiveness of wooden structures these ants rival or exceed that of termites along the B.C. coast. Telephone poles as well are often badly weakened, although the ants do not actually eat wood, but feed on other insects, and only use their excavations as nests. They are large black ants conspicuous because of their habit of running rapidly about outdoors on warm days.

The drawings of the insects are by Mrs. Mona Lambden of the Forestry Department, University of British Columbia.

Unfortunately management has to be undertaken within these hard facts of competition. Ideal forest practices, even though they may pay handsomely in the long run, cannot be put into effect if they mean a running economic loss.

So far the province has attempted to control forest operations largely by manipulating terms of private tenure, nearly always with unsatisfactory results. The usual effect has been to build up vested interests which cannot later be controlled by the original terms of the lease or licence without serious economic dislocation. The transferable timber licences are the classic example of this, but it remains to be seen whether the Forest Management Licences, or Tree Farm Licences as they are now called, will not make another. Industrial conditions are constantly changing and it is perfectly clear that long-term commitments in any form are a hazard. But forest management itself is long-term business calling for heavy investment, so there must be some measure of security. Owning, as it does, 93 per cent of all accessible mature forests, the province seems in a strong position. But this position can still be sacrificed if sufficiently flexible terms of tenure and taxation are not developed, and past commitments are likely to affect management for a long while to come.

The ultimate goal must be full management of young and healthy forest entirely in new growth. This cannot be realized for a very long while, but it will never be realized unless the goal is recognized and kept constantly in sight. In the words of *The Continuous Forest Inventory*: "The general forest situation justifies optimism, but demands skilful handling of every forest acre in the years ahead." Since the forest industries directly employ 70,000 people with an annual production worth 600 million dollars, and since about half of the provincial economy is based on this yield, it is not too much to say that the province's future largely depends upon "the skilful handling of every forest acre".

the extent of the resource CHAPTER 9

THOUGH BRITISH COLUMBIA is not one of the major agricultural provinces, accounting for only 5 per cent of national production, the yield of agriculture in the province is third highest among those of the natural resources. The annual farm cash income is 120 million dollars, which in turn produces an annual value of about 250 million in factory output of food and beverages. Only forests and minerals exceed these values.

Agriculture directly employs some 30,000 British Columbians and an additional fifteen to twenty thousand are employed in factories, packing plants and breweries. These totals of yield and employment are realized from something less than 5 million acres of occupied farmland, of which about a million acres are rated as improved farmland. Nearly four-fifths of the cash return and over two-thirds of the employment are provided by the improved land.

It is interesting to make a rough comparison of these figures with forestry statistics, which show that a hundred million acres of productive forest land yield 600 million dollars a year and employ 70,000 workers. On this basis, forest lands yield about six dollars per acre per year, while all farmlands together yield an average of 50 dollars per acre per year and improved farmlands yield over 250 dollars.

This comparison is of value only in emphasizing the widely different natures of the two resources and the varying quality of their use of land. It is quite clear that farming is the higher and more valuable use wherever the land is suitable and capital for development and improvement can be found. Farmland produces about eight times the return and more than ten times the employment from equivalent acreage.

Between four and five million acres of land in B.C. are rated as "potentially arable" – that is, they could be developed to a standard of agricultural production not too far short of that of the land already in use. Most of this acreage needs clearing, draining, dyking, irrigation or other heavy capital expenditure before it can be brought into production, and for various reasons, the needed capital simply is not coming forward at present; improved land is increasing at the rate of about 25,000 acres a year, but only one-third of this goes into crop. Against the increase must be set a loss of at least two thousand acres a year to urbanization, much of it highly productive land.

These circumstances, taken with an annual population increase of about 30,000, make the province an importer of agricultural products. Less than one acre per person of improved land is in production, as against the general United Nations' figure of 2½ acres considered necessary to supply a full and satisfactory diet. This is not altogether surprising, since most of the province's undeveloped agricultural land can only be brought into production at considerable cost; Canada as a whole is a great agricultural nation and British Columbia's other resources make her well able to afford to import food supplies. Agricultural experts in the province do not expect any spectacular change in the rate of development; they forecast instead a slow but steady increase over the next thirty years which will not quite keep pace with population increases. In other words British Columbia will continue to have rather less than one acre of improved agricultural land per person and will continue to import food supplies in large quantities. Some authorities believe that the proportion may fall off to half an acre or less per person rather rapidly. If this comes about it will reflect economic factors and presumably will fit into the trading pattern of the province in some way that makes economic sense. But it will also mean that a valuable resource is being left undeveloped and unused; and in the light of rapidly growing world population and increasing competition for world food supplies, it may well place the province in a suddenly precarious position at some later date.

British Columbia's agricultural production, like most of her other resource yields, is regional and widely varied. Apart from the Peace River plains and the grazing lands of the Interior Plateau, agricultural land is isolated in pockets of soil between high mountain ranges or near the mouths of rivers. Both the soils themselves and the local climates differ widely and so tend to bring about regional specialization.

The chief agricultural yields of the province, in order of farm cash income, are as follows: dairying, thirty per cent; poultry, twenty-two per cent; beef, thirteen per cent; vegetables and potatoes, nine per cent; tree fruits, eight per cent; small fruits, four and a half per cent; grain, four per cent; special horticultural crops, four per cent. This last classification includes production of flowers, nursery stock, bulbs, holly, hops, greenhouse crops and special seed crops. It represents the most intensive form of land use, since it is realized from little more than 2500 acres, mainly in the Lower Fraser Valley and on Vancouver Island. Mild winter climate is an important factor in these forms of specialization.

The Lower Fraser Valley is by far the most productive farming area of the province and accounts for nearly fifty per cent of the total value of provincial agricultural production. In addition to mild climate, good rainfall and rich alluvial soils,

The Fraser Valley, showing first-class agricultural land and its relation to urban development. Courtesy: Lower Mainland Region Planning Board.

it has the important advantage of being close to the centres of high population on the Lower Mainland, which provide markets for all that can be produced, and maintain a heavy demand for fluid milk.

Nearly 200,000 acres of Fraser Valley land are protected from river floods by over 300 miles of dykes. This low-lying land makes rich pasture and excellent silage for dairy cattle and the valley produces about two-thirds of the total dairy yield of the province. It also produces more than sixty per cent of the poultry products, and over half the provincial yields of vegetables, potatoes, small fruits and special horticultural crops. In sum, it is probably the most intensive and highly productive agricultural area in Canada, and it is this land that is slowly being buried under urban and industrial growth.

The south-east coastline of Vancouver Island offers somewhat the same farming conditions as the Fraser Valley, especially on the Saanich peninsula and in the delta lands near Duncan, Nanaimo and Comox, but the improved acreage is much smaller and the production less intensive. The main yields are dairy products, poultry, vegetables and potatoes, special horticultural crops and small fruits, in this order of importance. Seven hundred and fifty acres on Vancouver Island devoted to special horticultural crops produce one and a quarter million dollars annually or about thirty per cent of the provincial total in this field.

After the Lower Fraser Valley, the Okanagan Valley is by far the most important agricultural producer in the province. Hot dry summers and mild winters, with good soils under irrigation, have long made the Okanagan a magnificent country for tree fruits such as apples, pears, plums, peaches and apricots. Over ninety per cent of the provincial yield of tree fruits comes from the valley, and this is the only major crop of which the province grows an exportable surplus. The Okanagan also produces significant yields of dairy products, poultry, beef, vegetables and grain. It is a prosperous and well developed area with about 150,000 acres of improved land

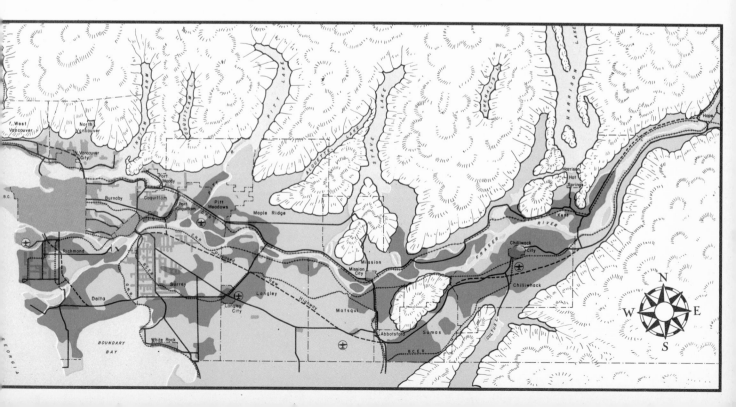

and a further potential of about half this amount. The farm population of the valley is 28,000 on over 6000 farms, which compares with a farm population of 45,000 on 10,000 farms in the Fraser Valley.

The Cariboo country produces about twenty-five per cent of the province's total yield of beef and the Kamloops area over thirty per cent. These two regions, with the Okanagan, contain all the best grazing lands of the Interior Plateau. Both regions support some dairying and poultry farming and the Kamloops region has the province's largest flocks of sheep. It is generally believed that the grazing lands are supporting a full capacity of cattle, but there are a hundred thousand acres of land in the Cariboo and seventy-five thousand in the Kamloops area that could be improved and brought under cultivation. The beef yield may also be considerably increased by bringing grain from the Peace River area and transporting cattle there for grain fattening now that the P.G.E. railroad has been completed to Fort St. John.

The West Kootenay region yields about 1½ million dollars' worth of dairy products yearly, with smaller values of poultry, grain, tree fruits, beef and small fruits. It has only about 40,000 acres in crop, with a further 160,000 acres capable of improvement. The East Kootenay at present yields beef, dairy products, vegetables and potatoes, and poultry, in that order of value. It has only 30,000 acres in crop, with a further potential of 400,000 acres. It is ironical that a considerable portion of this potential may be lost in the hydro-electric development of the Upper Columbia and Kootenay rivers just when industrial markets resulting from the development might justify their use.

The two remaining agricultural sections of the province, the Central Interior and the Peace River Block, have what is probably the greatest potential. The Central Interior, which includes the Prince George-Vanderhoof area and the Bulkley and Skeena valleys, has about 100,000 acres under crop and possibly a further one million acres unimproved; the Peace River has about a quarter of a million acres in crop and two million acres of undeveloped land. Both regions have important areas of degraded black soils, surrounded by much larger areas of grey-wooded soils, a proportion of which can be built up to fair arable standards, especially suitable for the production of legumes and grass seeds. Most development is so far centred in the degraded black soil areas.

Both regions lie well to the north of other agricultural areas and are to some extent limited by climate, ranging from 50 to 150 frost-free days annually and an accumulated temperature of from 1500 to 2000 day degrees over 43°F.* – figures which compare to 200 to 250 frost-free days and 3000 to 3500 day degrees in the Lower Fraser Valley and other more favoured parts of the province. The Peace River country is by far the largest grain-growing area in the province and produces over seventy per cent of the total crop. It also grows hogs, beef, poultry and forage seed crops in valuable quantities and supports some dairying. Dairying is the major

*See page 47 for definition.

farming activity in the Central Interior, closely followed by beef cattle, with some grain and forage crops. Minor quantities of seed, poultry, vegetables, hogs, small fruits and sheep are also produced, which suggests a diverse potential that should prove more and more important as local markets develop.

Since both regions now have railroad connections with other parts of the province, especially the beef-raising Cariboo country, they should play a very considerable part in future farm development. The Peace River, especially, is an area that will always produce the highest qualities of grains in quantities far beyond anything that can be used locally. Feeder cattle can now be carried in to take advantage of this and grain can be sent out to markets in the Cariboo and even in the Lower Fraser Valley. The Central Interior has felt some benefit from the aluminum development at Kitimat and is promised more when communications improve; but this area also has the greatest potential lumber cut in the province and is bound to benefit from increasing local markets as the main lumber cut gradually shifts from the coast to the interior. A favourable outlet towards Oriental markets from Prince Rupert should in time prove important to both the northern agricultural regions.

This broad survey of provincial agriculture disregards the upper coastal region and the far north, neither of which is considered to have significant agricultural potential; the first lacks any considerable areas of suitable soil and the second is obviously much limited by climate. There is, of course, some local production along the coast and there are pockets of more favourable climate in the far north, but there is nothing to suggest any significant development in the foreseeable future.

A typical pre-emptor's ranchstead of a few
hundred acres 30 miles east of Williams
Lake. It is stocked with from 40 to 75 head
of Hereford cattle and 8 horses and has four
buildings made of logs with shake roofs.
This type of unit is common on the eastern
margin of the ranching area.

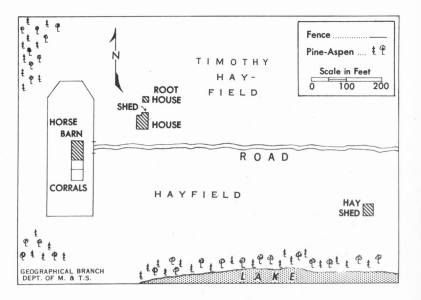

THE SLOW DEVELOPMENT of agriculture in British Columbia presents many contradictions. The province has only about one per cent of the improved agricultural land in Canada, while it has twelve per cent of the remaining forty million acres of uncultivated agricultural land. Yet the average yield of an acre of cultivated land in B.C. is $140 compared to the national average of $30. The province has good markets for agricultural products and imports large quantities of food supplies. Less than fifty years ago agricultural development was more than keeping pace with population and the province had over three acres of improved land per person; today this figure has fallen to less than one acre and shows every sign of falling still further.

The greatest single factor inhibiting the development of the remaining farmlands of the province is probably the high cost of initial improvement. Most of the land needs either clearing, irrigation, draining or dyking to yield a profitable return. Clearing costs are very high on the good forest soils near the coast; they are lower on the degraded black and grey-wooded soils of the north, but these soils call for a farm unit of two or three times as much acreage, so the advantage is not great. Irrigation or dyking of any lands not so far improved is likely to be a considerable undertaking calling for the co-operative effort of several farmers together and for the expenditure of a good deal of capital. In some instances it will call for capital expenditure beyond the scope of any co-operative group and may have to be undertaken as a joint federal-provincial venture.

In addition to clearing, the grey-wooded soils, which make up three-fifths of the province's unimproved land, need physical improvement to become productive. They tend to be low in organic matter, nitrogen and phosphorus; a succession of legume and grass crops, with manure and fertilizers, will bring them into useful production. But all this, in addition to clearing on a unit of two to four hundred

The Indian Gardens Ranch is of medium size located along the south side of the Thompson Valley in the vicinity of Savona. The site of the ranchstead is a knoll close to springs and a stream, and the ranch itself grazes 1200 head of cattle. The corrals include all the facilities usually found in the larger cattle ranches.

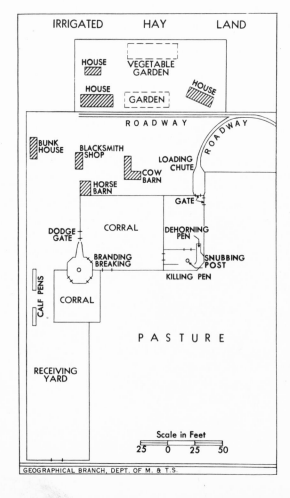

IRRIGATED HAY LAND

HOUSE
VEGETABLE GARDEN
HOUSE
GARDEN
HOUSE

ROADWAY

ROADWAY

BUNK HOUSE

BLACKSMITH SHOP
LOADING CHUTE
COW BARN

HORSE BARN

GATE

DODGE GATE

CORRAL

DEHORNING PEN

BRANDING BREAKING

SNUBBING POST

KILLING PEN

CALF PENS

CORRAL

PASTURE

RECEIVING YARD

Scale in Feet
25   0   25   50

GEOGRAPHICAL BRANCH, DEPT. OF M. & T.S.

These photographs and diagrams are reproduced through the courtesy of the Department of Mines and Technical Surveys, Ottawa.

acres which is about the minimum range for profitable farms on these soils, adds up to a considerable outlay before there is any significant return.

Even when he has good land, a farmer is not in business. He needs a house, barn, outbuildings, tractor, agricultural tools and livestock. It has been estimated that the average capitalization of a dairy farm in the Lower Fraser Valley is of the order of a thousand dollars an acre. A 70-acre farm of this type, well operated, may yield a cash income of $7500 a year, which leaves little enough for the labour of the farmer and his family after interest on capital; less successful farms of the same type and size yield incomes varying from $2500 to $4000. An average mixed farm on grey-wooded soil might be made to yield $5000 to $6000 a year.

It is important to realize that few men to-day are going to risk their capital and tie themselves to long hours and a seven-day week for such a return, dependent as it is on the vagaries of markets and weather. The only reason some people do so is that the life itself has important compensations. It offers challenge and independence, a sense of ownership, good surroundings in which to raise children and the association with the soil that remains a powerful and deep satisfaction to many human beings. The sort of citizens who respond to such factors as these, and the sort of communities they produce, are not to be lightly disregarded. They are assets of the highest order, which provide a core of stability and permanence to the life of any country. A sound and prosperous farm population is just as important for its human yield of valuable citizens as it is for its more commonly recognized yield of milk or potatoes or grain.

Early settlement in British Columbia, after the waning of the fur trade and the subsidence of the gold fever of the 1860's, was largely directed towards agriculture. Men wanted to settle on the land and the young province wanted food products. Transportation was slow and difficult and anything that could be grown or raised within easy reach of mines or logging operations or sawmills was sure of a ready market. Competition from outside the province was limited by long hauls and poor communications.

Under these circumstances men turned readily enough to the hard, slow work of clearing land, usually working at outside jobs to support their families while bringing their land into production. Other men formed groups and societies to implement dyking and irrigation projects. Development was fairly rapid and continued so at least until the First World War. Almost any arable land within reach of settlement seemed worth the effort of improvement. Beef cattle were raised on wild hay and tidewater meadows at the heads of the long inlets. Remote valleys grew potatoes and vegetables and other crops. Much of to-day's tree-fruit acreage was brought under irrigation and the dyking systems of the Lower Fraser laid the foundations of the great dairy industry.

Still another factor in land improvement developed under conditions of early settlement is the part-time farm. This is a household affair, designed to provide a family living and a certain basic security rather than any major income from sale of produce; cash income comes from work in the woods, commercial fishing or other seasonal occupation. The 1956 census classified farms into two groups, depending on whether their total production was more or less than $1200 per year. Those producing more than $1200 are rated as full-time units, the others as part-time units. Thirty-eight per cent of all farms in Canada and fifty-five per cent of all farms in B.C. are part-time units by this standard, so it is clear that such farms are significant in terms of total acreage. But the part-time farms of B.C. marketed an average of only $650 worth of produce per farm in 1956, compared to an average of nearly $9000 for full-scale farms, so it is equally clear that their impact on total production is insignificant – it represents less than 8 per cent of the total B.C. product. There are 13,500 of these small farms in B.C. and their average capitalization is a little less than $8000. Most of this is likely to be in the value of the farmhouse and the land itself, which emphasizes their importance as living units rather than productive units.

Under the present conditions of high wages and high employment, with unemployment insurance and improved social welfare in the background, the part-time farm is no longer such a powerful factor in family security and fewer settlers are willing to go to all the work of clearing and improving a small piece of land. But there can be no doubt that the small farm, in spite of its low production rate, is a most valuable and important land use, as well as a factor in bringing under culti-

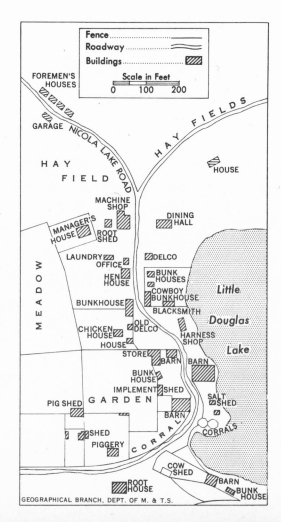

The modern company ranchstead shown here is the Douglas Lake Cattle Company, the centre of operations for the largest unit in Canada, grazing 10,000 head of cattle. There are, as well, three subsidiary ranchsteads. This main ranchstead comprises 42 buildings, two of which are large horse barns with haylofts, and which house a few of the 450 work and riding animals. A piggery with 50 sows is maintained in part by scraps from the mess house. A company store serves a permanent staff of 90 employees, extra hands during the hay season, and the neighbouring Indian reserve. Four modern bungalows provide homes for the ranch foremen and several bunkhouses accommodate the cow hands. An electric generating plant and water works provide modern facilities and all buildings are of recent frame construction and are painted.

vation land that might otherwise remain idle. Only when the provincial demand for agricultural produce becomes far greater than at present and all potential agricultural land has been improved will there be good cause to question the usefulness of these small farm units, and that time is still very far away.

Efficiency of full-time farms is another matter. The differences between a reasonable return on labour and capital and an over-all loss are so varied and so slight as to be difficult to assess. Inferior soil, small size, low production, inefficient use of labour, inadequate use of fertilizers all have their effects, but competent observers feel that it is a combination of factors rather than any one or two glaring inadequacies that makes the difference between failure and success. The Dairy Farm Improvement herds, which are closely watched by the Department of Agriculture and are all considered paying herds, have an average production of over 10,000 pounds per cow per annum; while the herds vary in size from 24 to 47 head, the average size is 32 cows. These farms use labour rather more effectively, achieve slightly higher production per cow and use slightly more capital per man than less successful units. But even these factors are not constant between farms rated as high income producers and those that produce medium incomes.

These difficulties of assessment emphasize that farming is still something of an art rather than an exact science. They also point up the fact that the business organization of farming has not kept up with the modern tendency of business to organize itself into large, integrated units instead of small, independent operations. In other words, the farmer has preserved his independence and his absolute ownership of the resource at the cost of increased efficiency, higher wages and higher capital returns. It is interesting to compare this with the condition of the small operator in the forest industry, who feels he is losing his independence to the competition of big firms, and that of the small operator in the fishing industry who bargains for prices through a labour union and so reduces his independence. Whether the intangibles of his way of life balance the relatively low financial rewards of the farmer is a difficult question; presumably they do in some measure for the farmer who is established or he would not stay in business. But it is arguable that they are not sufficiently attractive to draw much new blood into farming, or the province's unimproved arable lands would be taken up much more rapidly.

It seems likely that co-operation, not merely in marketing and in the maintenance of large-scale improvements such as dyking and irrigation, but in every phase of the work from beginning to end, would bring much better returns to individual farmers. But farm co-operation on this scale has never proved easy and has seldom been successful. Co-operation destroys many of the intangible values that are so important and it presents many practical difficulties connected with the nature of farming and the nature of farmers that are not easily solved. Perhaps it is especially difficult where the types of farming are so varied and, in themselves, so complicated as they are in British Columbia. Perhaps satisfactory methods of co-operation have not yet been worked out and perhaps the technology of agriculture has not yet reached the ideal stage for successful co-operation. It has been suggested that the future is in "vertical integration" from farm to ultimate market, rather than in "horizontal integration" at the various levels of financing, purchasing, selling or actual farm operation. Whether or not this proves to be the case, there can be little doubt that the future of successful agriculture, especially in British Columbia where arable land is limited and its use must become increasingly efficient, is in some form of co-operation.

Since the problem of finding capital is the big obstacle in the way of developing most of the province's unimproved arable land and since the returns from such investment would be at least as much in useful population as in actual produce, it is reasonable to expect that some sort of government action will be taken as markets develop. There is ample precedent for such action. It has been pointed out at several Resources Conferences that the Columbia Basin project in the State of Washington and the St. Mary's River project in Alberta, both of which compete directly in B.C. markets, were financed by government – the Columbia Basin a federal project of the United States and the St. Mary's project a joint federal-provincial venture in Canada.

The province now has about 150,000 acres of irrigated land using annually about half a million acre feet of water; it is estimated that a further half-million acres could be brought into useful production by irrigation, using less than 1¼ million acre feet of water a year. In comparison with amounts used for hydro-electric power, these are trivial quantities of water and would require only minor storage facilities. In some instances the storage would also contribute to flood control. While problems of competition in limited markets may delay such undertakings for some while, there is no doubt that they must eventually be realized, with great profit not only to the province but to the country as a whole.

Government assistance in land clearing is already available, but a policy of subsidy for mulch crops may be necessary before there can be any large-scale development of the grey-wooded soils, and there may well be delay in this since there are large areas of similar soils still undeveloped in other provinces. These soils make up over 3 million acres of the undeveloped arable land in the province, but it is believed their yield under mixed farming practices, when improved, could approach a national average of thirty dollars an acre. The degraded black soils, of which half a million acres in the Central Interior and 150,000 acres in the Peace River are still unimproved, do not present the same difficulties of development. They yield well in general farming and especially well under crops of grain, legumes and grasses. Careful farming is needed to prevent water erosion, especially in the Peace River where it can become a serious problem. The million or so acres of undeveloped brown podzolic soils are considered likely to yield within the provincial average of 120 - 140 dollars an acre, though the necessary clearing and draining or irrigation is likely to be costly and in some instances may be prohibitive.

The final factor in bringing new land into production or increasing the yield of

Fruit farming centres in the Okanagan Valley.

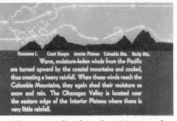

Photographs by the National Film Board.

Irrigation makes the soil fertile.

Flumes channel water to many of the orchards.

land already improved is technological progress. New varieties of grains and other crops, able to stand greater cold or drought, or capable of growing to maturity in shorter seasons, are constantly being developed. New fertilizers and new understanding of their uses, new crop sprays, new machinery, new methods of handling and feeding livestock, all tend to broaden the possibilities of economic production in difficult areas.

Agricultural research in British Columbia is conducted almost entirely by the Research Branch of the Canada Department of Agriculture and by the University of British Columbia. The first maintains a broad programme covering both long-term studies and short-term practical attacks on special problems, whose solution can be directly turned to the benefit of the farmer. The University examines many phases of agriculture, including dairying, soils, livestock, forage crops, horticulture, poultry farming, agricultural engineering and economics.

The diversity of agricultural conditions in British Columbia necessitates a widespread system of research stations, laboratories and experimental farms, each somewhat specialized to meet the needs of a particular region. Climate, soil and topography are all important factors in the growth and types of the crops grown. The scattered production areas, nearly always isolated from each other, have widely differing interests and problems.

The research station at Summerland, with substations at Creston and Kelowna, investigates the complex problems of the Okanagan-Kootenay tree-fruit area, one of the most important in Canada. Many of the projects are of national as well as regional concern. Vegetable production problems in the southern interior are being examined. In the field of animal science, studies are being made of the national problem of bloat in cattle.

The research station on the campus of the University is investigating the plant pathology and entomological problems of crops in the Fraser Valley and also has a special section studying fundamental aspects of plant virus diseases. The experimental farm at Saanichton on Vancouver Island is concerned with such special crops as bulbs and holly as well as with general matters in horticulture and agronomy. The farm at Agassiz, with substations at Abbotsford and Boundary Bay, is the dairy cattle research centre and does the major part of forage, cereal and small-fruit research in the province. At Kamloops there is a range research centre which specializes in ecology, carrying-capacity and livestock pests. The farm at Prince George, with substations at Smithers, is examining the problems of this relatively new agricultural area.

Sprinklers are another method of irrigation.

Pruning for a higher yield.

An orchard in bloom.

A cover crop prevents soil erosion.

Research of this type produces steady results which gradually improve techniques and increase the efficiency of agricultural practice throughout the province. Successful new varieties such as the Van cherry and the Spartan apple have been developed and virus-free strains of several important varieties of strawberries and raspberries have been established. The research stations showed that boron deficiency in soils was causing serious disorders in tree fruits, and also developed concentrate sprayers, which cut the cost of spraying in half. There are many other examples of direct contribution to improved production and better use of the developed agricultural lands.

Marketing problems are also matters of constant investigation and experiment. Grading of most agricultural products has been gradually developed under a system of federal and provincial acts, though grading legislation has been recognized as a provincial responsibility since 1935. Various forms of controlled marketing have been similarly evolved, initiated in most instances by the pressing needs of special-crop growers. The first provincial legislation, the "Produce Marketing Act", was passed in 1927 to protect and control the marketing of Okanagan fruit crops; it was closely followed by the "Dairy Products Sales Act" of 1929. Both these acts were found to be *ultra vires* in 1931 and were followed by voluntary agreements until 1934, when both federal and provincial governments passed "Natural Products Marketing" Acts. These acts were also found *ultra vires,* though three marketing schemes set up under the B.C. Act remain in force: the B.C. Fruit Board, the B.C. Interior Vegetable Marketing Board and the B.C. Coast Marketing Board.

It cannot be said that these efforts have been an unqualified success or that they represent the last word in what can be achieved. They have improved the general standards of produce offered for sale and have eliminated violent price fluctuations by ensuring a steady, controlled flow of fresh fruits and vegetables, but they are not considered to have affected consumer buying-habits or increased sales and they have not been met with unqualified approval even among the growers themselves. These are among the factors that suggest that the principles of "vertical" rather than "horizontal" co-operation should be further investigated.

A recent bright spot in the marketing of tree fruits has been the early success of cider from Okanagan apples. The product now sells at the rate of about a million bottles a year in western Canada, and there is hope of extending sales to eastern Canada and even to Britain and Europe, where the total cider market is of the order of sixty million gallons a year. Modern freezing processes have also been of

Spraying for pests.

Harvesting.

Seasonal help is vital.

Sorting and grading.

great benefit in the marketing of specialized crops such as blueberries, raspberries, strawberries and peas.

It could be said that there is not at present the same pressure for agricultural research and development in the province as there is for research and development in forestry. It is true that direct economic pressure is not so plainly felt – in other words, that money for the purpose is not so readily available. But pressures do exist. British Columbia has a growing population, and so, inevitably, a growing domestic demand for food products. World population is increasing at the rate of 20 million people a year and more than half the people of the world are underfed – world milk production, for instance, is less than half of what it should be to provide a proper diet for everyone, and other major food items are in similarly short supply in spite of local surpluses. If these things are not yet felt as economic pressures, they are certainly moral pressures. No nation can make a real case for reducing or abusing its agricultural lands, improved or potential.

While there is as yet no practical world approach to the problems of food distribution, it is difficult to believe that one will not be developed sooner or later. British Columbia, meanwhile, is a net importer of potatoes, vegetables, small fruits, beef, butter, cheese, powdered milk, poultry, eggs and hogs; in other words, it is far from feeding its own people. In addition, the province is allowing residential and industrial building to swallow up some of its most productive farmland and is sacrificing thousands of acres of potential farmland without question to hydro-electric storage. It permits logging operations that damage potential farmlands by removal of protective ground-cover and it tolerates overgrazing of rangelands. Finally, it has valuable idle acreage that could be brought into production by capital expenditure.

All these circumstances are the result of economic conditions, and all except the outright abuses make perfectly good sense in national or even continental terms. There is, for instance, no degree of popular feeling that would permit government subsidies to protect farmlands from real estate encroachment, and only the beginnings of conviction that some areas should be reserved by the establishment of green belts or other zoning regulations. But the long-term logic is that all the province's farmlands will eventually be needed.

It is difficult to suggest what forms of management are best designed to provide for this prospect. It has been pointed out many times that a resource only exists as a resource when it is in economic use or will be economically used in the foreseeable future. Any extensive opening of Asiatic markets or any large-scale world-wide attack on the problems of undernourished populations could produce sharp economic changes, but neither of these things, though they seem eventually inevitable, could be classed as "foreseeable" in any immediate economic sense.

Perhaps the province's first responsibility is further research. The soil survey is not yet completed and there is a good deal more to be learned about the nature of soils and their parent materials – the grey-wooded soils of the Peace River, for instance, are of saline origin and the only productivity information available is from work with grey-wooded soils of calcareous origin. It is possible that there should be a closer relationship between the soil expert and the agricultural expert – the Resources Conferences have suggested some differences of opinion that seem likely to be settled only by co-ordinated research. Studies of irrigation and drainage methods could well be undertaken, and all such work should be correlated with studies of water and climate. Work of this kind would give a much clearer idea of the real nature of the province's agricultural resources and of how they can best be protected and put to use when the time comes.

But the responsibility is by no means all governmental, nor can it be primarily directed towards some vague and uncertain future need. Private research is of great value in market studies, as well as in improvement of crop strains and agricultural methods. Controlled experiments in integration between farm supply firms, the producing farms and processing and marketing firms might be undertaken and these, if successful, could open up a whole new range of possibilities that would help to meet the economic conditions which at present limit development.

Soil is one of the basic resources and a strong case can be made for the point that agriculture is its most important use. To some extent this is recognized in British Columbia and agricultural use has a measure of priority. Development has been advanced by technological improvements in machinery and buildings, in varieties and breeds, in plant and animal nutrition, disease and pest control, soil management and business management; but on the whole these advances have not allowed the farmer to keep pace with similar advances in other industries. As a result farming remains a difficult, uncertain and somewhat less profitable business than most others. Land clearing and other development costs remain a problem in British Columbia and perhaps only time, with increasing markets and further technological progress, can overcome this. It has been estimated that the province should be using another million acres of improved land within the next twenty-five years, nearly twice its present development. Many factors, including population, transportation, organization and speed of technical advances, will influence this, but it is an indication that potentially valuable agricultural lands are of the utmost importance and must be protected from misuse if the province is to develop as it should. Eventual use of all potentially arable land can be forecast, but this is so far in the future that nothing more than continuing basic research and some early planning can be justified.

the fossil fuels   CHAPTER 11

ENERGY PUTS RESOURCES to use. For that matter, energy created them all in the first place – the sun's energy, the energy of the waters and the energy of the earth itself. From the beginning man has sought ways to use and control energy; his own energy, that of his fellow men, the energy of domestic animals, of wind and water and heat. His degree of success in this is the measure of the material side of modern civilization; what it may have done to the other aspects of man's being is more debatable, but fortunately need not concern us at the moment.

Man has used water-power and wind-power in simple mechanical conversion, to grind corn, drive sawmills and even to catch fish, from very early times. But the first great source of stored energy he learned to tap efficiently was coal. Coal, through steam-power, brought about the industrial revolution and set the whole pattern of development that has followed. Coal is still a tremendous factor in the world's economy and the world's coal reserves still add up to a mighty potential of energy; but through the past fifty years the petroleum oils have been slowly replacing coal as the world's major source of energy and, more recently, natural gas has been replacing coal gas and even oil in many areas.

Use of the petroleum oils to drive earth- and rock-moving machinery has had a good deal to do with the intensive development of water-power to produce electricity, and this in turn has still further reduced the uses of coal. Oil and natural gas, especially the latter, are being increasingly used to produce electrical energy, and further technical improvements, as well as further discoveries of gas fields, are likely to make natural gas a close competitor of water-power in many areas. Finally, the developments of nuclear fission within the next twenty or thirty years and of fusion within the next hundred years seem reasonably certain to supply man with energy far beyond his foreseeable or imaginable needs, if he can survive the shocks and surprises of discovery. Discussion of energy, then, is more beset with doubts and imponderables than discussion of other resources. Most experts are reluctant to project their ideas beyond the next decade and even in this they are cautious and seldom in close agreement.

British Columbia has an immense potential of energy, in nearly all its most valuable and useful forms. She has six billion tons of coal reserves that are accessible and workable – enough for several thousand years at the present rate of consumption. She has tremendous quantities of fuel wood, in spite of greatly improved techniques in the use of wood for other purposes. She has some 27 million firm horsepower undeveloped in her rivers, which would require an installed capacity of forty million horsepower in an ultimate integrated system. The expectation is that these figures will be revised upwards as northern rivers are investigated; at present only three million horsepower are developed. She has proven natural gas reserves of three trillion cubic feet, or enough to last for fifty years at the present rate of consumption, with prospective reserves of 70 to 90 trillion cubic feet now being more carefully examined. She has estimated oil reserves, also not yet proved, of 13 billion barrels, again with the distinct possibility that further quantities may eventually be proved.

This plainly is an embarrassment of riches. It poses the most difficult question in resource use in the province to-day: how best to develop and make use of this great potential of energy?

At present the province is importing over half of the total energy it uses, in the form of petroleum oils. True, it wastes a large proportion of this in oversized and underloaded automobiles, but it is still energy and it has to be paid for. It is also importing more than half the coal it uses, because better and cheaper coal is available from elsewhere. And industrial users of energy in the province are paying an average price of 54 cents per million British thermal units compared to 25 cents in Alberta – a higher price, in fact, than in any other province in Canada except Prince Edward Island and very much higher than the U.S. average. So British Columbia, in spite of her apparently vast resources of energy, is not at present competing very well.

Figures and statistics on energy are more difficult to understand and interpret than the figures and statistics of other resources, if only because they are expressed in so many different ways – electrical horsepower, kilowatt hours, B.T.U.'s, cubic feet of gas (in trillions), barrels of oil and tons of coal, to mention only a few. But the subject has a much more genuine difficulty in that it is constantly and rapidly changing; what was a good source of energy yesterday is less valuable to-day, and could be almost worthless to-morrow. At the present time, changes are so rapid and so far-reaching that forecasts are subject to almost yearly revision and any forecast beyond 1980 is of very doubtful value, if only because by that time nuclear energy is likely to be a powerful factor in the field.

Because energy is a highly competitive field and becoming increasingly competitive as well as increasingly diverse, it is further confused by politics and the special pleading of special interests. Though relatively useless by itself, it is the chief key to the modern economy and offers possibilities of power, wealth and service as nothing else does. For the most part it requires massive capitalization, such as can be undertaken only by governments and the largest of private concerns; it offers few opportunities for the small operator and so is difficult to fit into a philosophy of private ownership of natural resources. Government ownership and development at first seem the obvious answer, but the problem of finding the necessary capital for a succession of large developments would certainly be a burden to any provincial government and might delay development. Joint federal-provincial development would be a far more practical concept, were it not for jurisdictional, political and ideological differences that frustrate co-operation; most energy sources, except in their international aspects, are under provincial control, which ensures somewhat narrow thinking; and presumably federal credit would be seriously strained to provide for a multiplicity of large federal-provincial developments all over the country, to say nothing of the risk capital in oil and gas exploration, though not more so than it is at present by huge defence expenditures of highly debatable value.

The third alternative is to encourage private investment, and this can only be done by concessions and guarantees which, like railroad charters and forest management licences, heavily commit the future. Risk capital for exploration and development can be attracted only by the prospect of great rewards. Large energy developments, whether they are pipelines, transmission lines or plant construction, call

ENERGY CONVERSION FACTORS

Commodity	Physical Unit	B.t.u.*
COAL		
BITUMINOUS	ONE TON	= 27,000,000
ANTHRACITE	ONE TON	= 26,000,000
SUB-BITUMINOUS	ONE TON	= 19,000,000
LIGNITE	ONE TON	= 16,000,000
COKE	ONE TON	= 25,000,000
CRUDE OIL	ONE BARREL†	= 5,800,000
NATURAL GAS LIQUIDS	ONE BARREL	= 4,000,000
GASOLINE	ONE BARREL	= 5,200,000
DIESEL FUEL	ONE BARREL	= 5,800,000
FUEL OIL	ONE BARREL	= 5,800,000
RESIDUAL OIL	ONE BARREL	= 6,000,000
PETROLEUM COKE	ONE TON	= 30,000,000
NATURAL GAS	ONE CU. FT.	= 1,000
MANUFACTURED GAS	ONE CU. FT.	= 550
WATER POWER	ONE K.W.H.	= 3,412
FUEL WOOD	ONE CORD	= 20,000,000
LUBRICANTS AND OTHER (NON-FUEL) DERIVATIVES OF PETROLEUM	ONE TON	= 30,000,000

*The amount of heat required to raise the temperature of 1 lb. of water by 1 degree F.

†35 Imperial gallons.

for heavy capital outlays and therefore command long-term monopolistic rewards. They are one of the last remaining means of industrial empire building because they involve long-term concessions whose future can only be conservatively estimated in the light of to-day's values. It is always questionable whether such private investment and ownership can be regulated closely enough to protect the long-term interest of the public.

All these concerns, added to the natural interest of each proponent in his own special plan or energy source, naturally make for an extremely wide range of claim and counter-claim and forecast, a confusion still worse confounded by the claims and counter-claims of other resource-users whose interests will be affected by the developments.

British Columbia has moved, in pace with the rest of the world, from an economy based chiefly on energy from coal to an economy based chiefly on energy from the petroleum oils. Hydro-electric energy is another factor, and a considerably more important one than its percentage suggests, because it is renewable and the waste of petroleum oils – their consumption in activities that are neither productive nor truly satisfying – is so enormous. Natural gas has come into the picture only very recently, but its developments have been so rapid that any forecast is likely to underestimate its potential. Nuclear fuels are not yet in use in British Columbia and are not considered likely to become seriously competitive for at least twenty years. But they are already an influential shadow that must be considered in the planning of any long-term, large-scale project. The immense application of brains and capital throughout the world to the problems of controlling various nuclear fuels for constructive use promises – or threatens, depending on the point of view – a major breakthrough at any time; but even continuous progress at the present rate is a factor that must be considered.

In the course of a very carefully considered paper given at the 11th Resources Conference in 1958, Dr. John Davis, Director of Research and Planning for the B.C. Electric Company, gave the following table of past and future changes in the province's sources of energy:

BRITISH COLUMBIA'S CHANGING ENERGY SUPPLY

(*each source as a percentage of total supply*)

ENERGY SOURCE	1935	1957	1980
WOOD	26	15	2
COAL	50	17	10
OIL	17	55	40
NATURAL GAS [1]	Negligible	1	30
WATER-POWER	7	12	16
NUCLEAR ENERGY [2]	0	0	2
	100	100	100

[1] Including Natural Gas liquids.

[2] Measured in terms of its contribution as electricity.

Dr. Davis would be the last to claim that his projections are infallible, but he made the whole base of his paper very clear in its second paragraph: "I should therefore begin by describing my particular endeavour as that of adding the element of time to space; of bringing price as well as demand into our calculations; and, by stressing the importance of technological change, help to reconcile the widely different appraisals of our energy resource potential which have been made in the past." He was attempting a realistic approach to energy as a whole in the provincial economy during the next twenty years.

The steady decline of fuel wood as a source of energy requires little explanation. It is a variable and not too efficient source, expensive to harvest and expensive to transport. It can be economic only as a by-product, and higher uses are steadily being found for it. All in all, there is little to recommend it except availability.

Coal is a much larger question. Deep-mined coal at the pit-head costs about twice as much per unit of energy as natural gas at the well-head. It is nearly twice as expensive to transport as gas and three times as expensive as oil. Coal varies in quality and does not lend itself to use as fuel in modern transportation. These are the main reasons for its decline.

But it remains a potential resource and some experts believe it has not yet seen its greatest days. In favourable locations, especially where strip mining is possible, lignite coal is still producing some of the cheapest energy on the continent. Little success has been achieved in manufacturing gas from coal underground and feeding it to power developments at the site. So far the gases produced have been of low energy content, averaging about one-fourth that of city gas and one-tenth that of natural gas, and so will not bear the cost of transportation. Further research and experiment may greatly improve this quality, but in the meanwhile such energy is considered economic only when an electrical generating station can be established at or near the coal site. The fact that large-scale electrical energy from coal is still a realistic possibility in British Columbia is emphasized by the recent B.C. Electric Company purchase of the Hat Creek coal deposit, where open-pit mining is possible. Three hundred and forty million tons of coal are available in a square-mile area, with substantial reserves nearby; the thermal electric potential of the site is over 2½ million horsepower for a period of fifty years. It is said that "very cheap" power can be developed at this site within two years of the start of construction.

Another possibility is the manufacture from coal of synthetic liquid fuels that would be adequate substitutes for petroleum fuels. These processes are still too costly for use under normal North American conditions, but in view of the enormous consumption of liquid petroleum fuels the possibility must be considered important, although it is not likely to have any noticeable effect on the province's energy requirements during the next twenty years. B.C.'s 1957 coal production was slightly over a million tons, valued at about 7 million dollars, chiefly from mines near Fernie and from the Tsable River mine, on Vancouver Island. The chief coal reserves of the province are in the south-east, near Fernie, in the north-east near

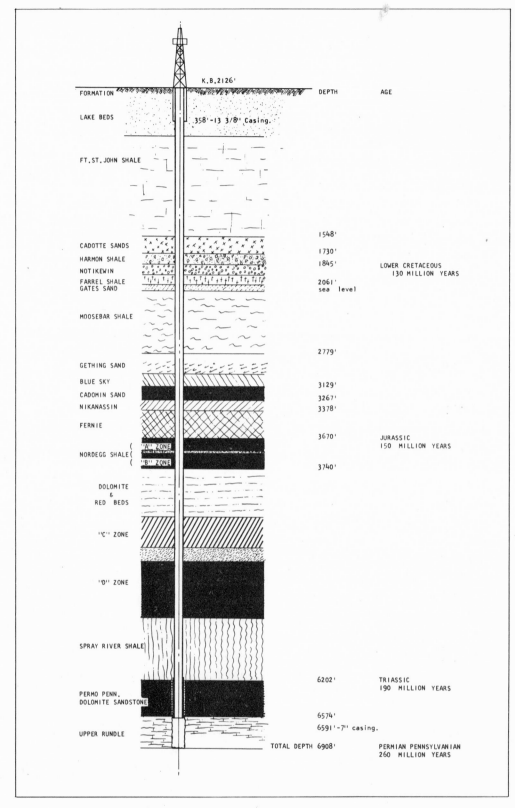

Diagram of strata encountered in the first successful gas well drilled in the Peace River region, 1952, courtesy Westcoast Transmission Ltd.

the Peace River Canyon, and on Vancouver Island. Large reserves on the Queen Charlotte Islands are considered extremely difficult to work profitably. There are smaller reserves at Telkwa, Atlin, Princeton, Tulameen and Merritt.

Most authorities on B.C.'s energy resources seem to concede that most of the coal reserves must be considered an "ex-resource", a resource that time has caught up with and passed by. While technology and the exhaustion of other energy reserves may bring it back into valuable use one day, this cannot be considered at all certain, since reserves of natural gas and hydro-power seem far more than adequate to serve the province's needs until energy is economically available from nuclear and solar sources.

So far as is known at present, British Columbia's oil and natural gas potential is limited to four areas: the Peace River district, northward to the 60th parallel and eastward to the Alberta boundary; the Flathead area, in the south-east corner of the province; the Nanaimo basin, which covers most of the Strait of Georgia including a small portion of the Lower Mainland and a narrow strip of the south-east coastline of Vancouver Island; and the Honna-Skidegate basin in the Queen Charlotte Islands.

The last two of these areas have broadly favourable geological conditions, but limited drilling has yielded no favourable results and it seems unlikely that further effort will be put into them in the near future. The Flathead area has more promising signs, and oil and gas are considered to be certainly present under the pre-Cambrian strata; drilling is being continued, with a deep test well planned for 1960.

The Peace River area has already become a substantial producer of natural gas and is now being subjected to one of the most intensive searches in the history of the petroleum industry. There is every reason to believe that it will shortly prove to be the province's greatest reservoir of energy and one of the greatest reserves on the continent.

The whole of the Fort Nelson, Fort St. John, Dawson Creek area between the Rocky Mountain foothills and the Alberta boundary is considered to be part of the Western Canada Sedimentary Basin, which has yielded such great petroleum discoveries in the prairie provinces. This sedimentary basin actually extends from the Gulf of Mexico to the Arctic Ocean and has at several times in the distant past been invaded by the sea; the oil-bearing strata, now covered by thousands of feet of overburden, are marine deposits of vegetable and animal life that were sealed off by sedimentary mud, which has now become rock or sand of varying porosity and depth. Gas and oil are trapped in faults and fracture zones and are held under tremendous pressures in the porous formations.

More than fifty million acres were under permit or lease by petroleum interests in the Peace River area during 1959. Drilling began in 1947, was given sharp impetus by the Pacific Petroleum discovery at Fort St. John in 1951 and again by the multiple and highly significant discoveries of 1959, following completion of the West Coast Transmission line. This pipeline, which passes through the length of the province to Washington and Oregon, has a capacity of 660 million cubic feet per day, the equivalent of 11 million electrical horsepower, but has already proved inadequate for the amounts of gas available. Construction will shortly begin on a second with double the capacity of the existing line.

Earlier gas discoveries centred on the Fort St. John and Dawson Creek areas, but exploration has been moving northward and the area around Fort Nelson and north to the Yukon boundary has been steadily growing in importance, with land near Clarke Lake, Kotcho Lake and the Petitot River promising discoveries that may far exceed anything so far found farther south. Nearly fifty per cent of the volume of gas so far discovered is in the Upper Triassic zone, while the Jurassic zone above it and the Permo-Pennsylvanian zone under it have excellent recovery conditions and together account for most of the remainder. The Mississippian and Devonian beds, at still greater depth, have shown some gas zones but have not yet been thoroughly explored. Although the main exploration effort seems to have worked northward and eastward, it is believed that the depth of the sedimentary zone thickens from an average of about six thousand feet in the north-east to a maximum of twenty thousand feet in the south-west, along the Rocky Mountain foothills, suggesting the possibility of foothill discoveries such as have been made further south in Alberta.

The progress of recent effort and discovery is roughly expressed in the following table of wells drilled and results on a succession of dates:

	1957	1959	1960
WELLS DRILLED TO DATE:	259	473	519
GAS WELLS PROVED:	112	179	196
OIL WELLS PROVED:	15	53	63
DRY OR INCOMPLETE:	132	241	260

It is noticeable that discovery has maintained a consistent average of one successful well for every two drilled, which is considered a particularly good rate since much of the work has been, and still is, exploratory.

It is difficult to find any solid, realistic base from which to discuss the implications of such rapid advances, but it seems reasonable to expect eventual discovery of not less than seventy trillion cubic feet of gas in the Peace River area, possibly very much more. A possible reserve of 75 to 90 trillion feet was suggested at the 12th Resources Conference of 1959 and the Minister of Mines offered an approximate figure of seventy trillion at the 1960 session of the Legislature.

To understand what a reserve of this magnitude can mean in terms of energy for the province, a few more figures are necessary. The present capacity of the West Coast Transmission pipeline is 660 million cubic feet per day, or the equivalent of 11 million electrical horsepower. A reserve of 70 trillion feet would support a flow of about 4 times the present capacity, or over 2½ billion feet a day for a hundred years. This energy would be the equivalent of 44 million horsepower, roughly the

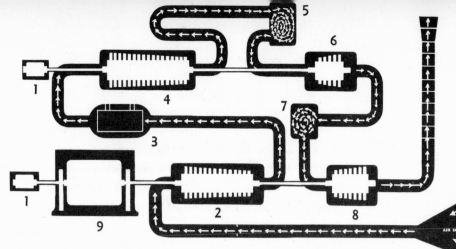

Above is a diagram of one unit of the B.C. Electric thermal plant at Ioco. *Starting motors* (1) turn the *high-pressure compressor* (4), *generator* (9) and *low-pressure compressor* (2) which sucks in air and drives it through the *intercooler* (3) to the *high-pressure compressor* (4). Natural gas is fed into the *high-pressure combustion chamber* (5) where it and the highly compressed air are ignited by a spark, after which combustion is self-sustaining. The super-heated air strikes the *high-pressure turbine* (6) which takes over spinning the shaft. The air continues to the *low-pressure combustion chamber* (7) where it is again ignited with natural gas, thus gaining the pressure to turn the *low-pressure turbine* (8) which takes over turning the *low-pressure compressor* (2) and the *generator* (9) which makes the electricity.

same amount as the entire hydro-electric potential of the province at optimum development.

The most efficient uses for natural gas are in direct heating and its use for the generation of electricity is therefore secondary and supplementary, but there can be no doubt that the whole picture of energy in the province is substantially changed by the prospect of these reserves. Natural gas is cheap, readily transportable, efficient and dependable. Gas-burning plants are cheaper to construct than hydro plants. They can be built close to the centre of the area of demand, thus reducing electrical transmission costs, and their maintenance and operating costs are low. The only critical question remaining is the cost of the fuel itself at the plant.

Peace River gas is now being delivered to companies in the southern part of the province at 32 cents per thousand cubic feet (one million B.T.U.'s) and the "crossing" or contract price at the international border is 22 cents. Authorities differ as to whether the 32 cents price could (or should) hold for some years. One view is that the demand for natural gas for thermal plants will have to compete with its demand for other purposes, with the result that prices will fluctuate and tend generally upward, as has been the case with Bunker "C" oil over the past ten years. The other view is that as pipeline capacity is increased and greater through-puts are achieved, the price will go down. With such a large potential in prospect, the second of these two views seems the more compelling. Prices closely reflecting cost are further assured by the powers of the National Energy Board to set field prices and to adjust demand levels by control of export permits.

Further indications that natural gas may be economic in producing base loads of electrical energy are to be found in the current construction of the B.C. Electric Company's thermal-electric gas-fueled plant at Ioco, which will have an eventual capacity of 1,200,000 horsepower. The plant is expected to yield electricity at six mills per kwh. or less, which would be closely competitive with either Peace River or Columbia River hydro-electric power in the same area. In the United States, some gas-electric plants in the gas source areas produce power for as little as three mills. Seventy-five per cent of all electrical power in the U.S. is now generated by thermal plants and this proportion is expected to increase to more than eighty per cent by 1970. By 1980 the Pacific states expect to be using hydro plants only for peak-load purposes, in spite of their massive hydro developments. The past twenty years have seen an improvement of almost thirty per cent in the efficiency of ther-mal-electric plants. Further improvement is expected with continuing development in metals and techniques, but it may be at a slower rate.

The largest and most important uses of natural gas are for the production of heat and energy, and these may be expected to remain paramount. But gas is a complex substance which can be broken down to supply important chemicals such as sul-phur, ammonia, methanol and carbon black. Large quantities of sulphur are al-ready produced in B.C. from acid gas waste, for sale to pulp mills and other users. But most of the petro-chemicals have to meet heavy competition from chemicals produced from other sources and there is no serious possibility that demand for them can affect supplies of natural gas for energy in the foreseeable future.

Significant oil discoveries in British Columbia are even more recent than natural gas discoveries. Proven oil reserves to date are of the order of sixty million barrels, which is by no means an important quantity since the province imports over 250 million barrels a year. But estimates projected from exploration work completed before 1959 suggest that the prospective reserve may be as high as thirteen billion barrels and it is believed that the results of more recent explorations may well lead to an upward revision of this figure. Reserves of this size are of importance and are certain to be developed sooner or later, even though they are remote from large markets. In 1959 the province produced about 800,000 barrels of crude oil, worth 1½ million dollars, but imported 113 million barrels of foreign oil and 151 million barrels of Alberta oil. The Transmountain pipeline delivers 185,000 barrels a day to B.C. and the State of Washington at the low transportation cost of 40 cents per barrel. Whether or not oil can be piped from the Peace River fields to compete with these sources of supply is still questionable, but an oil pipeline from the Peace River to Vancouver has already been predicted. Its completion would certainly throw still another large energy potential into the field of active competition with hydro and natural gas and coal. The present flow of the Transmountain pipeline, it should be noted, is the equivalent of 17½ million horsepower.

Coal, oil and natural gas are non-renewable resources. Conservation here is en-tirely a matter of skilful extraction and efficient and timely use. Economic recovery of both gas and oil depends largely upon maintenance of underground pressures in the fields. Gas and oil must be extracted from fields as fields and pools as pools, not from individual wells in haphazard competition. Regulation and planning are necessary. Rate of recovery and spacing of wells are important factors in maintaining pressures. Waning pressures can be increased by driving waste gas back into the wells instead of allowing it to escape, and by pumping in air or water or acids. All these methods of improving recovery or rejuvenating old wells are now standard practice, recognized by both government and industry. The recovery rate of natural gas has increased to ninety per cent of reserves, and recovery of oil, though less efficient, may range up to seventy-five per cent of reserves. Government can further ensure maximum recovery by proper allocation of markets among producing pools or fields.

Conservation continues at the surface, by the extraction of natural gasoline and butane from natural gas, and by improved refining processes and recovery of useful chemicals. If necessary, reserves can be protected for domestic use by limiting export permits, though excessive limitation may discourage exploration. Under to-day's conditions, the only large-scale waste of petroleum products is by the consuming public, and this is a matter of deliberate choice reflecting an economy of abundance. Under threat of scarcity, this could be even more readily controlled by government action than it is now promoted by extravagant advertising and the sale of inefficient equipment in the shape of overpowered automobiles. It seems that there is no threat of scarcity or else that there is complete confidence that other fuels will be developed to replace petroleum sources.

This last point seems of some interest. At the present time there is no fuel in sight that seems likely to replace the liquid petroleums for use in trucks, automobiles, locomotives, earth-moving equipment and most airplanes. If a shortage were in sight, coal deposits would become important again as one of the most likely sources of synthetic fuels.

Natural gas is expected in time to take over space heating, water heating and process heating in both domestic and industrial fields. It will be used to some extent in the production of electricity, chiefly on a low-cost, interruptible basis that can be integrated with other sources. Its contribution to the total energy needs of the nation increased from three per cent in 1949 to eight per cent in 1959; a further increase to between fifteen and twenty per cent is expected by 1970 and by 1980 it may be serving 25 per cent of all fuel and power needs. With extensive exploration work continuing throughout the north-eastern part of the province and greatly increased pipeline capacity running through the length of the province to reach and serve all major markets, there cannot be much doubt that British Columbia will share to the fullest extent in this development. It is a point of some importance that development and transportation of natural gas conflicts seriously with no other resource use.

LA JOIE DAM

MISSION DAM

BRIDGE RIVER

NO 2 POWERHOUSE

NO 1 POWERHOUSE

SETON LAKE

SETON DEVELOPMENT

FRASER RIVER

B.C. ELECTRIC BRIDGE RIVER HYDRO DEVELOPMENT

diagram courtesy B.C. Electric Co. Lt

UNLIKE THE FOSSIL FUELS, water-power is a renewable resource. It is in the hydrologic cycle that carries water in clouds from the oceans and drops it in snow or rain on the hills, to flow back to the seas through the river systems. Each year of the cycle restores the depletion of the previous year and the flow of water, drawn by gravity from the hills, creates energy that has only to be harnessed.

A river's flow is not even throughout the year; it fluctuates with rainfall and snow-melt in individual but recognizable pattern. Most British Columbia rivers fluctuate very widely between highs of spring and fall and lows of summer drought and winter freeze-up. River flows also vary in total from year to year, though these variations tend to compensate and average out over a cycle of years. This uneven quality makes it necessary to store water behind dams and level off a river's flow if power is to be produced efficiently and consistently. "Hydro-sites" are places in a river system that offer more or less favourable opportunities for building storage dams to regulate flow and drop water through a head to produce electrical energy. The capacity of such sites is measured in horsepower or kilowatts, and the actual output of energy is usually expressed in kilowatt hours.

Massive hydro development has always been a part of British Columbia's dream of the future and it remains so, in spite of the competition of fossil fuels and the impending competition of nuclear fuels. Most authorities who are closely connected with hydro-power believe that the whole hydro potential of the province will be put to use sooner or later, if only because it is a perpetual resource. A few less dedicated authorities believe that development will be markedly slowed and perhaps eventually stopped short of the full potential by economic competition of the thermal energy sources. Any long-term consideration is naturally confused by the unknown quantity of nuclear fuels; but it is clear that hydro has an important part to play over the next twenty or thirty years, though its development should be closely integrated with intelligent use of the fossil fuels, especially natural gas.

The reader will find tremendously wide variation in estimates of the province's hydro-electric potential. This is chiefly accounted for by the many different possibilities of storage, which in turn depend on engineering problems, costs, markets and other factors. The province's firm potential at the ordinary minimum flow of its important power rivers is about seven million horsepower. Well planned development and storage, by regulating river flows so that a maximum volume of water is available for turbine use throughout the year, and, in some instances, so that the regulated flow is available at several different sites on the same watershed, can increase this potential to at least 35 million horsepower, perhaps over forty million.

Hydro-electric potential, so stated, is not quite like an accessible reserve of oil or gas, or even a coal reserve. These reserves, especially the petroleum reserves, are available, once the pipeline or other transportation facilities are installed, in known quantities at fairly steady and predictable prices. Hydro-potential, or reserve if it can be called that, cannot be tapped as a whole. Each site is a separate development of its own, with its own special problems of cost, construction, transmission and markets, unless or until it can be fitted into an integrated system as part of a transmission network. Whether or not it can be economically developed at any given time is a matter for close and intense study. It exists only in theory until the final studies have been made and the proposed use found practicable. Even then unexpected construction difficulties, geological complications and other problems may upset the estimates.

If use of energy is to be properly planned, some reasonably accurate inventory of the resource is essential and work is constantly being done on the province's river systems to make the inventory as complete and accurate as it can be. At the end of 1958 B.C. had an installed-turbine capacity of slightly over 3,300,000 horsepower and an estimated further potential, at 70 per cent load factor, of over 40,000,000 horsepower. Some of this potential, which includes several major diversion possibilities, may never be developed, but there are other rivers such as the Liard, in the northern part of the province, that have not been considered, and integration, when possible, immensely increases capacity; so it is clear that the province has tremendous hydro resources. In Canada they are probably second only to those of Quebec province.

Heavy precipitation and high mountains are the base of these large water-power possibilities, and they are also the main obstacles in the way of early and easy development. River flows throughout British Columbia are subject to extreme seasonal fluctuations; rain and melting snow drain swiftly from the steep mountainsides and are swiftly carried through narrow valleys back to the sea. During winter freeze-up or summer drought the rivers are very low; during the thaws of spring and early summer and the wet months of the fall they are high and violent. Many of the coast streams have a ratio of a hundred to one or more between high and low flow; Bridge River's ratio is 158:1, the Skeena's 101:1, the Fraser's at Hope 33:1, the Columbia's at Revelstoke is 95:1, at Birchbank 35:1. These ratios compare with figures of 8:1 for the Nipigon, 9:1 for the Ottawa, 6:1 for the Winnipeg and slightly over 2:1 for the St. Lawrence, where the Beauharnois development will be producing two and a quarter million horsepower by 1961.

This flashy nature of the province's rivers means that very large storage is needed to control their flow and achieve a steady output of energy. At the same time the mountainous country and narrow valleys limit storage possibilities and make necessary high and costly dams, which can only be built at carefully chosen sites. From these sites, which are often remote, the electricity must be transmitted to the industrial and residential centres where it is needed. Here again the rough, mountainous country presents great difficulties and high cost, and long distances can make the difference between low-cost energy at the source and high-cost energy at the point of use.

In addition to these problems hydro-electric development nearly always comes into serious conflict with other resource uses. Storage reservoirs permanently flood large areas of land – a particularly serious matter in British Columbia, where valley land is limited and always important. High dams reduce or completely destroy valuable fish runs; forest; agricultural and recreational resources may all be affected, nearly always adversely. Roads, railroads and transmission lines must be relocated and future communications will be forced to by-pass the reservoir, often at very high cost because they are pushed back on to steep slopes.

In spite of these disadvantages, water-power remains a very attractive source of energy. It is a very flexible source, requires comparatively little supervision and may be readily and usefully integrated with any other source. In some instances storage dams can be planned to assist in flood control or irrigation projects. Above all, it is renewable and perpetual, short of major geologic or climatic changes, though it should perhaps be pointed out that power sites can in time be seriously reduced in value if silting in the reservoirs is not controlled, and maintenance costs of dams and other installations may be significant.

The largest single hydro-electric development in the province to date is the Aluminum Company of Canada plant at Kemano, which has a potential of 2½ million horsepower, less than half of it now in use. This is a diversion project which turns the main flow of the Nechako back through the coast mountains to take advantage of the steep drop to the Pacific. The electricity generated serves only the company's own plant and the community of Kitimat. The B.C. Electric Company operates fourteen plants for general service with a total of slightly over one million horsepower. The Consolidated Mining and Smelting Company has six plants which together yield 574,000 horsepower; most of this power is used for the company's own industrial purposes. The B.C. Power Commission, which is publicly owned, operates seven plants with a total of 377,000 horsepower; a large proportion of this goes to industrial users, especially pulp-and-paper plants on Vancouver Island, but the Commission provides electrification for many of the less settled parts of the province by thermal-electric and diesel-electric as well as hydro-electric installations. There are a number of smaller developments throughout the province serving both community and industrial purposes.

It is readily seen from this that the needs of the province have not so far been great enough to justify development of its larger hydro-electric sites. The single exception is the Kemano plant of the Aluminum Company of Canada and in this instance the most power-hungry of all industries has found cheap energy at tidewater sufficiently attractive to permit import of its raw material. Apart from this, hydro development has had to face the difficulties of scattered markets and the problems of long-distance transmission over most formidable terrain. It is natural that the smaller sites within fairly easy reach of markets should have been developed first.

At the present time most of the smaller sites still undeveloped no longer look especially attractive. Nearly all present construction or transmission difficulties that will make for relatively high-cost energy, or else involve sharp conflict with other resource uses. Development of smaller sites and expansion of existing plants will certainly continue, but the province seems to have reached the point where development of a major site is essential if hydro is to continue in competition with other energy sources.

Construction at a major site is a very large and complicated undertaking. It certainly involves provincial political considerations and almost as certainly federal considerations. It is likely to involve international complications, either in the form of essential markets or downstream benefits or resource damage. It must also involve some damage and loss and some measure of compensation within the province.

Any major hydro construction is a tremendous financial undertaking, a matter of hundreds of millions of dollars. Construction costs have been rising steadily ever since the war and there is every reason to suppose they will continue to rise. In major projects they are bound to increase, often unpredictably, during the course of construction. Transmission-line costs have also been rising in proportion to total investment. Financing of this order means enormous interest charges, accumulating over the non-productive years of construction, which can be justified only by advance assurance of very large markets. The output of such a plant must compete successfully, not only with other energy sources within the province but to some extent with those of other provinces and other countries as well. A major plant built ahead of its time – before the necessary markets are developed – must sustain very heavy losses and may significantly increase energy costs in the area it serves for an indefinite period.

British Columbia has eight watersheds with estimated potentials of over a million horsepower each. These are the Fraser, 7 million; Yukon-Taku, 5 million; Peace River, 4 million; Columbia, 3½ million ,plus downstream benefits in excess of one million; the Stikine, 2 million; the Skeena, 1½ million; the Thompson, 1½ million and Homathco-Chilko, 1 million.

Flood Line

Axis

ograph courtesy Water Resources Branch,
artment of Northern Affairs and Natural Resources.

PROPOSED DAM-SITE ON MICA CREEK

Of these the Fraser, the Stikine, the Skeena, the Lower Thompson sites (900,-
000) and the Chilko diversion to the Homathco involve problems in preserving
important migratory fish runs for which no solution is at present in sight. Two
smaller sites, the Nass and the Quesnel, with potentials of about 400,000 and 300,-
000 horsepower respectively, present similar difficulties. The Stikine, Nass and
Skeena are remote from important markets, though all three could provide energy
at tidewater. Yukon-Taku is remote from markets and presents international problems. The Peace River is remote from markets and the Columbia has international
problems that have been under discussion for more than fifteen years; but both
these projects are under very active consideration and are certain to be developed

within the next ten to twenty years if the energy demands of the province increase fast enough.

Of the two, the Columbia has many obvious advantages and certainly should be the first developed. The international complications mainly involve the downstream benefits that would be realized at developed sites in Washington and Oregon by well planned storage in Canada. The storage construction essential to development of the Canadian potential will, under proper control, achieve complete regulation of the river's flow – something that cannot be done on the U.S. side of the border. This regulation will provide greatly increased yields of firm power at American sites such as Grand Coulee, Rock Island, McNary, the Dalles, Bonneville and many others, and at the same time should provide complete flood protection for the heavily settled Lower Columbia Valley. In return for these benefits, Canadians are asking fifty per cent of the additional electricity produced. The mutual benefits are so enormous that it is impossible to believe the matter will not be settled very shortly, even though international negotiations at this level are notoriously ponderous.*

Apart from the international complications, the Columbia has everything to recommend it. It lends itself to phase-by-phase development, which reduces the initial heavy capital costs and should reduce the need for committing large blocks of energy to light-metal industries and other disproportionate users of power. Full development, including downstream benefits, will yield 50 per cent more energy in kilowatt hours than the total of the Peace River. The sites are in the southern part of the province and transmission lines would run through comparatively well settled areas. Mica Creek, the main Columbia site, is 290 miles from Vancouver by direct line and about 400 miles by the route the transmission line would take, compared to distances of 475 and over 600 miles from Finlay Forks on the Peace. In addition, the Columbia offers possibilities of integration with the American transmission grid and would provide a valuable base for a grid covering southern British Columbia. The Columbia would be financed by federal and provincial governments, owned by the public and controlled by the public. Its development in no way depends on export of power. It has been estimated that Columbia power can be delivered at the coast for 4 - 4½ mills per kilowatt hour. This may be over-optimistic, even allowing for downstream benefits, but at least there is a good chance of coming within the 6-mill limit that is usually competitive under modern conditions. This would allow for at-site cost of 3½ mills and transmission costs of 2½ mills.

With the Columbia fully developed, the province would be within one million of the nine million horsepower of hydro energy it is likely to need by 1980. But in the

---

*Agreement between Canada and the United States for development of the Upper Columbia was reached late in 1960, approximately on the terms outlined above. It appears likely that a treaty between the two nations will have been signed before this book appears in print. The matter is still confused by some provincial-federal disagreement as to details of financing, but an early start on construction is to be expected.

meanwhile it will almost certainly be necessary to go ahead with some of the dual purpose hydro-electric flood-control dams recommended for the headwaters of the Fraser by the Fraser River Board preliminary report of 1958. The Clearwater and McGregor River projects alone would provide 8 million acre feet of effective flood-control storage, or nearly seventy per cent of the total needed for complete protection, and about 750,000 horsepower. Full implementation of Plan A of the Report, which can be achieved "without serious damage to salmon runs", would provide complete flood protection and about 1,300,000 horsepower.

The Peace River project is estimated to be capable of a production of 4 million horsepower for sale at site at about 4 or 4½ mills per kilowatt hour. The proponents of the project believe the power could be delivered to the international border at a price of about seven mills. Other authorities believe that transmission would at least double the price to 8 or 9 mills.*

Transmission distance from the Peace River site to the Vancouver market is over 600 miles and very little is accurately known of electrical transmission over such distances. Certainly until 1952, the principle that "electrical transmission is much more expensive than transporting energy by gas or pipeline" was sound and unquestionable. Since that time experiments with extremely high-voltage transmission have shown that some savings are possible. Before 1952 long-distance voltages of 220,000 were fairly standard – the equipment for higher voltages was not available. Voltages on some European lines have since been increased to as much as 400,000 with an apparent measure of success. The B.C. Electric is using voltages up to 345,000 and estimates that transmission costs can be held to 2 mills per kwh. over 300 miles at high-load factor. The advantage is that twice as much energy can be transmitted over such a line as over a 220,000-volt line for approximately the same maintenance costs and only 15 - 30 per cent higher construction costs. Line losses of electricity in transmission are no greater in percentage with high voltage than with low.

The question so far unanswered is: how far can this principle be extended in terms of both distance and increased voltage? The Peace River project is predicated upon alternating current voltages of 500,000 over a 600-mile transmission line. This has never before been attempted. The Russians are said to have transmitted 600,-000-volt direct current over considerable distances, but direct current cannot be generated or used at high voltages, so elaborate conversion installations are needed at both ends of the transmission line, thus materially reducing or entirely wiping out the savings in construction costs.

Any really important advance in transmission practices, with significant reductions of cost, would be of great benefit not only to the Peace but to hydro projects

*The exact cost of power delivered to Vancouver markets from the Peace and Columbia projects remains a matter of some dispute and involves many uncertainties. Late in December of 1960 the provincial government ordered an investigation by the Provincial Energy Board, which should be completed early in 1961.

PROPOSED DAM AND POWERHOUSE
IN THE PEACE RIVER CANYON

*diagram courtesy Peace River Po[...]
Development Company Ltd.*

in many parts of British Columbia. But progress has been fairly slow to date and along expected lines; there is nothing so far to suggest revolutionary developments or to affect the belief that lengthy transmission must add substantially to the cost of delivered energy. The Peace River sites should enter the province's natural development of hydro projects when energy from the Columbia has been fairly well absorbed by existing markets. By that time it is reasonable to suppose that markets will have developed in northern areas much closer to the site, and integration with a provincial grid should be a strong possibility. Simultaneous development of both the Peace and the Columbia has been considered a possibility, but does not bear serious consideration. Both projects would be prejudiced by overstraining of the construction force, with increased costs an inevitable result, and the province would face a dislocation of economy that could set it back for a long period. A surplus of hydro-power would be created, with resulting losses to both projects and, again, probable increase of cost to the consumer. Effective development of a provincial transmission network might well be delayed by many years. These are very serious matters of proper resource use which should not be slighted and which are all too likely to be slighted in the confusion of politics and special interest that, as I have already suggested, plagues such major projects.

It has been too often stated, almost as an article of provincial faith, that a surplus of cheap power attracts industry all by itself. This simply is not so. An assured supply of cheap power has been available on the northern coast ever since the completion of the Aluminum Company's plant at Kemano in 1954. It has the additional advantage of being available at tidewater. Industry has not moved to it because there are no other resources in the area ready for development, nor are there any considerable nearby markets for a finished product. Now, in 1960, the B.C. Power Commission plans to transmit some of this surplus to Terrace for general industrial and domestic use. In other words, power has moved in search of industry rather than vice versa. This point was clearly made by T. M. Patterson, Director of the Water Resources Bureau of the federal government at the 11th Resources Conference. "The fact is," said Mr. Patterson, "that power alone is not enough to attract industry; there must be some other primary resource available locally or within economic access to create a need for power."

It is important to realize that energy is by no means equally important to all forms of industry. In all primary manufacturing industries in Canada, fuel and electricity costs average 7 per cent of the gross value of production, while in all secondary industries the average is only 1.5 per cent. Some idea of the importance of fuel and energy costs is given by the following percentages, again in terms of gross value of production, for the heavier energy users: Cement, 20; Nitrogenous fertilizers, 17; Aluminum, Lead-zinc, Dissolving pulp, Clay products, each 13; Newsprint, 10; Crude abrasives, Magnesium, both 9; Primary steel, 7; Nickel-copper, 6; Sulphate pulp, 5. It will be noticed that a number of these industries are already important users of energy in British Columbia.

Even in the case of these relatively heavy users of fuel and electricity, the cost of energy alone can rarely be the deciding factor in the location of a plant. In the case of aluminum and light metals generally, where the raw material needed is abundant and readily transportable, it will be. In the case of such products as newsprint, dissolving pulp (rayon), primary steel, and sulphate pulp, it is clear that low-cost energy is of little value without an abundant source of raw material close at hand.

In over-all planning of energy use – and planning of this sort is essential in a modern economy – the desirability of certain industries that are exceptionally heavy users in proportion to employment and local materials used is questionable. Light-metal industries use tremendous amounts of energy in proportion to employment of labour and so are of disproportionately low value in building population and adding to the development of a country. Aluminum refining uses 137 kilowatts for each worker employed, compared to the 1950 U.S. average for all industry of about 6 kilowatts. Another source estimates that aluminum uses 55 times as much power in relation to manpower employed as other industries. In Norway, which is the largest per capita producer and user of hydro-electricity in the world, the supply of power to the electro-chemical and metallurgical industries has already been limited.

Massive power uses of this sort have their place and may well be sound at remote sites where other resource uses are not affected and transportation of the necessary raw materials is possible. They also appeal to promoters of large projects who need to sell a lot of power as quickly as possible to cover interest on the capital costs of development; but so used they can also defeat the very purpose of a major development by rapidly committing power away from the more useful industries. This in turn may force premature development of high-cost sites or of sites that seriously conflict with other resource uses. Either is bad for the country, though in British Columbia at present the rapid development of natural gas reduces such dangers in some degree.

Where a remote site such as the Peace River or Yukon-Taku is under consideration, large users such as the metallurgical industries are likely to be the only sound reason for the original development. In this case, the values may be reversed; the high-consumption industry may make available to other local or nearby industries a power source that could not otherwise have been developed.

It has been suggested, for instance, that the Peace River site might fit well into the economy of the nation as a whole by providing a large block of low-cost energy for enrichment of uranium. This is a far-sighted concept, involving national policy and international markets. Canada does not make enriched uranium at present, and her present research programme is directed, rightly or wrongly, to the production of commercial energy from natural uranium. The United States has a world monopoly in enriched uranium, which tends to limit the existing world market because importing nations are not anxious to depend on a single source and therefore limit their research and development to processes that use natural uranium.

Canadian uranium depends on the United States market and is already feeling the pinch most sharply. Uranium is enriched by a series of diffusion processes that use large amounts of energy; each process makes a smaller package of more powerful fuel and there seems little doubt that a great deal of the future use of nuclear fuels will involve moderately enriched uranium. By establishing a place for herself in this world market, Canada would not only put some of her remote northern hydro sites to good use, but would ensure the future of her own uranium mines and increase her chances of achieving low-cost nuclear energy of the best possible type.

An enrichment plant of medium size would use from ¾ to 1½ million horsepower of low-cost energy. Three mills per kwh. has been mentioned as an acceptable unit cost of electricity, though the figure presumably could be rather higher. The value of the raw material used and the eventual product is so high and the quantities are so small that the remoteness of the site matters little – if necessary, natural uranium could be flown in and enriched uranium could be economically flown out to markets no matter how distant. This naturally means that several major sites in the Canadian north could be considered, but the Peace River certainly qualifies as one of these.

Discussion of this sort may seem speculative, but it is at least as realistic as any in consideration of remote hydro sites. With steadily increasing capital costs, tremendous transmission difficulties and increasing competition from thermal power sources, the value of remote sites for any but highly specialized uses seems to be rapidly receding.

As has already been suggested, no resource use conflicts so drastically and frequently with other resource uses as hydro. Though essentially a sound and valuable use of water (the over-all efficiency of a hydraulic turbine system is about 85%), it is made a clumsy and awkward use because of the immense storage facilities needed and the massive construction that must be undertaken to achieve them.

Hydro's worst conflicts in B.C. are with salmon fisheries, and by far the worst of these concerns the main-stem hydro sites of the Fraser River, which will be discussed more fully in another chapter. The Fraser has the greatest power potential of any river in the province. It is also the greatest salmon river in the world, and being steadily improved. The power potential of the Fraser is probably worth 400 million dollars annually. The salmon potential is probably not much over 50 million dollars annually. But the problem is by no means as simple as this. The salmon runs exist and are used. The river's energy potential exists only in theory and so do the industries that might be built on it. Power can be realized economically in many other ways for many years to come; so far as is known at present, the yearly salmon crops can be realized in no other way than by full use of the river system and its lakes. Hydro energy may be important only for a short space of time, perhaps thirty to fifty years ahead. The salmon runs are a protein food resource that will become progressively more important and more valuable as world population increases.

For the time being, no one seriously suggests development of the Fraser's mainstem hydro sites, and the need for development may never arise. But the conflict is clear and it is typical of a hundred or a thousand lesser conflicts between salmon and hydro energy throughout the province.

Some measure of conflict is implicit in all hydro development, because every storage site means flooding land useful for forests or agriculture or for residential purposes. Very often such land is critical wintering area for wildlife. It may or may not be important scenically or for other recreational purposes. It may be grazing land or park land, or land reserved for some other purpose. Inevitably, in every storage project, some damage will be done. Financial compensation means little, because the loss is in resource values.

The evil practice of flooding land without first clearing the timber seems to have been forever abandoned. Flooding of the great circle of timbered lakes in Tweedsmuir Park without clearing was the last example; and the clearing of the shoreline of Buttle Lake in Strathcona Park is a good indication of the beneficial results that can be achieved by a well planned operation. Full recreational values of storage lakes are almost impossible to preserve except in arid countries because of periodic draw-down. But drowned timber will stand for scores, if not hundreds, of years to destroy both recreational and transportation values.

In some instances multi-purpose storage dams are possible; some of the dams proposed for the headwaters of the Fraser River system are good examples. A measure of flood control, useful irrigation possibilities and better balanced stream flows for migratory fish may well be achieved in combination with hydro-power. Usually some modification of the hydro-potential itself is necessary, but if a proper proportion of construction cost is charged to the secondary purposes the resulting energy should be produced at reasonable cost. This is good and desirable resource use.

It is unfortunate that the great developments in natural gas production within the province are so recent that they have not yet been properly fitted into discussions of energy at the Resources Conferences. It is perfectly clear at this writing that thermal-electric installations using gas are already competitive with hydro-electric stations, unless the latter are close to load centres. As construction costs continue to increase, thermal installations are bound to seem increasingly attractive, unless some revolutionary advance in methods of electrical transmission is achieved. The province's future should hold a carefully integrated development of energy supplies from hydro and natural gas, probably with some use of coal as well. Integration, not only of the various energy sources themselves, but of the distribution of energy throughout the areas of demand, can be the greatest single factor of proper use in this resource as in most others. Population and development in the province are now reaching the point where integration is a practical possibility, and its application is briefly discussed in the following chapter.

integration of energy

"INTEGRATION" IS A WORD that has many applications in resource use, its exact connotation varying with the context. In connection with energy it has at least two possible applications – the co-ordinated production and distribution of electrical energy by means of a transmission grid, or a carefully planned and interrelated development of all energy sources to ensure that community and industrial needs are met with maximum efficiency and minimum interference with other resource uses. Both are important steps in proper use of the energy resources, but the second cannot be fully realized without the first, and even the first implies a fairly advanced stage of development. In British Columbia the possibilities of integrated production and transmission of electrical energy are only beginning to be examined.

In all areas where electricity is extensively used there are seasonal and daily variations of demand; these may vary from one area to another in accord with climatic differences, time differences, differing types of industry and other factors. It follows that if such areas are linked by effective transmission lines, diversity in demand can be balanced to a more uniform level.

As already pointed out, British Columbia rivers have extreme fluctuations of flow. Storage dams may be installed to level off these fluctuations and in some instances complete control may be achieved; where this is so, the full capacity of the river may be realized in constant energy output. In other words, the development permits a firm commitment to supply every kilowatt hour the stream is capable of producing at an even rate throughout the year. Such ideal storage is rarely possible or economic and most installations "spill" water at certain seasons of the year – that is, they must allow it to run downstream unused instead of turning it through the turbines. The water spilled in this way can be used to produce energy if additional turbines are installed, but the energy so produced can be sold only on an "intermittent" or "interruptible" basis.

Energy that is available on a year-round basis is known as "firm power". The "base load" of a system is the minimum load carried during a given period. The system is committed to produce continuously the amount of energy necessary to meet the base load. A "peak load" is the maximum load carried during a given period, which may be well in excess of the base load and may be supported in one or more of several different ways: by an auxiliary thermal plant, by extra turbine capacity taking advantage of seasonal run-off or simply by skilful use of storage so that the peak is met, thus satisfying firm power commitments.

In any area as large as British Columbia and with such wide variations of climate and precipitation, the times of high and low flow vary between river system and river system. Coastal streams, for instance, are likely to have periods of high run-off in spring and early summer and again in fall and early winter; interior streams are likely to have relatively high run-offs from the break-up in late April through most of the summer, with peak flows in June or July, but may have little or no fall recovery and will continue at low run-off throughout the winter. Even between adjacent river systems of approximately similar climate and precipitation, there will be at least minor variations in the timing of run-offs. An integrated transmission system, by tying together all such energy sources under a central control and by permitting transfers of energy, is able to take advantage of the variations and convert much of the interruptible power into firm power. It can reduce over-all costs because it needs less reserve generating capacity than do separated systems.

Sources of coal for thermal power

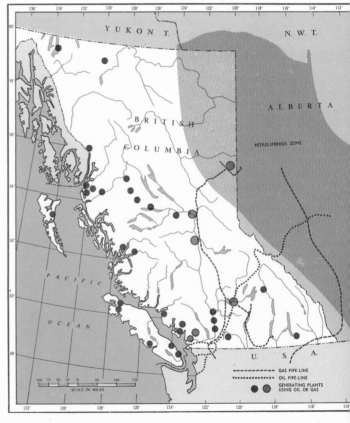

Sources of gas and oil for thermal power

The larger the system and the more varied its sources, the closer it will come to realizing the full benefit of the river systems committed to it.

Integration of energy sources in British Columbia has so far reached only elementary stages. Each of the several power systems is to some extent integrated within itself and there are some minor exchanges between systems, though these last may represent only interconnection, not integration. The B.C. Electric's Lower Mainland system is connected with the B.C. Power Commission system on Vancouver Island; in the southern interior, the East Kootenay Power Company connects with the West Kootenay and Consolidated Mining and Smelting system, which in turn connects with the B.C. Power Commission services based on Kamloops and Vernon. The Lower Mainland system is also connected to the Bonneville Power Administration circuits south of the border. But there is no connection across the province and no connection between southern systems and those of the north.

Since the main settlement and most developed power sources are in the southern part of the province, it is clear that any integrated transmission network must grow from south to north. In the use of energy perhaps more than in that of any other resource, the geographical divisions of the continent have a powerful influence on the efficiency of development. Some measure of integration with the transmission grids of Oregon and Washington is a logical early step and will certainly be realized with development of the Upper Columbia and return of downstream benefits. Development on the Columbia in Canada will call for a transmission line probably

Principal hydro sources, 1961

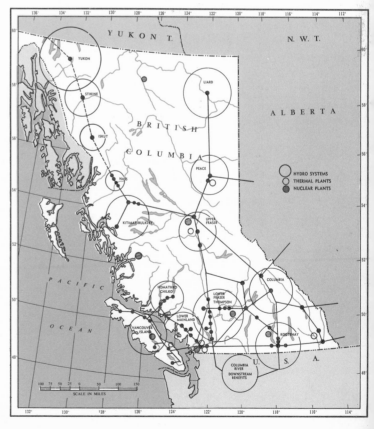

Possible future electrical energy grid

through Kamloops to Lillooet to link with the southern interior and Lower Mainland systems. This presumably would be connected with the Kootenay systems to provide an important measure of integration south of the fifty-first parallel.

The cost and difficulties of long-range electrical transmission are such that a transmission grid can only work well when loads and power sources are distributed throughout its length. This means that careful choice of projects in proper sequence, designed to promote integration, may prove of critical importance. Once the Upper Columbia developments are under construction and integration with the Bonneville Power Administration is fully established, such projects as the Homathko development may become very much more attractive than they are at present. Any of the three systems proposed by the Fraser River Board's Preliminary Report (1958) on flood control and power development for the headwaters of the Fraser watershed would fit well into a progressive northward expansion of the transmission grid. System "A", preferred because it should cause only minor damage to salmon runs, provides power and storage sites at Olsson Creek and McGregor River, as well as on the North Fork of the Quesnel and on the Clearwater at more central locations. These would link eventually to the B.C. Power Commission's extension of Kitimat power to Terrace and so provide a sound framework for further developments through the southern half of the province.

Considered in this context, early development of the Peace River, with a high-voltage transmission line to Lillooet, would call for careful examination. A direct current line, for instance, could not be fitted easily or economically into a transmission grid and might well delay development of the grid or increase costs excessively. If developed first for use at site, it seems likely that Peace River power would fit readily into a provincial grid once the network is properly extended to include Prince George. It would then make a splendid northern anchor for a still growing system.

In this rough outline of the way in which an integrated transmission network may be developed, emphasis has been placed on hydro sites as the main sources of energy. This is in keeping with the fact that 95 per cent of all electrical energy generated in B.C. during 1959 was produced from hydro sources. But it must be remembered that the province now has the first stages of a natural gas transmission grid in the shape of the West Coast Transmission pipeline, which runs through one of the main lines of settlement to the chief industrial areas, branches east as far as Trail and will shortly be extended to Vancouver Island. British Columbia has also a number of strategically placed coal reserves and the probability that nuclear power sources will be available in the not too distant future.

While it is generally considered that hydro sites will continue for some while to be the chief sources of electrical energy, natural gas is expected to enter more and more rapidly into both industrial and domestic space heating, water heating and process heating. The last two of these have been heavy users of electricity in the past, so the availability of natural gas must certainly have an important effect in releasing electricity formerly committed to them. Natural gas will also have its effect upon future demands for electricity; in this direct function of providing heat it will fit usefully into any province-wide system for the distribution of energy. It may also prove useful in thermal-electric installations to firm up seasonal power or to fill out gaps in the network where hydro sites are not available. Coal, because it must generally be used at site to be economic, is much less flexible, but it is possible that one or more of the known deposits may fit well enough into a developing power-grid to be useful. Nuclear power remains an uncertain quantity, but some authorities believe that it will, in time and possibly with other thermal sources, take over the base loads in most areas, leaving hydro-power, which can be turned on and off at will, to handle peak loads.

A transmission network multiplies advantages at every stage of its development and can well be said to be essential to the proper use of energy resources. Every step in balancing loads, every step in hydraulic integration between river systems and in the co-ordination of thermal and hydro sources means a greater total of usable power and may mean significant reductions in cost. A well integrated system can call upon different power sources or combinations of sources to fit the need of every hour of day or night, thus ensuring that the fullest possible use is made of both storage and run-off and that the cheapest available source is put to best use. Carefully planned northward spread of the network should ensure that large northern power sources can eventually be brought into it on a sound economic basis. Connection with networks developed or developing south of the border will take advantage of important climatic differences between north and south, which influence seasonal demand and loads, and should achieve a safe means of exporting whatever true surpluses of energy the province may be able to develop.

British Columbia is well supplied with energy sources for all foreseeable needs. There are some problems of reconciling these with other resource uses, with political considerations, both national and international and, to some extent, with each other. Development has so far tended to be local and on a relatively small scale. The stage has now been reached at which power transfers from one area to another are essential to efficient development, and it would seem that all future projects should be tested against the over-all needs of an integrated system that will eventually serve the province as a whole. This means that the various energy sources must be regarded as complementary rather than competitive, and regulated in such a way that each fits into the broad scheme in its proper place. Planning of this sort will not only ensure the best possible use of existing conventional sources, but will also allow every advantage to be taken of new sources, such as nuclear fuels, and of advances, technological or otherwise, in the use or availability of conventional sources. Co-ordinated development of the different energy sources, conceived provincially rather than on local scales, should also help to reduce conflicts with other resource uses.

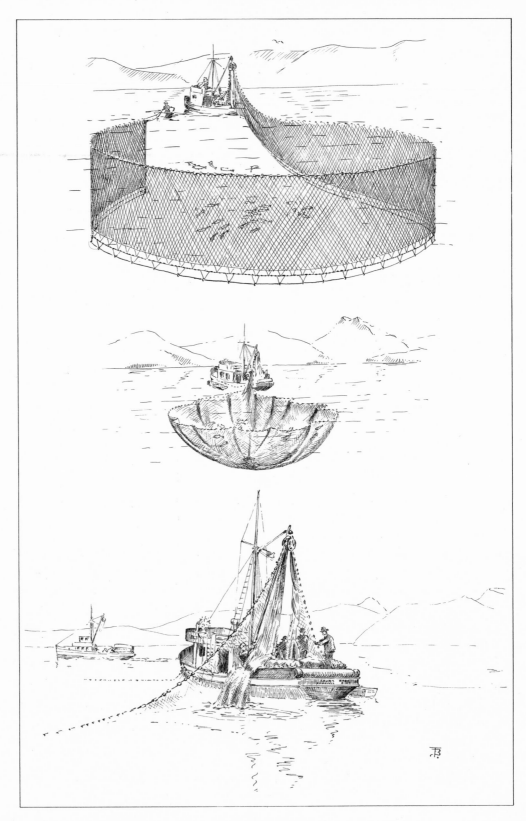

THE PURSE SEINER

general inventory CHAPTER 14

ACRE FOR ACRE, the waters of the earth are richer and potentially more productive than the land. We know less of them and generally use them far less intensively. The intensity of use varies directly with the concentration of human population on the nearby land surfaces. The world's fish landings amount to thirty million metric tons a year, having increased about 50% during the past ten years. Seventy per cent of this comes from the temperate regions of the northern hemisphere. Within the northern hemisphere the European Atlantic accounts for twenty-five per cent of world landings, the American Atlantic ten per cent; the Asian side of the Pacific has thirty-one per cent, the American Pacific three per cent. British Columbia fisheries account for only one per cent of the world's fish landings, yet the value of this catch is between sixty and a hundred million dollars annually.

It is perfectly clear, then, that the province is using only a small part, though a very valuable part, of its fishery potential. There is no economic demand at the present time that would justify the research, effort and risk that further development would entail. Yet in world terms and in human terms a most powerful demand does exist, just as it exists for agricultural products; over two-thirds of the present world population is underfed and the population is continuing to increase more rapidly than the available food supplies – since World War II population has increased by twelve per cent while food production has increased by only nine per cent. So far the ingenuity of mankind simply has not been able to work out a means of transferring the abundance of one area to the needy people of another area without extreme economic dislocation, though it is perfectly clear that such means must be found. For the time being, it is more sensible to send scientists and technicians to, for instance, Ceylon, to show the local fishermen there how to achieve a better yield from nearby waters, than it is to develop B.C. fisheries whose yield would have to be processed and transported over great distances to serve the same purpose.

But although this demand has not the economic means to make itself proportionately felt, it is felt in some degree; and the increasing population of the North American continent itself is gradually and inevitably developing markets that justify expansion. The herring fishery has increased steadily throughout the past fifty years and yearly landings since the war have begun to approach the desirable limits of use. Ground-fish landings, though still far below the potential, have increased from a yearly average of one or two million pounds before the war to present levels of about twenty-five million pounds. Increases of this type and expansion into new fisheries are certainly the trend of the future. Whether the increases and expansion can be speeded beyond the rate of the past few years depends at least as much on the possibility of improvements in the technology of finding, catching, processing and transportation as it does upon the possibility of great economic changes.

In an average year, British Columbia's fisheries have a market value of between sixty and seventy million dollars. The 1958 value was over ninety-eight million dollars, but this was the year of the great return of sockeye salmon to Adams River; while similar returns may be expected not only in the cycle year of this run, but in other years as other great cycles are restored, it seems best for present purposes to consider the average years of the past. In such a year, salmon make up a total of about sixty-five per cent of the value, herring sixteen per cent, halibut ten per cent and all other fish the remaining nine per cent. Price, demand, strikes and variations in abundance of the chief species can markedly affect these values from year to year, but they give a reasonably close idea of the present composition of the fishery. In weight of fish landed, the salmon amount to about a hundred thousand tons, or about half the weight of the herring catch; halibut landings are ten or twelve thousand tons. In terms of the world's fisheries, these values are exactly reversed; British Columbia's halibut catch is between twenty-five and thirty per cent of the world's total, second only to the U.S. catch; her salmon catch yields between fifteen and twenty per cent of the world's canned salmon production – probably one-third to one-half of the U.S.-Alaska production and approximately equal to either Japanese or Russian production; her herring landings amount to about two-thirds of the Canadian total and Canada ranks fifth in world totals.

All these figures are approximations, which may vary from year to year because of the uncertainty of fish and fishing; it should be noted, for instance, that F.A.O. statistics for 1954-7 give average national shares of the *total* salmon catch as follows: U.S.S.R. 30%, Japan 29%, U.S.A. 28%, Canada 13%. But they give a rough idea of how important in proportion to population are the province's three chief fisheries, and they emphasize the very high commercial value of the salmon catch. The salmon and halibut fisheries are fully exploited at present, though the herring fishery may not be – further research is needed to clarify the point. But all three fisheries are considered capable of increased yields under sound management. The salmon, which use both fresh and salt water extensively, present many problems in use and management which must be dealt with in another chapter.

The length of the mainland coast of British Columbia is nearly 4500 miles; with the adjacent islands the total coastline is well over seven thousand miles. From the coastline the bed of the sea extends for an average distance of about thirty miles at a depth of a hundred fathoms or less, then drops rather sharply towards the ocean floor and depths of one to two thousand fathoms. This shallow area between the shore and the hundred fathom line is known as the continental shelf and practically the whole of the present fishery is carried on within its limits. A great part of the area, in the long inlets and behind the islands, is more or less sheltered water and lends itself to independent fishing by small operators who have a limited investment in boats and gear. This relatively sheltered water, with its large stocks of resident or migratory fish, has naturally been exploited first. But the more exposed waters of the west coast of Vancouver Island, Queen Charlotte Sound, Hecate Strait and Dixon Entrance are regularly and extensively fished for the principal species to the limits of the continental shelf.

It is in these waters that one major fishery problem arises, that of international competition. Beyond the three-mile limit offshore, except in territorial waters such as the Strait of Georgia, the seas are open to all. The only possibility of achieving the control, regulation and understanding of the fisheries necessary to proper use is by international agreement. Fortunately the only competition in the province's offshore waters so far has been from American fishermen and co-operation between the two nations has been excellent. In 1923 the governments of the two countries signed a treaty for regulation and investigation of the halibut fishery that has resulted in complete restoration of what was a declining resource. In 1937 a similar treaty was signed for the regulation and investigation of the Fraser River sockeye salmon fishery and again the results have been outstandingly successful. In 1957 this treaty was extended to include investigation and regulation of the pink salmon

LONGLINING FOR HALIBUT
The halibut, being a bottom feeder, is usually caught by longlining or groundlining, and this line may be anything up to eight miles long and be furnished with up to 4000 baited hooks. The halibut schooners are large vessels, up to 85 feet, and may have a crew of ten men, they make long voyages to the fishing grounds and may be out for three weeks at a time.

fisheries. International agreements governing whaling and pelagic sealing are also in force and are observed by Canada. Finally, the North Pacific Fisheries Convention, signed in 1952 by the United States, Japan and Canada, has led to extensive investigations that should prevent excessive exploitation of fisheries in any of the waters covered and which should add greatly to common knowledge of deep-sea resources.

All fisheries are under the exclusive legislative authority of the federal parliament, which facilitates international negotiations and undoubtedly has provided strong protection to a resource that is very much open to the abuse of over-exploitation by both foreign and domestic users. Federal research has been ambitious and effective, and in recent years control and regulation based on this research has brought about a situation in which almost every phase of the resource is not merely holding its own, but showing active promise of increased yields that, short of natural disasters, can be indefinitely sustained.

It may well be that further treaties will be necessary to protect this position – the exploitation by Alaska fishermen of salmon stocks raised in northern B.C. rivers, for instance, may threaten the proper management of the runs unless some sort of agreement is reached. Except in the case of the Fraser salmon runs, the pattern of such agreements in the north-east Pacific so far has been to ensure protection of adequate breeding stocks and proper breeding environment first, and only then to consider proper distribution of the allowable catch. This, and no other, pattern must be followed if fishery yields are to be maintained and increased. But the proper pattern of agreement will become increasingly difficult to determine and perhaps increasingly difficult to enforce as the fisheries work farther out to sea and more and more nations compete.

It has often been suggested that the limit of territorial waters should be extended to twelve or thirty miles offshore or even farther to meet this threat. It is clear that the old three-mile limit, based on the ancient range of naval guns, has become meaningless under modern conditions, but any other limit can only be properly effective through international sanction and, as has already been shown in the fisheries dispute between Great Britain and Iceland, this is not easily attained. In narrow waters such as the English Channel, extended limits would present almost insuperable difficulties. Possibly there is a case for continental limits within which neighbouring nations would set protective limits by mutual agreement; but even this would raise problems of established rights, such as those of the ancient European fishery off Canada's east coast – a fishery far older than Canada itself, upon which many Europeans depend and which played its part in the earliest settlement of Canada. And there are the established rights of the neighbouring nations themselves, such as the U.S. halibut fishery in Hecate Strait, between the Queen Charlotte Islands and the mainland. This has not only the sanction of usage, but the far more significant one of the Halibut Convention, which by joint effort restored the fishery and made it one of the best managed in the world. Canada's recent proposals before the United Nations were for a six-mile limit to territorial waters and a further six-mile limit beyond this for complete control of fisheries. Acceptance and enforcement of these limits would affect Canadian fishermen working American waters as well as American fishermen who work the Canadian banks, so there seems to be basis for negotiation, though the Canadian position is opposed to any recognition of "historic rights". Whether national control would serve the resource any better than international control already has, seems highly debatable.

The strongest claim to a fishery that any nation can possibly put forward is that it is already using and managing that fishery properly – that is to say, to the fullest yield that is consistent with sustained renewal. This principle is recognized in the North Pacific Fisheries Convention of 1952, accepted by Canada, the U.S. and Japan, and it must always carry preponderant weight in any honest negotiation among nations.

Every fishery presents its own special management problems and these are never easily recognized or understood. Fish live and travel and feed for the most part out of sight of man. They live in an element that is less fluid than air and possibly less subject to climatic change; but water is still fluid and climatic changes can occur in it; when they do occur their effects are likely to be just as far-reaching as similar changes on land, perhaps even more so because the creatures that live in water are less tolerant of change. It is only by intensive and often highly ingenious research that the habits and movements of fish, their abundance and the factors that influence that abundance can be determined. Such research is usually dependent upon an established and fairly intensive fishery – satisfactory answers can only be found through extensive sampling and observations and by season to season comparisons. Such modern devices as echo-finding, electronic fishing and underwater television may be helpful in advancing research ahead of intensive fisheries by enabling scien-

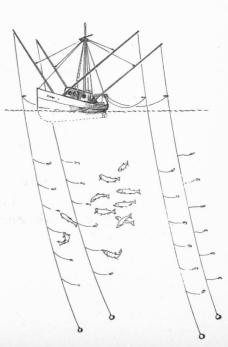

SALMON TROLLER

The only two species of Pacific salmon which really count for the troller are the spring and coho salmon, though other fish are occasionally caught. The gear varies considerably, particularly in different waters. The trollers off the west coast of Vancouver Island may use gear as shown with "cannonball" weights to get deep down. Spoons and plugs are the usual lures and as many as forty may be used at a time.

tists to find new stocks of fish, estimate their size and suggest effective use of them; but it will probably remain the case that really thorough and accurate work can only be done after the fishery is well established.

The British Columbia herring fishery is based on the Pacific herring, *Clupea pallasi*, a fish that is closely similar to the European herring, *Clupea harengus*. Herring are extremely abundant and with modern equipment they are easily found and easily caught in great numbers. Taken at the right season, well before spawning, they are very rich in oil and have long been important in world food markets. They are immensely important also in the food chain that mounts from the diatoms, which synthesize sunlight and minerals, through crustaceans and other forms of life, including the herring hordes, to grow the salmons, cods, halibut and many other fish of commercial importance.

Herring have been fished in British Columbia fairly regularly since 1877, when seventy-five tons were taken. In 1904 the dry salt industry began and the Oriental market for salt fish held until the early nineteen-thirties, when it declined and the fishery fell off to 30,000 tons. The reduction industry, by which herring are converted to oil and meal for use in cattle and poultry feed, was established in 1924; so little was known of the stocks and real potential of the fishery that this industry developed very slowly until catch quotas were set and expanding markets sharpened interest in the late thirties. Within a few years the annual catch was averaging one hundred thousand tons and several new fisheries had been developed.

As the fishery expanded, research began to reveal that previous ideas of conservation had been unsound. The herring population is made up of about ten year classes, of which three-, four- and five-year-olds are likely to be preponderant in the catch. Exceptional abundance of any year class appears to be quite unrelated to heavy or light spawning in the year it was hatched; frequently a light spawning year will yield a larger year class and a heavy spawning will yield a very small year class. A single year class of special abundance can make itself felt through several years of fishing; on the other hand, a succession of years of low yield will inevitably reduce catches until more abundant year classes began to come into the fishery.

From this it seems fairly clear that the fishery itself has little, if any, effect on the yield from the spawning of any given year. On the other hand, natural conditions may have very great effects. Herring lay eggs which sink in shallow water and stick to rocks, weeds and brush in the inter-tidal zone. Freezing weather, drying winds, heavy surf and large concentrations of gulls, diving ducks, cormorants and other predators may cause great losses. Both weather and oceanographic conditions – shifts of current and unusual temperatures, for instance – may have even more serious effect on the survival of herring larvae. So a relatively small spawning under excellent conditions may well produce a very large year class of adult herrings, as happened in 1943, while a heavy spawning followed by poor conditions may produce a weak year class.

These observations strongly suggested that quotas might be not only unnecessary, but undesirable, and for some years no quota was applied in the fishery on the west coast of Vancouver Island. The results of this experiment confirmed the impression that the fishery, as presently conducted, makes little difference to the abundance of succeeding years.

Since the mortality rate of herring three years old and older is about fifty per cent and since the growth rate at three years is only about twenty-five per cent and decreases steadily with age, it appears that the present fishery is well short of maximum yield. The next logical step is to determine the smallest spawning escapement that will ensure a maximum year class under satisfactory conditions, and intensify the fishery to the point at which the maximum catch consistent with this escapement is achieved. Most authorities believe that the yield can be increased by at least twenty per cent, possibly as much as forty or fifty per cent over the present average of about two hundred thousand tons a year.

There are believed to be seven or more separate herring populations along the British Columbia coast from south-east Vancouver Island to the north-east of the Queen Charlotte Islands, all of which are at present being used. Fishing is almost entirely by purse seine and hauls of up to three hundred tons are not uncommon; echo-sounding is used to find the fish and recently mercury arc lights have been used to attract them to the surface at night. Radio telephone is used to summon nearby seine boats to a concentration of fish. With these devices there is no serious problem in attaining any catch the market can use. Prices of meal and oil fell off in the 1959-60 season because of heavy Peruvian competition in world markets, and the British Columbia fishery closed in mid-season. Prospects for early resumption depend upon adjustments both in the world market and in the fishery itself, though there is no doubt that fishing will be resumed in the end.* While the reduction industry, which produces cooking oils and soaps as well as cattle and poultry feeds, has used about ninety-eight per cent of the catch in recent years, there is every reason to believe that British Columbia herring must be used sooner or later directly for human consumption. Markets for canned or dry salted fish may be revived or some new and more economical process of preserving the fish may be found. But even when used in the reduction industry, the herring make an important contribution to world food supplies.

The Pacific halibut, *Hippoglossus stenolepis*, has been fished commercially in British Columbia since 1888. The main halibut banks are off the west and north coasts of Vancouver Island, in Queen Charlotte Sound and in Hecate Strait, though mature halibut move extensively and individuals have been known to travel as far as two thousand miles to spawning areas. British Columbia fishing boats go north as far as the waters off Bristol Bay in Alaska in search of halibut and American fishermen compete in waters off the B.C. coast.

*Fishing was resumed in November 1960, at reduced prices to the fishermen under conditions that may limit the use of the more distant grounds.

The halibut is a very large flounder that lives on the bottom in depths from ten to a hundred and fifty fathoms and more. It feeds on crabs, squid, herring, clams, worms and other marine life. The females grow faster than the males and usually live longer; a really large female may attain an age of thirty-five years and a weight of over four hundred pounds, while the males rarely exceed twenty-five years and forty pounds. Most fishing is by "long-lining" – set-lines fifty fathoms long that rest on bottom, with lighter lines at every ten or fifteen feet carrying baited hooks – though salmon trollers have turned increasingly to the fishing within recent years.

In the early years of the fishery, the built-up populations of the British Columbia halibut banks were soon discovered and intensely fished by both American and Canadian fishermen. The British Columbia catch reached a peak of nineteen million pounds in 1915 and then sharply declined to an average of less than nine million pounds in the years from 1916-35. The combined American-Canadian catch, from all waters south of Cape Spencer in Alaska, declined from 60 million pounds in 1912 to 22½ million pounds in 1930. The abrupt fall-off from 1915 figures led to the signing of the International Halibut Convention and the work of the International Pacific Halibut Commission, which began in 1923.

Investigations of the Commission soon established that the depletion was due primarily to overfishing. Halibut are slow-maturing fish and closely limited in distribution. The main halibut banks, not only of the North Pacific, but of the world, show bottom temperatures varying between 37° and 46°F.; outside this range the fish are scattered and the fishing is poor. The females mature at an average of twelve years of age, the males somewhat earlier, and though the eggs and larvae drift with the ocean currents at varying depths, there are indications that local stocks may depend upon local spawning. Under the intense fishery, few fish were able to reach maturity and spawn and fewer still were able to attain the ages at which they would be making maximum annual growth.

Carefully calculated regulation of catches and seasons, with some protection of nursery banks with the high concentrations of immature fish, have brought about a steady increase in the stock and from 1936 on improved catches have reflected this. Since 1946, the average Canadian catch has exceeded the 1915 record of nineteen million pounds and in 1954 the total American-Canadian catch was seventy million pounds, the highest figure recorded in the whole history of the fishery to that date. The Canadian share of this was twenty-seven and a half million pounds. The 1959 total was seventy-one and a half million pounds with a value of thirteen million dollars.

Halibut is sold both fresh and frozen. Recent improvements in filleting, quick freezing and packaging have tended to increase the popularity of the fish and offset competition from other species; demand is steady and, though prices fluctuate from time to time, the total production has always been marketed.

The Commission considers that the present take is probably approaching the maximum that can be achieved, but some authorities believe that judicious har-

vesting may yield further increases of as much as forty or fifty per cent. Unlike herring, the halibut show a close balance between growth and mortality rates, which
limits this last possibility; and past experience has shown that it is all too easy to
reduce the yield by exploiting the fish too heavily before they have had a chance to
grow to moderately large size.

"Ground-fish" is a catch-all name given to those bottom-feeding fish that are
members of the cod and flatfish families. The cods include lingcod, grey or "true"
cod, sablefish or blackcod and rockfish. Lemon sole, brill, rock sole, butter sole and
Dover sole are the flatfish chiefly used at present, though many others, such as the
starry flounder, rex sole, sand sole and turbot (long-jaw flounder) come into the
catch. Though many of these fish have European names, they are not the same fish;
there are no members of the family Soleidae on the Pacific coast, for instance, and
the Pacific brill is *Eopselta jordani*, unrelated to the European *Scopthalmus rhom-
bus*. The Pacific species are usually fairly similar fish, at least in general appearance, and were named by early European settlers and fishermen. The common
names given above are those generally accepted in commercial usage in British
Columbia.

The flatfish are caught entirely by otter-trawling and the cods by both long-line
and otter-trawl. The trawl is a large net which is dragged over the bottom and held
open by two heavy boards bridled to force away from each other against the resistance of the water; the sides of the net slope back at an angle to the narrower codend, where the fish are collected. When the net is brought home, the codend is
lifted by a winch, the opening at the back end of it is tripped and the fish pour out
on the deck of the trawler to be sorted.

Trawl fishing began in B.C. in a very small way in 1911, with one boat fishing
in English Bay and off the mouth of the Fraser. It was extended during the First
World War and for a short while after, but developed very slowly until the Second
World War brought increased need for food. Demand has been maintained and
even increased since the war by the market for frozen fillets and fish sticks. The
yearly catch by American and Canadian boats off the B.C. coast now averages
about fifty million pounds and the Canadian share is approximately half of this.

Demand varies from year to year and between species, and fluctuation in the
abundance of individual species influences fishing effort, so the fishery is by no
means stable in spite of fairly equal annual totals. It is considered that some of the

LEMON SOLE

BRILL

ROCK SOLE

TRUE OR GRAY COD

A valuable food fish, usually caught on halibut longlines or in trawls. It is closely allied to the cod of the Atlantic.

more popular species, such as brill and lemon sole, are being fairly intensively exploited while others such as the Dover sole, which is difficult to handle and process because of excessive slime, are under-exploited. The fishery as a whole is certainly far less intensive than either the herring fishery or the halibut fishery, and at the same time far less is known of the life history, abundance and habits of most of the ground-fish than is known of herring and halibut. Unquestionably there is room for expansion and in all probability the increased effort of expansion will reveal some new stocks of fish. There has been some criticism of trawl fishing as a destructive method in that it may modify the sea bottoms and affect the living conditions of fish other than those sought. The consensus of opinion seems to be that excessive trawling on soft bottoms may cause serious damage, but that the present intensity of the fishery in B.C. does little damage. One authority has suggested that moderate trawling, like moderate harrowing of fallow land, may even be beneficial.

The grey cod has been increasingly taken by trawling and is now the dominant species in trawler landings. But important line fishing is still done for lingcod and especially blackcod. These are long-established fisheries and appear to be fairly stable, though in some areas the blackcod may be overfished.

Still another factor in the trawl fishery is the increased demand for "scrapfish" which are used as mink feed. Turbot and whiting are the species chiefly landed for this purpose and in 1959 totalled about four million pounds, approximately twenty per cent of the B.C. ground-fish total.

Though ground-fish stocks are at present generally under-exploited, it is important to recognize that they are fished for mainly in water beyond territorial limits and the Canadian fishermen face American competition. This means that sooner or later there will have to be control by international agreement if the yield is to be sustained. Quite obviously this control must be brought into effect before stocks become depleted, to avoid the losses of a long, slow build-back such as has been necessary with the halibut.

The dogfish, *Squalus acanthias*, has probably been more abruptly in and out of demand than any other B.C. species. In the nineteenth century dogfish oil, extracted from the livers, was highly valued for both lubrication and lighting. It lubricated the engines of naval ships, lighted Nanaimo coal mines, Vancouver saw-mills and coastal lighthouses. A heavy duty killed export to the United States and reduced the fishery to the point where dogfish became a nuisance. During the First World War there was a large market for the flesh and the fishery was again intense. After the war dogfish became a nuisance again and a reduction industry was started. During the Second World War and for a while after it there was a heavy demand for dogfish liver for its Vitamin A content and the fishery became so intense that stocks were reduced and catches fell off. Since the war synthetic vitamins have been developed and by 1950 the demand for livers was at a very low level. Stocks are now fully replenished and the dogfish is again a nuisance.

The present abundance of dogfish in B.C. waters is estimated to be of the order of one billion pounds. It is interesting to speculate on the possible use of the dogfish as a multi-purpose tool in fishery management. It is a very slow-growing, viviparous fish, which produces from three to fourteen young in alternate years, so it is quite easily controlled by intense fishing. It is a potentially useful fish – the flesh, extensively used in Europe, is palatable and nutritious, and large quantities of oil and meal can be realized by reduction; only the difficulty of competing at present prices prevents these uses. On the other side of the picture, the dogfish in its present numbers is a harmful nuisance to other forms of fishing; it damages nets and may load both trolling lines and long-lines to the point at which fishing for other fish becomes uneconomic. This nuisance value is recognized by the present government price subsidy of a quarter of a million dollars annually, which has so far proved insufficiently attractive to establish population control.

But the dogfish is also both a predator and competitor of other more desirable species. It feeds heavily on herring, and a billion pounds of active dogfish conceivably represent enough herring to make a significant difference to commercial

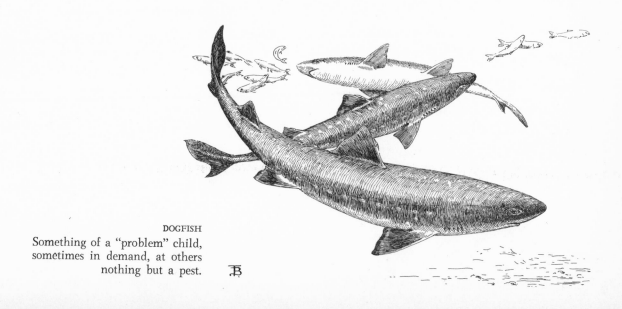

DOGFISH
Something of a "problem" child, sometimes in demand, at others nothing but a pest.

catches. In feeding on pilchards, anchovies, smelts, lance fish and pink feed as well as on herrings, the dogfish is a direct competitor of the salmons, halibut and cods. Besides competing with the adults of these species, it may well be a significant predator of their young.

Assessment of all these factors presents many difficult problems and only a costly and painstaking research programme could provide the answers. But it seems wholly possible that a reduction industry based on a subsidy designed to control dogfish to 25 per cent or less of their present abundance might be shown to be economically sound if their competitive and predatory proclivities, as well as their nuisance value, were accurately calculated.

Several other sharks, such as the soupfin, basking shark, blue shark and mackerel shark, may offer limited commercial possibilities in B.C. waters. Only the first has been actively fished, yielding some 40,000 pounds of liver a year during and shortly after the Second World War. Even this short-lived fishery seems to have made sharp inroads upon the stock, as catches fell off abruptly after a peak year in 1944.

Three smelts of some importance are taken, the eulachon, the silver smelt and the capelin. The eulachon has long provided an important subsistence fishery for Indian peoples on the coast; the Nass fishery has been estimated to yield as much as 900,000 pounds in a year and the normal catch in the lower reaches of the Fraser is about 300,000 pounds. The catch of silver smelt has declined from a high of 450,000 pounds in the early years of the century to the present average of less than 50,000 pounds; overfishing and pollution of spawning beaches in the Vancouver area are believed to be responsible for the decline.

Of the pelagic or open-ocean fish, the albacore tuna and the pilchard have both provided intermittent fisheries of some value. These are warm-water fish that range northward when stocks are high and shifts in ocean current produce favourable conditions. Tuna have not been caught in substantial quantities off British Columbia since 1951, but deep-sea exploration and oceanographic studies may reveal stocks within reach. Pilchards have not been available in significant numbers since 1945, either because over-exploitation of the main California stocks has limited reproduction or because of environmental changes. A small anchovy fishery from in-

SOUPFIN SHARK
As its name implies the fins are used for the making of soup, much prized by Chinese. Like the dogfish, the livers are rich in vitamin "A" but with laboratory-produced vitamin much of the value of these two fish has gone.

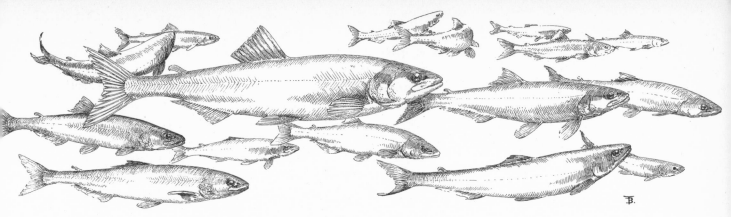

shore spawning stocks produced catches of up to five million pounds during the years from 1939 to 1945, but demand has fallen off and the fishery is at present negligible. The potential of inshore stocks is not accurately known, but they are probably inadequate to support a rewarding fishery; ocean stocks have not so far been exploited and their size and distribution are unknown.

Pacific mackerel, jack mackerel, scad, saury and brown ragfish are other pelagic species known to be present offshore in some numbers. There is little doubt that one or more of them will one day support important fisheries as world demand develops. Oceanographic studies already in progress for other purposes are likely to yield at least some knowledge of stocks and movements, and might conceivably lead to earlier development than would otherwise be the case.

The province has good stocks of shellfish and there is a clear possibility of increased yield from several species. At present fluctuating markets make for rather unstable year-to-year production. Crabs have been fished commercially for over seventy years. The major fishing grounds are in Hecate Strait and Dixon Entrance, along the west coast of Vancouver Island and in Boundary Bay and Burrard Inlet. The annual yield is from three to five million pounds and at the latter figure known stocks are probably being quite fully exploited. Shrimps and prawns yield from one to one and a half million pounds a year and while some known stocks are not yet intensively exploited, new discoveries are being made with some frequency. It seems clear that considerable increases in yield are to be expected.

The Pacific oyster, *Crassostrea gigas*, is a successful introduction from Japan, now firmly established both on leased and open grounds. Until 1951 nearly all seed was imported from Japan because conditions in the Strait of Georgia allowed a natural set of spat only about once in ten years. Since then the oysters have become firmly established in favourable areas, such as Pendrell Sound, where spat sets regularly and plenty of seed is available. The present fishery yields from five to nine million pounds* a year and can certainly be increased as demand dictates. The small native or Olympia oyster, *Ostrea lurida*, is largely disregarded at present, but it is a gourmet's delight; it is sensitive to sudden temperature changes and to pollution, but should the feeding habits of the province's human population ever develop even a mild degree of sophistication, intensive cultivation could supply an important yield of high value.

*"Green" weights – shell included.

EULACHON
This little fish runs up the Fraser River in the spring to spawn in its millions, and similarly in the Skeena and other rivers. It is very rich in oil and can be dried and a wick threaded through it which can be ignited, hence its name of "candlefish". The Indians dry it for food and also render it down for its oil. It grows up to about a foot, but 8 or 9 inches is probably average.

Butter clams, razor clams and little-neck clams of two species are extensively harvested from many parts of the coast. Butter clams yield from 2½ to 5 million pounds* yearly, razor clams perhaps 200,000 pounds and little-necks about 500,000. The Japanese little-neck or Manila clam was accidentally introduced with oyster seed about thirty years ago and since 1953 has become more important than the native. Exploitation varies from place to place on the clam beds and probably averages twenty per cent of stocks for the province as a whole. Individual beds may become "dug out", but this is a temporary condition since there are always enough clams left on adjacent beds and below zero tide level to provide new set.

Abalones and scallops are both present in B.C. waters but limited search so far has not revealed any large commercial concentrations. There is a small fishery for abalones. Mussels and cockles are abundant, but there is no commercial demand. Small quantities of octopus and squid are landed from time to time but no important fishery for either species has yet been developed. There is no doubt that production of all these edible molluscs can be greatly increased when demand develops.

There has been a whale fishery off British Columbia from aboriginal times, when the Nootka men went out in dug-out canoes with mussel-shell harpoons. The modern industry was established in 1905 and has been continued since almost without a break. Blue, finback, humpback, sei and sperm whales all contribute to the catch; grey and right whales are completely protected. Since 1948 the fishery has been limited to one station, Coal Harbour on northern Vancouver Island, and six

*"Green" weights – shell included.

IDENTIFICATION CHART OF
WHALES OCCURRING ON
THE BRITISH COLUMBIA COAST
Dept. of Fisheries, Ottawa

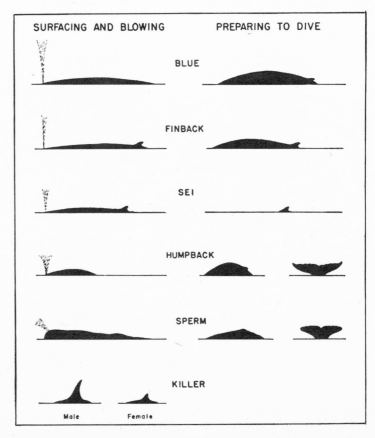

KILLER WHALE

This whale is often wrongly called "blackfish", the Pilot whale being the real blackfish. The Killer is often seen round our coasts and one's attention is often attracted by the sound of it blowing. In the picture a male is blowing and a female has seized a hair seal. As its diet consists largely of mammals, such as seals, walrus, porpoises etc. the Killer, which is so often damned as a vicious predator, may have a lot to be said in its favour by fishermen.

catcher boats. The average catch is about 600 whales a year, nearly all taken within 150 miles of the station, between April and September. It is not considered that this catch can be materially increased from a shore station, or even several stations, because the value of the carcasses is too much reduced by deterioration on longer tows. The whales caught are transients, moving between the summer feeding grounds in the north and the breeding grounds in the south. The industrial yield is oil, whale meal, concentrated protein "solubles" and frozen mink feed. Depressed world prices caused suspension of the whale fishery during 1960.

Other sea mammals of possible commercial value on the B.C. coast are sea otters, fur seals and sea lions. Sea otters were, to all practical purposes, exterminated by early and excessive exploitation for skins. There is a small colony remaining in California and a larger one on Amchitka Island in the Aleutian chain. Experiments in transplanting from the latter colony are now being made and there is some slight hope that this very attractive animal may once more become naturalized in British Columbia waters, if only for its historical and aesthetic values.

The fur seal was saved from similar extinction by the treaty of 1911, among the United States, Russia, Japan and Great Britain (for Canada), which outlawed pelagic sealing and allowed nations controlling the breeding islands to regulate the kill. Since 1958, under the North Pacific Fur Seal Convention, Canada has been receiving fifteen per cent of the U.S. kill from the Pribilof Islands and a similar share of the U.S.S.R. kill on Robbin Island and the Commander Islands. A small pelagic kill by Canadian aboriginals using native weapons decreased from a peak of nearly 3000 in the years from 1921-5 to 54 in 1953. Since 1953 this activity has entirely ceased.

Sea lions are a nuisance to fishermen since they rob and damage nets and troll lines. Some control is attempted and further investigations are to be made. Counts of animals hauled out on the rocks in the known colonies have varied from 14,000 in 1938 to 9,000 in 1955, suggesting only a moderate abundance and limited commercial possibilities. The hides make good leather and the carcasses have some value as mink feed. Conceivably, subsidized control combined with some commercial return might be economic, but the limited stocks make this a far less promising possibility than would be a similar effort to control dogfish.

The province has an intricate and abundant salt-water fishery that has not yet felt the stimulus of active and sustained demand except in so far as salmon, halibut and herring are concerned. These three fisheries are at or near maximum exploitation, though sound management and continued research may still lead to increased yields. The other fisheries, which are largely under-exploited, can only be increased in response to increased demand. To some extent this will be brought about by natural increase of population, but increased efficiency in catching and handling, improved processing and imaginative marketing can all help to bring the final product within reach of present demands.

Nearly all stocks are at present being used within the safe limits of sustained yield, though continued research will be needed to ensure this. There are some possibilities of over-all management policies that might be used to the benefit of several fisheries at once, though these may have to wait upon more intensive and stable development. Conflict with other resource uses presents few problems as yet except in the salmon fishery and in some local pollution of inshore waters. Conflict between fisheries themselves presents some problems and these may increase in time, but the system of unified federal control, guided by sound research, should be able to anticipate such conflicts and limit their effects.

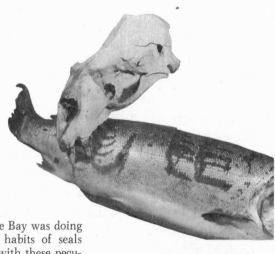

The Biological Station at Departure Bay was doing some research into the predatory habits of seals when this salmon was brought in with these peculiar markings. They turned out to be the teeth marks of a seal, as shown when this skull was matched up with them. It must have made several grabs at this relatively large fish before it escaped.

THE PACIFIC SALMONS make up by far the most important and valuable section of the province's fisheries. The chief value of all fish to mankind is that they collect into their own bodies the wealth of the seas and make it available to man in useful form. The salmons are not only particularly efficient collectors, ranging widely and making extremely rapid growth, but they render their collections into an especially rich, popular and readily processed form. Under proper conditions they are prolific and abundant fish. They return predictably, from their widest rangings, to make themselves available to man at the peak of their growth and condition, in the shallow inshore waters, the river mouths and the rivers.

It is this last point that sets the salmons apart from most other fish. They use and need not only the salt water, but the rivers and lakes and the streams above the lakes. In returning to the rivers they expose themselves so completely to man that they could be caught up almost to the last fish by the equipment that is at present available; so catches must be controlled. And they depend upon fresh water absolutely, not only for their breeding and spawning, but for the hatching of their eggs and the nursing of the fry and fingerlings to the point at which they are ready to go down to the sea and make their rapid growth. So the freshwater conditions must be protected so far as possible from change or abuse. Where change or abuse is inevitable, compensating action must be taken.

The province has five species of salmon that are of commercial importance, all of the genus *Oncorhynchus*: the sockeye (*O. nerka*), the pink (*O. gorbuscha*), the chum (*O. keta*), the spring or chinook (*O. tschawytscha*), and the coho or silver (*O. kisutch*). Each of the five has different habits, life history and abundance; and each divides again into separate stocks or races that frequent different river systems, and often yet again into separate runs within the river systems. All the fish, of every species, race and run, die almost immediately after spawning; and all are quite highly specialized to the particular habits and tolerances of the races and runs they belong to. Under natural conditions any interchange among the groups is so slight as to be negligible and it is quite difficult, often impossible, to force interchange by artificial means such as transplanting. In other words the total of the fishery depends not upon a single stock of fish but upon a very large number of separate stocks, each with its own special needs. Successful management depends very largely upon understanding the various stocks and their needs, so that the fishery can be properly regulated and the necessary protection can be provided to the freshwater conditions that are vital to the fish.

The bulk of the salmon catch, somewhere between sixty and seventy per cent, is canned and the average annual pack is about 1½ million cases. The make-up of the canned pack varies by species from year to year according to the runs, but in general it can be said that sockeye, pink and chum salmon each produce between three hundred and six hundred thousand cases, while springs and cohos together produce about one hundred and fifty thousand. These last two species are largely marketed fresh or frozen, which accounts for a further twenty or twenty-five per cent of the total catch; the remaining five to ten per cent is made up as offal meal, mild-cured salmon, bait and other minor products. In value the average canned salmon pack represents some seventy-five per cent of the total while fresh, frozen and mild-cured together account for over twenty per cent.

While all these figures are necessarily imprecise, they give a fair idea of how the salmon are used and they emphasize the point that by far the greatest part of the catch is sold directly for human consumption. This is in sharp contrast to the herring fishery, where ninety-eight per cent of the catch is reduced to meal and oil, and reflects the keen and steady world demand for salmon. There is every reason to believe that the future demand will not only continue to match, but will probably exceed, any increases of supply that can be realized by good management.

The most valuable of the five species is the sockeye, because the colour and texture of the flesh hold up supremely well in canning. It is also the most highly specialized fish and the one which makes the greatest use of freshwater habitat. The majority of sockeyes spend a little over one year in fresh water after hatching and from 2½ to 3½ years in salt water before coming back to their rivers to spawn at weights varying from three to fifteen pounds and averaging about six pounds. Almost invariably they spawn just above or just below a fairly large lake; after hatching, the young fish move up or down stream into the lakes and spend a year feeding on minute crustaceans; from the lakes they go down to the sea in the second or third spring of their lives. In the salt water they travel or are carried by prevailing currents in a general north-westerly direction, feeding chiefly on marine crustaceans. So far as is known at present, Canadian fish move rapidly offshore and scatter northward through the Gulf of Alaska, a few reaching the mid-Aleutians. Alaskan fish work more directly westward; the important Bristol Bay stocks move southward through the Aleutian chain and are found in considerable numbers at and beyond mid-Pacific points. The abundance and dispersal of these fish is at present under investigation by the International North Pacific Fisheries Commission; considerable concern is felt as to the possible effects of the Japanese ocean fishery on Alaskan stocks, and as to the American catch of Canadian fish in Alaskan waters. Assessment and control of these effects is essential to management of the fisheries on a sustained-catch basis.

The major part of the B.C. sockeye catch comes from five areas: the Fraser, Skeena and Nass rivers, Rivers Inlet and Smith Inlet. The Fraser River is by far the most important of these, yielding the largest present catches and having the greatest potential for future development. The watershed has about twenty lake systems, eight of which are or have been major producers. It is almost certainly the greatest sockeye producer and quite probably the greatest all-round salmon river in the world.

The Fraser River sockeye stocks have been heavily exploited ever since the first cannery was established in 1866. By the end of the century the fishery was so intense, by both Americans and Canadians, that it probably approached full exploitation of the runs, though sheer abundance of fish often overloaded the cannery facilities and excessive numbers of fish escaped to the spawning areas in some years.

How long the fishery would have held up under these conditions is extremely doubtful. Sooner or later cannery facilities would have caught up with the catching equipment, the pressure on the runs would have become too great and a decline would have set in, as it did with the halibut fishery. In all probability some runs and cycle years were already being overfished by the early years of the twentieth century. The Fraser sockeyes are preponderantly four-year-old fish on their return to fresh water, so each year's return reflects the spawning escapement, hatching and rearing conditions of four years earlier. After a pack of nearly a million cases in 1899, the 1903 return produced only 370,000 cases, the 1907 return less than 160,000, the 1911 return just over 185,000 cases; the 1900-4 cycle years had fallen off after a heavy pack in 1900; the 1902-6 cycle year was also yielding well below the 1902 peak of 633,000 cases. Only the superabundant 1901-5 cycle year was still holding up and produced its peak of nearly 2,400,000 cases in 1913.

The year of this immense return was also the year of the disastrous rock slides that blocked the upstream passage of the spawners at Hell's Gate canyon. The worst of the slides were removed, but the major part of that year's spawning was lost and the runs of succeeding years were delayed at various stages of the river's flow by changes in the channels. These delays resulted in decreased spawning efficiency which continued the decline. The pack reached its lowest point in the 1923-6 cycle, when the four years together produced a pack of 465,000 cases, about one-fifth of the single year pack of 1913 and a little over three-fifths of the annual average of 700,000 cases that had held through the previous twenty years. There was some recovery after 1926, especially in the Adams River run, but it was slow and incomplete; the continuing annual loss to the fishery has been estimated at

HELL'S GATE

about 25 million dollars. In 1937, the International Pacific Salmon Fisheries Commission was formed by treaty between Canada and the United States, its purpose being to restore the sockeye runs as the Halibut Commission was restoring the halibut stocks. The Commission at once made a careful investigation of the delays to the runs caused by the Hell's Gate obstruction at various stages of the river. These were found to be significant. Special fishways were designed and were installed in 1945 and 1946. Since that time salmon have been able to pass freely at all stages of the river and the way has been opened for complete restoration of the runs and probable increases in most of them.

The next step was carefully calculated control of the fishery to permit the best possible escapement of spawning stocks to depleted areas, which lasted from 1946 to 1950; control is still maintained to ensure that catch and spawning escapement are accurately balanced to provide maximum yield with safety for the future, a policy which permits a spawning escapement of 30% or less, and as low as 13% in years of great abundance. In addition to the fishways at Hell's Gate, passes were built at Bridge River rapids and in the Chilcotin River to eliminate delays and reduce mortality. Some spawning areas, whose runs had been completely wiped out, have been brought back into minor production by transplanting. Small man-made obstructions, such as the logging splash dam on Adams River, were removed. This wretched little structure probably caused greater salmon losses in every year of its existence than the total value of all the logs it helped to move; it is still causing losses, because the runs to Upper Adams River are not yet rebuilt.

The success of the Commission's policies was fully shown by the magnificent return of 18½ million fish in 1958, chiefly to the Lower Adams River. There is every reason to believe that this cycle year will maintain itself at a very high level. The 1959-63 cycle year, depending on the lesser Adams and lesser Chilco runs, remains weaker than the others. The big Chilco runs of the 1956-60 cycle years suffered less from the Hell's Gate obstruction and are holding at a high level, probably increasing. The 1961 cycle year matches 1913 and the cycle years before it of the Fraser's biggest runs. It is chiefly made up of Quesnel and Stuart Lake fish and may return to something of its glory in 1961, when the Quesnel is expected to bring back ten million fish.

In spite of these improvements, there is every reason to believe that still greater returns can be expected over the next twenty years. Many spawning streams that were once outstanding are still poorly stocked; some of the runs are not properly timed to reach the streams when they are at their most favourable spawning temperatures and distribution of spawners in the restocked areas is not ideal. There is good reason to believe that the four-year cycles can be brought back to their original abundance before the full productivity of the lakes is realized; and it is already clear that the individual years will be much more evenly productive than they were originally.

Even when full restoration of the runs has been achieved, further improvement is by no means impossible. The limiting factor in sockeye production appears to be the nursing capacity of the important lakes. It is probably significant that a very large run such as the Adams or the Chilco is followed by a lesser year and two successive minor years before the big run comes off again. Lakes such as Shuswap, which supports the Adams run, and Chilco on the Fraser watershed produce an annual average of about 15,000 fish to the square mile, while Owikeno Lake at Rivers Inlet produces more than twice as many. One or more of several factors may be responsible for the difference – a lower rate of plankton production, improper distribution of fry and fingerlings in the lake or an excessive drain on plankton stocks in the big years, followed by slow recovery. While it is true that no spawning area has ever had more than one really large cycle year in four, it is perfectly possible that a better understanding of the factors involved may suggest ways of overcoming or circumventing them.

This brief account of the Fraser's abundance, decline and restoration gives some idea of the problems involved in salmon management. The abundance of the fish is primarily dependent upon their freshwater environment; modification, even in details that are apparently small, can cause serious damage. While salt-water conditions can, and occasionally do, affect abundance, there is always a sufficient return to maintain the stock. Control of the fishery can ensure an adequate spawning escapement; but no abundance of spawners can overcome unsatisfactory freshwater conditions. Once these are seriously affected, decline is inevitable.

Of the province's other major sockeye areas, the Skeena has undergone a decline through overfishing in the early years of the century and is now making a slow recovery. A serious rock slide in 1951 on the Babine River, the chief spawning area, caused heavy losses for two seasons, but was cleared in time to allow an escapement of 750,000 fish in 1953; careful control of the fishery in 1955, 1956 and 1957 should bring rapid recovery. A fishway at Moricetown falls and other improvements are expected to increase the Nanika River run. Babine Lake, which is the main nursing area for Skeena watershed sockeye, produces an average of only a little over three thousand fish to the square mile, about one-fifth of the production of the Fraser watershed lakes and one-tenth that of Owikeno Lake. It is believed that the young fish at present do not spread properly through the lake to take advantage of its potential and that redistribution of spawners by regulating the escapement may correct this.

The Skeena River sockeyes mature and return mainly at four and five years old, in contrast to the Fraser where mature fish are nearly all four-year-olds. The Nass has a return of four- and five-year-olds with one year of freshwater life and five- and six-year-olds with two years of freshwater life. Not too much is known of Nass watershed, but it is estimated that the spawning escapement is about fifty per cent of a total return of 300,000 to 500,000 fish. The nursery lakes produce at the low level of 4500 fish to the square mile, suggesting that improvement may be possible. Rivers Inlet and Smith Inlet fish are mainly four- and five-year-olds and the catch is about 65 per cent and 75 per cent of the runs respectively. Both inlets have exceptionally high-producing lakes, with total returns of half a million fish or more in good years. Catches have held up well over a long period and are expected to continue at a satisfactory level. A number of other lakes in the province, especially on Vancouver Island, produce fair numbers of sockeyes and probably provide an annual catch of about half a million fish. Most of these watersheds have not been closely examined and regulation of the fishery is probably not ideal. The yield of fish per square mile of lake surface is known to be as low as 340 in several instances and it would seem that more intensive management should produce increased catches.

The pink salmon is the most widely distributed of the salmons and the simplest. The fry go to sea as soon as they are hatched from the gravel and return two years later as mature fish weighing about four or five pounds. The average annual catch is about 11 million fish from the stocks of well over a thousand different B.C. streams. The flesh of the pink salmon cans well and commands a good market.

The present abundance of pink salmon is considered to be far below that of the early years of the century. A combined U.S.-Canadian catch of 22 million fish was made in 1917, but even that probably did not reflect the true abundance as the fishery was not intensive enough to take full advantage of it, and stocks had already been heavily reduced by the Fraser River rock slide of 1913.

The pink salmon's unvarying life history and its habit of frequenting small streams makes it particularly vulnerable to disaster. A major flood, a river block or severe drought may wipe out or heavily reduce a run, and if this happens there is little chance of replacement except by chance straying from other streams or a slow build-up over many years. Perhaps as a result of this about half the pink salmon streams have a very large run in one year and little or nothing in the next. Runs have been reduced by overfishing, because control was extremely difficult, especially in international waters, until 1957 when responsibility for the investigation and control of the Fraser runs was vested in the International Salmon Commission. Logging operations have blocked streams or damaged spawning beds from time to time and clear logging has dried up or greatly reduced the flow of many streams that once supported good runs.

Fortunately the simple life history and habits of the fish also give a very real hope that something can be done to restore and perhaps surpass the original abundance. Since it is a short-lived and uncomplicated fish, pink salmon research is easier and can be completed more quickly than other salmon research. Since it does not depend on lakes and needs fresh water only for spawning, the hatching of its eggs and passage to and from the sea, there is a much better chance of increasing the numbers of migrants by artificial means.

At the present time a number of important experiments are being conducted on pink salmon streams in the province. Since 1954 an artificial spawning stream, fed by water from Jones Creek, a tributary of the Fraser, has been producing an extremely high survival rate – over 30 per cent from egg to fry – from both artificially planted and naturally spawned eggs. The stream bed has been built to provide ideal

ENTRANCE TO JONES' CREEK DIVERSION
When Wahleach (Jones) Lake was dammed for power by the B.C. Electric, the flow of the creek from the lake to the Fraser was affected. Just below the Trans-Canada Highway water is diverted through a controllable sluice into a channel which runs almost parallel to the creek for some quarter-mile before rejoining Jones' Creek. The latter is screened, shown on the left of picture, and ascending salmon are compelled to turn into the diversion. This is about twenty feet wide and one or two feet deep, gradually dropping by shallow steps forming pools carpeted with good spawning gravel.

THE SPAWNING OF CHUM SALMON
These photographs, showing chum salmon actually spawning, were taken by Mr. C. Groot as part of his work on a doctoral thesis on spawning salmon. He is working in association with the Fisheries Research Board of Canada at the Biological Station near Nanaimo.

gravel conditions and the flow of water is controlled to the best possible speed and depth for spawning and hatching. Extension of these principles obviously holds tremendous possibilities.* Other experiments that promise well are control of flows in smaller streams by low-cost dams and new techniques in hatchery propagation, especially a more natural form of release to the migration stream, which seems to yield a far higher survival than has been achieved by older methods. Control of the fishery will remain a problem, but in spite of this prospects for an increased yield on a sustained basis are very good.

Chum salmon mature at 3, 4 and 5 years of age and an average weight of 12 pounds. Like the pink salmon, it has a very short freshwater life and it favours the short coastal streams of the province even more exclusively than the pink. It is somewhat less abundant and is marketed fresh and frozen, occasionally smoked or dry salted, as well as in cans. The same management policies are likely to apply to chums as to pinks, but any major increase of stocks will probably lead to competition for available spawning areas. It is likely that management would favour the pinks in this event, since they command a steadier market and would give quicker results.

Coho salmon nearly all mature as three-year-olds, after one year of freshwater life which is usually spent in a stream or river rather than a lake. About 3 million coho a year are taken commercially, two million of these by trolling, from a total estimated stock of 5 million. The fish average between five and ten pounds in weight and are largely used in the fresh and frozen fish markets, though a fair number are canned. There is an important sport fishery, chiefly centred on the Strait of Georgia, in which at least 300,000 fish a year are taken, many of them at immature stages.

Like the pink salmon, the coho runs to a very large number of small streams – more than a thousand in various parts of the province. Since it depends absolutely

*A similar project at Robertson Creek on Vancouver Island, with some improvements, produced a 95% survival from 1.64 million eyed eggs planted in 1959. The return from these migrants is expected in 1961.

Male "nosing" and pushing female to gravel patches.   Unwilling female is bitten in tail by male.

on a nursing year in fresh water, it is far more susceptible to drought than the pink salmon; it has been shown for at least one major stream that the catch and return almost exactly reflect the minimum summer flows of two years earlier. So far the commercial catches have held up fairly well, probably because increased fishing intensity has coincided with decline in abundance. There is no doubt that many coho streams have been damaged by logging, fires, local stream diversions and other factors that increase floods and silting and reduce minimum stream flows. Regrowth of logged land and improving logging practices may compensate to some extent for past damage, but increasing population with its danger of industrial and agricultural pollution and its careless treatment of small streams will almost certainly cause further damage. Stream protection and control of flow, with elimination of obstructions that now limit spawning areas, could do a great deal to maintain the runs; really intense management of this type would probably increase them and the growing importance of the sport fishery may well justify such action.

The springs or chinooks are the largest of the salmons, averaging from ten to thirty pounds, according to the run and the season. Individual fish commonly weigh over fifty pounds and a few have been caught at over one hundred pounds. The present commercial catch is estimated at about a million fish a year, with a sport-fishing catch of well over 50,000, and probably represents about two-thirds of the stock. Spring salmon are powerful and vigorous fish which ascend the longest rivers to their limits of accessibility, though some numbers spawn in smaller streams, often quite close to salt water. The fry usually go down to the sea within a few months of emerging from the gravel, but a certain proportion spend a full year in fresh water. In migration they tend north-westward along the coastline, apparently keeping nearly always within the limits of the continental shelf, so numbers of American fish enter the Canadian fishery and Canadian fish are taken in Alaskan waters. Most spring salmon mature at four or five years, though the full range is from three to eight years, with a strong tendency towards later maturity in the more northerly rivers.

About two-thirds of the British Columbia catch is taken by trolling and most of

Male and female at beginning of courtship standing over just-started bed.

Female digging bed.

the remaining third by gill-nets; most of the troll catch goes to the fresh-fish market and commands a good price. The fishery has been maintained at a steady level since accurate records have been kept, but this reflects an increasing intensity of effort rather than sustained maintenance of stocks; the great Columbia River stocks, impaired by overfishing in the early part of the century, have been prevented from recovery and gradually still further depleted by dam-building; the total decline to date has been estimated at about 85 per cent of original abundance, and there is strong reason to believe it will continue. This has been reflected by a decline in the proportion of Columbia fish in the open-water catch along the B.C. coast from fifty to less than thirty per cent, though the more intense fishery by both Canadian and U.S. boats has maintained the total catch. It is considered that this catch probably represents the maximum available from present stocks. Some Canadian spring salmon streams, such as the Puntledge on Vancouver Island and the Nechako, a major tributary of the Fraser, have already suffered industrial damage. Unfortunately spring salmon, which use mainly the larger streams, do not offer the same possibilities of constructive management as do coho, pink and chum salmon. There is little or no immediate prospect of increasing the runs and since some stocks are probably already being overfished, careful regulation of the fishery seems essential.

Some 50,000 steelhead trout, averaging rather over ten pounds, are taken each year in the commercial fishery, mainly by gill-nets. These fish are not especially sought after since they have heavy bone structure and do not can well. They have great value as game-fish and probably should be protected from all commercial effort, but since most are caught by gill-nets set for the various species of salmon, this is difficult to achieve. Fortunately many runs occur at times and places where there is little commercial effort.

This brief account of the habits, life history and abundance of the species that make up the B.C. salmon catch gives some idea of the complexity of the resource and the difficult management problems it presents. The multiplicity of species, runs and races that make up the salmon resource has not been developed fortuitously, but in direct response to environment. It is generally supposed that the retreat of

Female "crouching" into bed, testing depth of hole with stretched anal fin.

The spawning act – eggs and milt are being released simultaneously.

the last glacial ice sheets played a great part in this development. As the ice withdrew farther and farther, there were always a few maturing fish with sufficient body reserves to press on upstream, spawn successfully and establish new runs adapted to the new conditions. The result is that each race and run is composed of highly specialized individuals that must find exactly the right conditions to spawn successfully and whose progeny must find exactly the right hatching and nursing conditions if they are to develop successfully to the migrant stage.

This limited tolerance is quite clearly shown by the fact that most sockeye salmon die within five days after spawning. Fish delayed only ten or twelve days at the Hell's Gate obstruction simply did not reach their spawning grounds; others, delayed for shorter periods, reached the spawning grounds but did not reproduce satisfactorily. In the same way, salmon can only survive temperature or other changes in water conditions if these are held within very narrow limits, as they usually are under natural conditions. The freshwater environment as it is and has been for the past ten thousand years is the real base of the resource. The individual runs and races are closely adapted to make the best possible use of that base. It follows that not only must the freshwater environment be adequately protected and cared for, but the fishery must be regulated in such a way that proper proportions of each individual species and run and race reach the spawning areas at the right time. Nothing short of this will ensure that the catch will be brought to its maximum potential and sustained there.

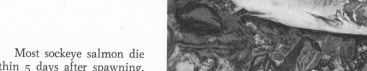

Most sockeye salmon die
within 5 days after spawning.

CHAPTER 16 *salmon management*

IT HAS BEEN POINTED OUT that the salmons are easily caught fish. The runs follow predictable routes to the narrow objectives of river mouths and it is only necessary to set enough gear of the right kind across these routes to ensure a catch of any desired size. Four or five years of uncontrolled fishery with existing gear could wipe out practically every salmon run in the province.

By the same token it would be possible to maintain an extremely efficient fishery with a system of strategically placed fish traps along the migration routes and near the river mouths. Such a system would be quite predictable in its operation and would be far more easily controlled to ensure proper escapement of the various spawning runs and races than is the present mobile and varied operation. In all probability it would land the required catch at considerably lower prices.

The reasons British Columbia does not have such a fishery are entirely sociological and philosophical, though with some measure of economic sanction; were it not that salmon command high prices in fairly steady markets, the province probably could not afford its present fishery. As it is, the principle of public ownership of the resource and reasonable opportunity for everyone in the labour and profit of realizing its yield is more closely observed in fisheries than in any other resource. Any citizen who purchases a licence for one dollar is free to fish in accordance with the regulations. He can fish and sell his fish from a rowboat costing less than a hundred dollars, or from a seine boat or halibut boat or dragger worth a hundred thousand dollars. He may invest what he can afford and will probably realize a return in proportion to his investment, his skill and the hours he puts in.

All this has been of immense advantage to the province. It has spread settlement along the coast into many places where there would otherwise be little reason for settlement. It has given the Indian peoples of the coast an ideal chance of self-realization in an occupation for which they are particularly well fitted. It has been an attractive force for immigrants of independence and determination, and it has developed a large body of men with an intimate knowledge of the narrow waters and intricate coastline that could have been acquired in no other way.

British Columbia has over twelve thousand independent fishermen who operate upwards of nine thousand boats, nearly a thousand of ten tons or more, about eight thousand under ten tons. In 1959 there were twenty-six salmon canneries, twelve reduction plants, seventeen processing and cold storage plants. In addition to these the industry supports boat yards, net, twine and rope manufacturing and contributes largely to many service industries. Altogether more than ninety thousand workers in the province are directly or indirectly dependent on fisheries for all or a substantial part of their livelihood. Besides taking a very active part in the commercial fishery, many of the province's Indian peoples still depend to an important degree upon subsistence fisheries, especially for salmon, in which fish are taken during upstream migration and smoked or salted for future use.

The chief fishing methods used in the industry are gill-netting, purse seining, drag-net trawling, trolling with hook and line and long-lining. A few fish traps are still operated in the Strait of Juan de Fuca. Trawl nets are used for ground-fish, dogfish and shrimp. Long-lining is used for halibut and dogfish. Salmon are the chief troll catch, though salmon trollers also go out for halibut. Purse seines are used extensively for salmon and account for nearly all the herring catch. Gill-nets, the most widely used gear of all, are mainly fished for salmon but occasionally also for dogfish and herring.

Since World War II, increased prices and increasing runs of fish have encouraged more people to take advantage of the open policy and very low licence fee, so that competition has increased considerably. At the same time cost of boats and gear has gone up. While it is true that a measure of success is still possible with very limited equipment, most small gill-net boats, with their nets, represent an investment of at least $3000, while the better boats are worth over $10,000. Good trolling boats represent a similar investment. Halibut boats are likely to cost upwards of $40,000 and good seine boats over $75,000, with proportionate investment in nets. Many of the better boats are equipped to take advantage of more than one kind of fishing. Modern equipment such as echo sounders and radio telephones is standard on the better boats. New devices such as the drum seines and the power block used on ordinary seiners have been developed in the face of competition and consequently make the competition still more intense.

The natural result is an increasing tendency on the part of fishermen to ask for limitations on gear and licensing. The original policy, which had always prevented the establishment of large vested interests that might limit participation in the fishery, has now had the effect of creating a great number of small vested interests. At the present time the authorities seem to have every intention of maintaining the principle of an open fishery and relying on the effects of competition to keep the quantities of gear within reasonable bounds. Since increasingly close regulation of the catch is essential to sustained yield there is no doubt that competition will eventually bring about a balance between the amount of gear and the fish available; but with increasing stocks of such high-priced fish as sockeyes and the periodic "big" years, it may be some while before this happens.

Since spawning salmon work their way into nearly every stream in the province except those of the Arctic watershed, the resource has always suffered from competition and abuse. In the days of the gold-rush, destruction of spawning gravels by placer mining operations almost precipitated war between the Indians and the miners. Early farmers had such contempt for the spawning fish that they pitchforked them on to the fields for fertilizer. Minor irrigation diversions and channel obstructions for logging or other purposes were constructed with thought only for the purposes immediately in hand. Mine effluents were turned without hesitation into the rivers – it was convenient. The salmon, like the forests, were so abundant that nothing could affect them.

Later the large-scale logging operations altered the face of the land and the flow of its waters; sawmill and other industrial wastes used the rivers for drainage. The first few hydro-electric projects were installed. These things were progress and nothing must interfere with them. They might injure a run here or a watershed there, but there were many runs and many watersheds. It was not clear then, as it is to-day, that the salmon are a total of all the watersheds open to them and that repeated injuries to little parts of the resource cannot be continued indefinitely without serious damage to the whole.

Besides all these things, there was overfishing. This gradual depletion, a combination of many factors, would sooner or later have drawn attention to itself. But before that could happen the Hell's Gate slide produced a more dramatic depletion. In just two cycles the Fraser's big year pack of 2,400,000 cases dropped to 143,000 cases. And it did not recover. There has been no comparable disaster to a natural resource in the province's history – even the greatest of forest fires cannot compare with it – yet it served the useful purpose of showing, once and for all, that the salmon resource could be utterly destroyed if its freshwater needs were not respected.

From the very early days of the fishery many people hoped that artificial propagation could be used to maintain or increase the runs. The first salmon hatchery in B.C. was established on the Fraser, just above New Westminster, in 1884, and 1,800,000 sockeye fry were released from it the following year. Additional hatcheries were established at Shuswap Lake, Harrison Lake and Stuart Lake on the Fraser watershed soon after the turn of the century. Several others were operated at Rivers Inlet, at Lakelse Lake, on the Skeena River and on the more important Vancouver Island watersheds. By 1927 the hatcheries had released twenty million chum salmon fry, 85 million cohos, 72 million springs, 82 million pinks, 1.68 million steelhead and over 2 billion sockeye fry. No one really knew whether all this had done any good. Most people hoped and believed it had.

Hatcheries were based on the idea that there are heavy losses to the eggs in the gravel between spawning and hatching. In the early 1930's Dr. R. E. Foerster showed, by an exhaustive series of experiments at Cultus Lake, that artificial propagation as then practised gave no better results in the production of fry than did natural propagation. He was also able to show very clearly that the total effort of all the hatcheries then in production could not possibly make a significant contribution to the numbers of returning adult salmon. A reduction of only twenty thousand cases in the salmon pack, for instance, would let enough spawners go through to produce 480 million eggs or about ten times the total handled by all the Fraser hatcheries in 1927.

Foerster's experiments have since been confirmed many times by other researchers and no professional biologist to-day believes that hatcheries can ever be successfully used to replace natural salmon runs. It has been pointed out that the hatcheries needed to maintain one cycle year of the Fraser run would involve a capital outlay of half a billion dollars and annual operating costs of 125 million. Even this would probably lead to a gradual decline of the natural abundance and would entail serious risk of more rapid decline by disease. Hatcheries have a place in the management of salmon fisheries, but it will always be supplementary to that of the natural runs. Some of the new techniques of artificial propagation, or rather assisted propagation, such as artificial spawning beds and controlled lake and saltwater rearing, also promise well; but these, too, are supplementary measures which may increase the total yield but can never replace the great natural runs that are the true resource.

In the history of the B.C. salmon fishery, nothing shows the advantages of maintaining and improving natural conditions more plainly than does the recovery of the Fraser River runs under the management of the International Commission. It is not too much to say that within a few years the yield of these runs will not only be restored to its previous peak but will be greater than it has ever been – if this type

Microphotograph of a sockeye salmon scale, showing growth-rings. The number of growth-rings in the central portion reveals the lake in which the fish was reared. The International Pacific Salmon Fisheries Commission in New Westminster analyses scales continually during the fishing season, and is thus enabled to control the catch to the point that at least 20% of the fish from each lake are allowed to return to their spawning beds.

of management can be continued. Further, it is equally certain that major runs throughout the province can eventually be increased well beyond previous yields.

But it is also true that the salmon runs of the province are entering their time of greatest danger from industrial developments of every kind. Some of the old dangers will persist; an increased logging cut will almost certainly mean an increased acreage of poorly controlled run-off; agricultural developments will mean increased use of water for irrigation; more pulp mills, greater population, larger cities, more industries, all putting out waste, will mean increased danger of pollution in many areas. Pollution from agricultural sprays is an increasing risk and pollution from forest sprays has already proved disastrous in a single experiment on northern Vancouver Island.

Some of these possibilities are legitimate conflicts in resource use that can be worked out by good management, perhaps with advantage to both sides – sound logging practices, for instance, can be as beneficial to forestry as to fisheries. Some of the pollutions, such as those from pulp mills, offer opportunities for management and intelligent compromise, as has already been shown in the case of the Alberni Canal. Others are simply abuses that benefit no one in the long run and should be rigidly controlled.

By far the most serious threat to salmon runs in the immediate future is that of hydro-electric dams. Dams of moderate height such as Bonneville on the Columbia, which has a maximum head of 65 feet and a normal head of 45 feet, do not present insuperable problems, although they cause some losses. Unfortunately the nature of British Columbia streams and terrain generally calls for the use of very high dams and often a series of dams on the same stream. In spite of the expenditure of hundreds of millions of dollars during the past twenty or thirty years, especially in the United States Pacific North-west, there is absolutely nothing so far to suggest that major salmon runs can be successfully maintained in the face of a really high dam, much less so against a series of them.

The Columbia River was a seriously damaged salmon producer before any of its major dams except Rock Island was built. Many of the upstream spawning areas had been carelessly cut off by small logging and irrigation dams, serious losses had been caused by unguarded irrigation ditches and overfishing had continued for many years. But it was still one of the world's great salmon rivers and full restoration of its runs could have been achieved without serious difficulty. Timing, which I have suggested is a major factor in resource development and management, was entirely against this. The Pacific North-west States entered a period of expansion and heavy power demand at a time when there were few alternatives to hydro power and when knowledge of salmon was totally inadequate to provide a sound answer to what would happen to the salmon under such development; real knowledge of how to compensate for the effect of the dams was, of course, no more available than it is to-day. Over 200 million dollars has been spent on the Columbia in efforts to maintain the runs, 50 million dollars of it on hatcheries alone; but the yield of the river has now declined to about 15 per cent of its original level and de-cline of the upriver races is likely to continue. At Grand Coulee, the highest of the dams, no effort was made to pass salmon because it was perfectly clear that any such effort would be futile.

In British Columbia, both timing and prospects are quite different, though hydro-electric dams are still a serious threat to the runs. Industrial development has been slower and power demands are neither so immediate nor so immense, though there is a very great demand which must be met. Construction costs of hydro projects have increased tremendously and are still increasing. Natural gas has begun to establish itself as a source of energy and nuclear power must be ser-iously considered in any long-term planning. At the same time rehabilitation of the salmon runs has advanced to the point at which these are an increasing instead of a declining asset, and the potential value of a fishery that can clearly be maintained indefinitely into the future is much too great to be written off for what may easily prove to be very short-term gains.

On some streams salmon losses have already been accepted under pressure for hydro development – the Nechako River and Seton Creek, both Fraser tributaries, are examples, as are the Puntledge and Ash rivers on Vancouver Island. In all these projects, which are comparatively small, compensating devices have been used and losses are smaller than would otherwise have been the case; some reha-bilitation may be possible in the future. The Quesnel River, considered a potential hydro project at the time when its salmon runs were still negligible, was abandoned in favour of salmon production and is expected to produce ten million fish in 1961.

A large number of power sites are under consideration at the present time and it is impossible to consider them all, but a few instances will give some idea of the problems involved and possibilities of compromise. The Homathco project on Bute Inlet would seriously damage salmon runs only if it incorporated water diversion from Chilco Lake. Since substantial quantities of power can be realized without this diversion, it is reasonable to expect that it will be avoided and that the minor problems that do develop can be solved. A multiple development proposed for the Nass River presents many problems; partial solutions could be found for some of them and runs of pink, chum and coho salmon below the main 240-foot dam would probably suffer the least harm; but it is unlikely the river could remain a major producer. A dam proposed for Great Central Lake on Vancouver Island raises the difficult problem of saving a run of lake-spawning sockeyes. A high dam suggested for the Nimpkish River would threaten quite large runs of all five species and would present the classic problems of upstream and downstream migration, as well as the more uncertain ones of modification of lake conditions above the dam.

Both biological and engineering research have made steady advances in solving the extremely diverse problems that are presented by the different projects, but it remains true that most solutions are partial, entailing compromise that is almost always detrimental to the total of the salmon runs. On large multiple projects, where cumulative effects build up, partial solutions almost inevitably mean little more than a gradual decline to extinction instead of a sharp one.

The real difficulties of reconciling the needs of salmon and hydro projects are not so much in the simple fact that dams obstruct passage of upstream and downstream migrants as in the sharp changes of freshwater conditions created by dams and in the very limited tolerances of the fish themselves. In the case of major projects on rivers like the Fraser which has really large runs, and even on rivers like the Nass, changes in environment and conditions are so manifold and so complex that they remain to date completely insuperable. Each adverse effect may be separately countered, usually at high cost, with some degree of success, but the total will be failure.

The Fraser watershed is by far the largest salmon producer in the province; it is also, potentially, one of the largest power producers. Realizing its full power potential would entail construction of a large number of main-stream dams, which would completely change the character of the watershed and wipe out every important salmon run. But the construction of even one of the projected main-stream dams, the seven-hundred-foot dam proposed for the Moran Canyon site, 23 miles above Lillooet, would destroy every major sockeye run on the watershed except possibly the Adams run.

A dam such as this would create many problems whose effects are obvious as well as a number whose effects can only be guessed at. It has been estimated that the dam may create a temperature difference of 10°F. or more between the river below and the lake behind it; this by itself might well be enough to change the pattern and timing of all runs entering the river and it would certainly cause a major problem in adjustment for both upstream and downstream migrants, since an abrupt temperature change of this order is normally fatal to salmon. At the peak of the upstream runs, it would be necessary to transfer as many as ¾ million fish a day from the foot of the dam to the lake above it without serious delay to any of them. Whatever facilities were used for this would have to be operable over a range of 200 vertical feet, the potential draw-down of the lake above the dam. This lake itself, which would reach to Quesnel, 160 miles upstream, would present totally unfamiliar oxygen, temperature and flow conditions which would almost certainly confuse and delay the upstream movement.

If these problems were solved and the salmon reached their spawning areas in time to spawn successfully, which is totally unlikely, the downstream migrants would face the same difficulties of changed environment. Migration through the 160-mile lake would be slowed from a few days to a period of at least two or three weeks; there is a strong chance that large numbers of young fish would not migrate at all under the changed conditions but would land-lock in the lake. Those that did choose to migrate would have to be steered into safe by-passes by some means not yet discovered, in spite of extensive research. And once past the dam they would be faced with a possibly lethal difference in temperature between the water that carried them down and the water emerging from the turbines to make the main flow of the river below.

Colour photographs taken by the International Pacific Salmon Fisheries Commission

ADAMS RIVER SOCKEYE MASSED ON SPAWNING GROUNDS

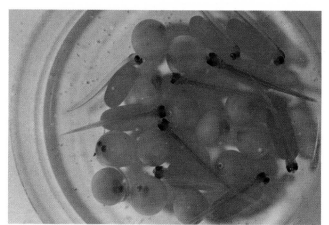

SOCKEYE EGGS, HATCHING EGGS AND ALEVINS (LARVAE)

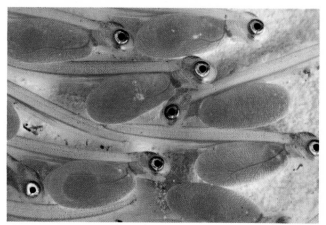

NEWLY HATCHED SOCKEYE ALEVINS

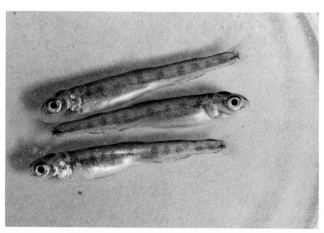

SOCKEYE FRY AT THE EMERGENT STAGE

SOCKEYE SMOLTS (FINGERLINGS)

These considerations, and the inevitable conclusion to be drawn from them, have been enough to protect the Fraser watershed from power development for the time being. Perhaps equally important, they have served to direct attention to alternative possibilities on other rivers and on the Fraser watershed itself. A number of lesser sites are available and would produce important quantities of power, distributed through the watershed in such a way as to reduce transmission costs and encourage development of a power grid. In addition, most of these sites would also provide some measure of flood control, a few offer irrigation possibilities and some might even permit management that would benefit the salmon runs.

At least two other watersheds offer major alternatives to Fraser development – the Peace and the Upper Columbia. The salmon problems of the Upper Columbia were solved for all time when Grand Coulee blocked the runs. The Peace also is without salmon runs and can create no problems unless its waters are diverted into the Fraser; in this event there would be serious risk of transferring a fish parasite, *Triaenophorus,* to the salmons through the Northern Pike. This would not be disastrous to the runs, but could prove extremely costly to the industry since the parasite infests the flesh and seriously reduces the selling quality. Avoidance of such a risk seems no more than common sense, when plenty of power can be realized without diversion. The Columbia and the Peace together can provide enough hydropower to supply the province's needs until 1980 and well beyond. By that time many issues, both in salmon management and in energy development, will be much clearer than they are to-day and better decisions can be made than would now be possible.

In this writer's opinion fisheries research in British Columbia, largely carried out by the Fisheries Research Board under the federal government, has been outstand-

Invertebrate Sea Life
PAINTED BY MRS. GLADYS CLAWSON
The British Columbia Coast harbours one of the richest collections of invertebrates in the world. Some of the animals pictured here are eaten as rare delicacies in other parts of the world, and could be termed one of our great unused resources.

1. *Sunflower Starfish* – PYCNOPODIA HELIANTHOIDES
2. *Rockweed* – FUCUS
3. *Pacific Octopus* – OCTOPUS APOLLYON
4. *Giant Chiton* – CRYPTOCHITON STELLERI
5. *Eel Grass* – ZOSTERA
6. *Slime Star* – PTERASTER
7. *Sea Lettuce* – ULVA
8. *Giant Kelp* – NEREOCYSTIS LUETKEANA
9. *Plumose Anemone* – METRIDIUM SENILE
10. *Leather Star* – DERMASTERIAS IMBRICATA
11. *Immature Red Algae* –
12. *Tubeworm* – EUDISTYLIA POLYMORPHA

13. *Pink Starfish* – PISASTER BREVISPINUS
14. *Blood Star* – HENRICIA LEVIUSCULA
15. *Oregon Triton* – ARGOBUCCINUM OREGONENSIS
16. *Lyre Crab* – HYAS LYRATUS
17. *Long Rayed Star* – ORTHASTERIAS
18. *Prawn* – PANDALUS PLATYCEROS
19. *Red Sea Urchin* – STRONGYLOCENTROTUS FRANCISCANUS
20. *Tunicate* –
21. *Giant Nudibranch* – DENDRONTUS
22. *Blue Mussel* – MYTILUS
23. *Slender Starfish* – EVASTERIAS TROSCHELLII
24. *Green Sea Urchin* – STRONGYLOCENTROTUS DROBACHIENSIS
25. *Sea Pen* – LEOPTITUS
26. *Common Pacific Starfish* – PISASTER OCHRACEUS
27. *Hermit Crab* – PAGURUS
28. *Sea Cucumber* – STICHOPUS CALIFORNICUS
29. *Japanese Oyster* – CRASSOSTREA
30. *Green Anemone* – BUNODACTIS ELEGANTISSIMA
31. *Edible Crab* – CANCER MAGISTER

ing over a long period. Salmon management is soundly conducted by the Department of Fisheries within the limits of departmental finances, and knowledge of the fish is quite enough to ensure sustained-yield operation of the fishery, with reasonable expectation of substantial increases in allowable catch, so long as the freshwater environment remains unimpaired. Unfortunately major threats to the runs are now all caused by competing resource uses, especially the use of rivers for disposal of wastes and for hydro-electric projects.

The first of these, more commonly called pollution, is a completely destructive use which can and should be prevented at whatever cost. The second is a constructive use which presents problems that must be faced. Intensive research and costly experiments, not only in Canada but all over the world, have not so far yielded even distant promise of solution to problems that would be caused by a structure such as the Moran dam on the main stream of the Fraser, much less several such structures. Perhaps it is short-sighted to suggest that adequate solutions may never be found. But it is not too much to say that if they are found it will be through fundamental research in salmon biology, not through special programmes designed to solve specific problems. Fundamental research of a high order is at present being carried out by the Fisheries Research Board and also by the Institute of Fisheries at the University of British Columbia. It involves such matters as oceanographic and lake studies, examination of the energy resources and biochemical reactions of the fish and many other considerations that will lead to much fuller understanding of the salmon's needs and behaviour. Work such as this offers the only real prospect, however remote, of finding some answers to the problems posed by other resource uses. At the same time it offers an excellent chance of finding ways of increasing salmon runs well beyond the maximum figures that can be foreseen at present.

PIKE OR NORTHERN PIKE

At present unknown in the Fraser watershed but native to the Peace - Liard - Mackenzie systems. Its food consists almost entirely of fish and its presence in trout and salmon waters is not looked upon favourably. Many of the British Columbia rivers are not ideal waters for pike, which is at home in more sluggish waters. However in any lake it could do untold damage, particularly in those lakes where immature sockeyes spend their first year.

mineral resources   CHAPTER 17

AFTER THE FUR TRADE, mining is the oldest of British Columbia's industries. Coal mining began under the Hudson's Bay Company and was well established at Nanaimo when the first gold discoveries on the Thompson and the Fraser rivers started the gold-rush of 1858. For the next few years, gold was everything, or almost everything. It opened roads, brought population, paid for government administration – in short, it wrote history, establishing the Crown colony of British Columbia and paving the way for confederation with the rest of Canada some thirteen years later.

Gold was found in many parts of the province and the search for it led to the discovery of other important minerals. By the turn of the century there were over nine thousand miners in the province, mining some 400,000 tons of ore a year with a total value of nearly twenty million dollars. The Granby Consolidated Mining and Smelting Company's operations in the Boundary District were by far the largest producers.

To-day the province's mining industry produces about 150 million dollars a year, employs about 9000 miners, 4200 workers in concentrating and smelting plants and perhaps 80,000 to 90,000 others indirectly in various industries and services. In the years from 1900 to 1960, many mines have failed or played out, many new mines have been discovered, some old mines have been rejuvenated. Yet a strong measure of stability and growth is evident in the figures; in the past hundred years, mining of all kinds has produced a total of over four billion dollars in British Columbia and the annual value of production has increased from a few million dollars to a peak of over 190 million in 1956, fluctuating sharply downwards only at times of world-wide economic dislocation – shortly after the First War, at the start of the great depression and during the later years of the Second War – for brief periods. This growth in value and relative stability of operation in what seems at first sight a wasting and extremely uncertain resource is, in fact, in the very nature of the

FORMATION OF A TYPICAL METALLIFEROUS MINERAL DEPOSIT

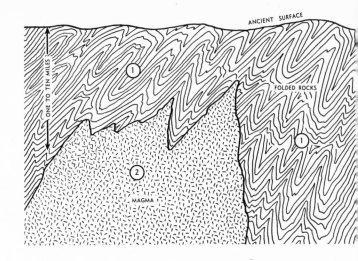

Folded volcanic and sedimentary rocks (1) are intruded by molten silicate material called "Magma" (2). The magma comes to rest and begins to crystallize at depths ranging from as little as one mile to more than 10 miles below the ground surface. The resulting mass of granitic rock, known as a "Batholith", is of irregular shape and is apt to have a jagged upper surface. As the various silicate materials that comprise the granitic rock crystallize, metals present in minute proportions in the original magma become residually concentrated deep within the mass, in a shrinking volume of highly mobile fluid composed of materials such as water, carbon dioxide, sulphur, and silica. This residual fluid is under extremely high pressure, so that if any cracks develop in the batholith as a result of earth movements (3), the mineral-bearing fluid streams up such passageways towards the surface. As the fluid ascends, the temperature and pressure decrease, and as a result ore and associated minerals are precipitated at one or more places along its route, forming mineral deposits. A hot spring at the surface may represent the mineralizing fluid depleted of its metals. During the following geological ages weathering and erosion remove thousands of feet of the overlying rocks, finally exposing the batholith at the surface that we see today (4), for example, along the coast of British Columbia. Deeply engulfed parts of the ancient roof rocks, preserved after erosion as remnants completely surrounded by granitic rock are known as "roof pendants" (5). These are favoured places for ore deposits such as the Britannia Mine on Howe Sound.

resource and still more in the nature and present state of the province, as well as in the nature of the times.

Mining is not a renewable resource. The ore body of even the largest mine is necessarily of limited extent and can yield its value only once, though new techniques or increased demand may make it profitable to rework tailings or to extend the operation into mineral deposits of lower grade. But it is also true that mining itself often leads to discovery of new ore bodies or to disclosure of unexpected extent in an old ore body; an increasingly intensive industrial civilization multiplies demand for minerals, raises prices, expands the search and brings prospects once economically unsound into useful production. These factors operating in a large, sparsely settled and only partly explored province of great mineral promise, almost inevitably lead to increasing production.

The word "promise" as used here is intentionally imprecise. It expresses promise shown by favourable geology rather than by known presence of minerals. Minerals are usually buried underground; they cannot be seen. They were formed, for the most part, in regions where major disturbances and granitic intrusions occurred millions of years ago. Mineral deposits are commonly associated with mountain ranges or once great ranges long since reduced by erosion. An ore body may reveal itself by surface indications; it may be detected by geological reasoning or electronic survey or by geochemistry; but its precise nature and quality and size can only be determined by intense physical exploration, which is so difficult and costly that it is normally undertaken shortly in advance of intended development. The usual practice, even then, is to explore only far enough to find reasonable assurance that the size and quality of the ore-body will yield the necessary capital return with some profit. Further exploration is undertaken during the course of the mine's operation and, if the results are successful, may lead to expanded development.

Important mineral deposits in nearly all parts of the world are commonly associated with intrusive rocks – granite masses either thrust up from a great depth in molten form or else altered and crystallized under very high temperatures and pressures. The early stages of mountain-building produced a great deal of folding and

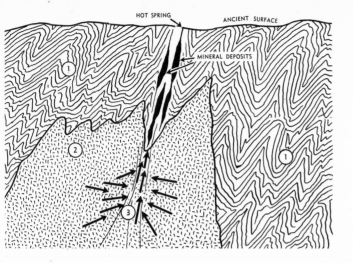

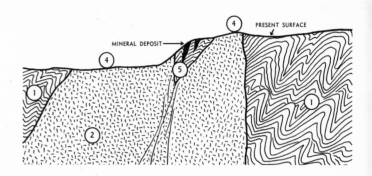

faulting and it is believed that minerals in solution were forced through the channels and passages so formed to deposit themselves in veins and host rock at greater or lesser distances from the earth's surface. The erosion of millions of years since that time of creative violence has worn away the surface rock to expose the granites and sometimes the ore deposits with them. These "surface showings" are what the ordinary prospector looks for and learns to recognize. They are most likely to be found along or near lines of contact between the intrusive granites and older volcanic or sedimentary rocks or in areas where there are signs of folds or faults; they are usually recognized by coloration or by other minerals that bear the metal sought or are likely to be associated with it, rather than by the presence of the metal itself in native state. Nearly all the world's important mines have been first discovered by surface showings of float, staining or outcropping.

Except in the far north and in the remote or inaccessible parts of the Coast Range, most of British Columbia's areas of exposed rock have been closely prospected. This does not mean that their possibilities have been exhausted; every miner knows that search near the sites of abandoned mining camps can be rewarding and there are many known mineral deposits that may be sooner or later made economically useful by improved transportation, cheap power sources or increasing world demand. There may even be undiscovered ore bodies in some of the most heavily prospected areas. But it is reasonable to suppose that the unprospected areas will sooner or later disclose ore bodies of important value.

The largest areas of intrusive rock in the province are in the Coast Range batholith, which extends from north to south through the entire length of the province, along the coast or paralleling it inland behind the Alaska Panhandle. The batholith is massive and comparatively uniform but its igneous rocks vary widely in age and composition, giving good promise of metallic mineral deposits at contacts with older rock. High elevations and rugged terrain have limited close examination of the rock exposed above timberline in many parts of the range, and heavy timber with overburdens of soil, gravels and broken rock has made prospecting very difficult in the more accessible areas. Logging operations are opening up and sometimes exposing the batholith at lower elevations. Helicopters will help greatly in prospecting the inner sections of the Coast Mountains and are already credited with one major discovery, at Granduc, which is expected to become an important copper producer.

In many other parts of the province that are known to have promising geological features, the forest overburden has greatly slowed prospecting. Once basic geology has been mapped, modern methods of aerial survey with magnetometer or electro-magnetometer can be used to cover extensive forested areas and direct ground search to the more favourable locations. The same methods can be used on the ground for more detailed work such as tracing rock formations and outlining faults or folds. While both aerial and ground methods penetrate only to shallow depths and indicate many unusual features that are quite barren of metal deposits or other useful minerals, their cumulative effect is an important addition to knowledge of the province as a whole; and where favourable formations are shown they are a useful, though expensive, stimulus to conventional methods of search.

These advances, together with the gradual opening up of the province by settlement and new transportation routes, give the "promise" of continuing mineral discovery real substance. Any sudden "unlocking of vast mineral wealth", as politicians and newspapers love to phrase it when singing the praises of some new development, is most unlikely. Discovery will, as always, be slow and painful and costly. But it is reasonable to hope that the province's immense areas of covered rock will sooner or later yield as many mineral deposits in proportion to their extent as have already been found in the much smaller areas of exposed rock.

Without enormous and unjustifiable expenditures, the province's mineral potential cannot be assessed more accurately than this, and without detailed knowledge of the potential any attempt at conservation, or rather "rationing the production of minerals", can make little sense. The logical course at present is to move ahead as economic and other circumstances permit, making discoveries, proving them wherever possible, working them as and when markets make it profitable to do so. There is good enough reason to believe that the production rates of most useful minerals can be maintained at a high level for many years to come; they should be adequate to allow for major export and still supply domestic needs in the face of the greatest foreseeable population increases. While it is true that such widely used base metals as copper, lead and zinc are quite scarce in terms of over-all world supply, the steady and rapid development of substitutes and alternatives is certain to continue under modern industrial conditions. The substitutes and alternatives are by no means always inferior; some offer strong special advantages, such as the lightness of aluminum in high-tension wires, and continued development may tend in time to make conventional metals less, rather than more, desirable. If prices should increase with increasing scarcity rather than decrease in the face of competition from substitutes, the province would still find itself in a favourable position. Increased prices would stimulate search and development and at the same time would bring into production many known mineral deposits that cannot now be economically worked.

Mining production in British Columbia falls under three main headings: metals, fossil fuels and industrial minerals. The fossil fuels have already been discussed under the section dealing with energy. Oil and natural gas clearly have a strong future as fuels and their mineral by-products will be available whenever there is a demand for them. Coal, which has played a large part in the provincial economy for over a hundred years, is in temporary eclipse. Some coal bodies will almost certainly be used to produce electrical energy at site. Others may yield synthetic liquid fuels if technological advances bring prices within competitive range of the petroleum fuels. But the immediate future offers little hope of a return to heavy and consistent production, since Alberta coals are already competing successfully in what is left of the limited domestic market.

Industrial minerals, which will be examined in detail later in this chapter, include many heavy and bulky substances, such as limestone, clay and shale, that are used in construction. Since their value is small in relation to bulk and weight, they are valuable mainly for domestic use near the point of origin. Cassiar asbestos, a long-fibred, high-quality grade which is in short supply and commands a high price, is a notable exception; almost the entire output is exported. Most of the indus-

TASU DEPOSIT

AN AERO-MAGNETIC CONTOUR MAP

This is a section of an airborne magnetometer survey of an area of Moresby Island, Queen Charlotte Islands, made by the B.C. Department of Mines. The contour lines form themselves into "anomalies" at points of high magnetic concentration, which can result either from metal deposits or from geologic or topographic effects. Frobisher Explorations Ltd. carried on further ground surveys of this area and discovered the Tasu iron ore deposit, which shows here at the upper left as the largest anomaly on the map.

trial chemicals produced by mining, like the construction minerals, cannot absorb high transportation costs, and also serve domestic needs. Consumption is expected to increase roughly in pace with population and reserves are generally considered adequate, though some of the more convenient deposits will in time become worked out.

The province's chief mineral values are in the non-ferrous metals – gold, silver, lead, zinc and copper have yielded about seventy-five per cent of the total value of mineral production to date. Minor quantities of antimony, bismuth, cadmium, indium and tin are recovered as by-products of other ores. Tungsten was produced in some quantity for several years until the Salmo operation closed in 1959 and mercury was produced from the Pinchi Lake deposits during the war and for some while after. At least one nickel deposit is known. Molybdenite, palladium, selenium, chromite, cobalt, magnesium and manganese have been produced for trial shipments or at times of high prices. Some platinum has been recovered with placer gold. Iron ore has been exported at the rate of several hundred thousand tons annually since the war.

Placer gold caused the rush of miners in 1858 – first the fine flakes on the sand and gravel bars of the Fraser River, later the nuggets and coarser gold that deep digging found on the blue clay and bed-rock of the creeks of the Cariboo. By 1863 placer mining had reached it peak yield of nearly four million dollars and from there it declined gradually until about 1880, then more sharply. Since 1900 its annual value has rarely exceeded a million dollars and at times has dropped to a quarter of a million or less. The 1957 yield of placer gold in the province was only a little over eighty thousand dollars, reflecting the discouraging effect of the controlled value of gold. Revaluation would certainly bring about increased activity and some increased yield, and it is at least possible that some new discoveries would be made.

Mining of lode gold began in the 1890's and production reached nearly three and a half million dollars by 1900. It reached a peak of over 22 million dollars in 1940 and now is holding fairly steadily at seven or eight million dollars.

Total gold production in British Columbia has been in excess of 500 million dollars. Gold occurs in many parts of the province and in a great variety of rocks, though only minor deposits have been found east of Kootenay and Upper Arrow Lakes. It is often in association with other minerals and some twenty per cent of the province's lode production is a by-product of base-metal mining. Some major gold-producers of the province have been the Silbak-Premier Mine, the Rossland properties and Surf Inlet Mines on Princess Royal Island, Sheep Creek, Hedley and Polaris-Taku, all of which are now inactive. Present production comes mainly from the Bridge River area and the Cariboo, and the Bralorne Mine at Bridge River is now the province's leading producer.

Like placer mining, lode-gold mining has been faced with a fixed price for its yield through a time of steadily increasing costs. Naturally this has forced a number of mines altogether out of production. The others have generally been forced to mine higher-grade ore in order to meet costs and stay in production. This represents serious and probably permanent loss. Should gold be revalued at a higher price, the low-grade ore which might have been profitably mined at the same time as the high-grade ore will probably still be uneconomic and will be left in the ground, thus shortening the lives of the mines.

It could be said that the whole future of gold-mining in the province rests in this matter of revaluation. Until the price is increased there can be little incentive to search for new deposits, much less to develop them, and the producing mines must inevitably find increasing difficulty in proving reserves of high-grade ore. Gold is not a particularly useful metal. It is beautiful, it serves as material for international poker chips and it is a money-producer within the limits set by the world's governments. Waste of low-grade deposits has none of the implications of later critical scarcity that may be in the wasted ore of the useful metals, but it does represent waste of what would have been a cash yield under the right circumstances.

The province's total yield of copper has so far been about the same as that of gold – approximately 500 million dollars, over one-sixth of the national total. Copper is found chiefly in the central and western parts, especially along the coast and islands and in the southern interior west of Nelson. Britannia Mine on Howe Sound has long been the principal copper producer of Western Canada and recent discovery of a new ore body suggests it will continue to produce well. Copper Mountain, near Princeton, Anyox, near Prince Rupert, and the Granby Mine at Phoenix and the Mother Lode Mine near Greenwood, have all been major producers. The Granduc property in the Unuk River area is a new development of promise, as are Craigmont and Bethlehem in the Merritt-Ashcroft area.

Copper prices have fluctuated widely in the years since the war and remain somewhat unstable. Any marked increase in price would bring response from the very large established copper-mining companies in other parts of the world and therefore might not hold for very long, but it would certainly produce activity in British Columbia. Some older developments might be brought back into production and there would be a sharp increase in prospecting which might lead to new discoveries. Since the Coast Range batholith has already yielded two large producers, Anyox and Britannia, and since copper showings are common throughout its length, new discovery of importance is a real possibility. Several copper-smelters have operated in the province at various times, but at present ease of water transportation favours the American smelter at Tacoma.

By far the most important mines of the province are the silver-lead-zinc properties in the south-eastern part. These have produced in total nearly a billion dollars worth of lead, almost the same value in zinc and over 250 million dollars in silver. These totals represent about ninety per cent of the lead, fifty per cent of the zinc and fifty per cent of the silver produced in Canada as a whole.

The south-eastern section of B.C. chiefly responsible for this very large production has had a relatively long history and has been intensively prospected. Outcropping at the site of the Bluebell Mine on Kootenay Lake, for instance, is said to have been first noticed by David Douglas, the botanist for whom the fir is named, in 1826. Father de Smet commented in 1845 on the "abundance of lead in many parts" of the Kootenay and noted further that "it is of such fine quality there is little doubt that it is mixed with a certain amount of silver." The prospectors came first in search of gold, and they found gold; but silver, lead and zinc have made the great mines.

Of them all, the Sullivan Mine at Kimberley is by far the largest lead-zinc mine, not only in B.C., but in Canada. It was first discovered in 1892, but for many years its complex sulphide ores could not be successfully processed. Since 1923, when new metallurgical processes were applied, the mine has been a steady and immense producer, yielding commercial quantities of cadmium, tin, antimony and bismuth as well as silver, lead and zinc. In large measure the Sullivan Mine supplies the big C.M.S. smelter at Trail and the whole southern interior of the province reflects its prosperity.

There are a number of other silver-lead-zinc properties in the Golden, Nelson, Slocan and Fort Steele mining areas, some of which are active only intermittently, at times of high prices. The Slocan area especially had many rich deposits which are, unfortunately, noted for their unpredictability. The Monarch and Kicking Horse mines, abandoned since 1952, were the only important metal mines so far discovered in the Canadian Rockies, where the thick cover of sedimentary rock has not been sufficiently eroded to reveal the batholith. Estella and several other mines were established in the rocks of the Purcell Group east of the Rocky Mountain Trench. Other mines are producing near Revelstoke and Invermere. The whole of this general south-east area of the province has been so thoroughly prospected that it is considered unlikely any new surface outcroppings remain to be discovered. But there is a very real possibility that new ore bodies will be found through the exploration work of active mines or by close re-examination of older properties, such as the Blue Bell.

Tungsten was produced at the Red Rose Mine near Hazelton and at the Emerald, Dodger and Feeney mines south of Nelson, which were the largest producers in Canada. Tungsten is also found in the Cariboo and Bridge River districts and small quantities have been shipped. Tungsten has only been produced in quantity in times of acute world shortage. 1958, the last full year of B.C. production, yielded two million pounds with a value of six million dollars, and represented ninety-five per cent of the Canadian total.

Mercury deposits have been found near Kamloops, in the Tyaughton Creek area and in the Pinchi Lake belt near Fort St. James. Mines in this last area produced over four million pounds during the Second World War and accounted for nearly all Canadian production. No mercury mines are active at this writing, in the year 1960.

Several small deposits of iron ore have been known for many years t
the southern coast and in the islands. Since 1951 several of these have b
oped and concentrated ore has been exported in some quantities. These
tite ores, some of which contain sulphur and copper, though the sulphu
often quite low. One of the better placed and more productive deposit:
ada Island in the Strait of Georgia. Bog iron deposits, built by the filte
sulphates through mosses and other vegetation, are found on the eas
Coast Mountains. Deposits near Terrace and on the Taseko River are estimated to
contain 500,000 and 670,000 tons of limonite ore respectively.

While there are no known deposits of iron ore in the province to compare with
the great eastern deposits that supply major steel industries, the small, high-grade
magnetite deposits are becoming increasingly important and are being rapidly expanded by intensive exploration and development work. Among the most important are those at Zeballos, Nimpkish Lake, Quatsino, Tasu Harbour, Harriett Harbour, Port Renfrew and Kennedy Lake, all of which occur in zones of lime silicates
along or near contacts between granite intrusions and limestone. There is much
favourable geology for this type of iron deposit along the coast and especially on
Vancouver Island; possibilities of further discoveries are considered excellent.
Though a steel mill on the coast is probably still years away, there is now little
doubt that iron reserves to support it can be found once the local market has expanded to justify the very large initial expenditure. In the meanwhile each new
development has its importance in producing revenue and employment as well as
in promoting road construction, harbour improvement and other works that open
up the country.

Antimony, bismuth, cadmium and tin are produced mainly as by-products of the
Sullivan Mine and though the totals are small, they represent a major part of Canadian production. Nickel is produced near Hope, and small quantities of molybdenum, cobalt and chromium have been produced from near Salmo, Hazelton and
Greenwood respectively.

This brief account gives some idea of the quantity and diversity of the metallic
minerals so far found in the province and tends further to support the promise that
new discoveries will be more or less constantly forthcoming. The rather large number of high-cost, low-grade mines at present inactive is by no means written off.
The future of many of them may be threatened by the development of alloys and
other substitutes or by the possibility of more economic, large-scale discoveries. But
the constantly expanding use of metals of all types, except possibly gold, makes it
far more likely that increased prices will sooner or later bring them back into
production.

In value, asbestos is by far the most important of the industrial minerals produced in the province. The Cassiar Asbestos property, the only significant producer,
is in the extreme north centre of the province, on the Liard watershed about sixty
miles south of the Yukon boundary. The mill was opened at this remote site in

1953 and since then production has steadily increased to the present yield of over thirty thousand tons annually with a value of about ten million dollars. The quality is high and the output is mainly exported.

Small quantities of barite, diatomite, flux, gypsum, mica, fluorite and larger quantities of sulphur are also produced. All these minerals, which have relatively low value for bulk, are available in larger quantities if demand increases.

Structural minerals such as limestone, clay, sand and gravel and stone are quite readily available in many areas and have so far felt little but the demands of local use. Some limestone is exported to the State of Washington and this market is expected to increase; growth of the pulp-and-paper industry within the province will increase use, as will any development in local manufacture of iron or steel; the cement industry also increases demand at a steady rate, more or less in keeping with growth of population. Many known deposits of limestone are in areas where there is as yet little demand, but indicated reserves of suitable stone near tidewater on the coast are considered to be "very great" and there is an adequate quarry near Trail, where significant demand is also felt.

Sand and gravel, rock and brick clays are also considered to be common and well-distributed throughout the province. No shortages are anticipated in the near future, which is hardly surprising in view of the generally rocky and mountainous nature of the country and its recent glaciation. Altogether the structural materials, including the manufacture of cement, brick, tile and similar products, produce about 25 million dollars a year.

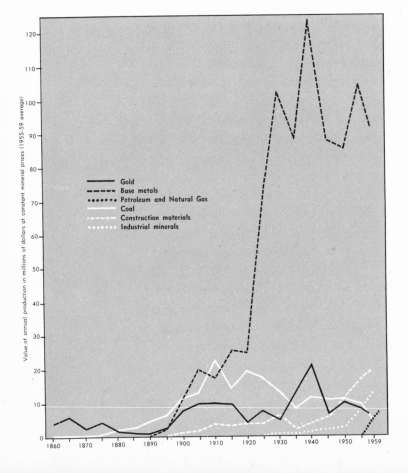

THE ANNUAL VALUE OF MINERAL PRO-
DUCTION FROM 1860 TO 1959. The early production has been adjusted to appear at the same dollar value as current production, so that the decrease in the value of the dollar over the years has been eliminated, and a truly relative picture of production can be seen on the graph.

extraction and use of minerals

SINCE MINERALS ARE NOT a renewable resource it follows that the closest man can come to sustained yield is by maximum use – that is to say, by maximum recovery of ore from the earth, maximum extraction of metals from ore, careful manufacture of the metals themselves and proper re-use of scrap. At the present time North American civilization, and industrial civilization generally, pursues only the first of these ideals and that not always. There is a profound belief, which may or may not be well founded, that technological progress will take care of the future. All the metals, it is true, are available in immense quantities in the oceans, and magnesium is already being commercially extracted from salt water. Bauxite and magnesite deposits, which yield aluminum and magnesium respectively, are very large and are available in many parts of the world; magnesite is found in B.C., bauxite is not. Beyond these known sources of metals that might be expected to meet any critical world shortage in the near future are the unknown but certainly considerable possibilities in alloys and substitutes that constant metallurgical research is bound to yield. There is also the distinct probability of further technical progress in mechanical aids to prospecting, in extraction processes and in the physical problems of mining itself.

The mining industry in British Columbia is generally considered to be progressive, venturesome and up-to-date; the province has many sound geologists, mining engineers and metallurgists, some of whom have pioneered developments in their own special fields. It is a mining area of importance and standing; yet the province's total of mineral production is quite small in world terms and it has little or no real influence on world prices.

It is said that an area with important mineral resources goes through three well-defined stages of development. In the first of these it is found to have an increasing number of mines shipping out ores or concentrates. In the second stage a smelting industry develops, producing metals to be manufactured into finished products elsewhere. In the third stage, which depends on population growth or the existence of large markets within economic reach, secondary industries are established to make finished products.

British Columbia can be considered to be in the second of these three stages, chiefly because of the great Consolidated Mining Company smelter at Trail, and to be just edging into the third stage. The Gordon Commission has anticipated the establishment of a second smelter and an iron and steel industry within the province by 1975.

Some idea of the progress that has been made in the handling of mineral ores during this century was given in a paper at the Seventh Resources Conference. A "representative" silver-lead-zinc mine operating at the rate of a thousand tons a day was considered; the ore of this hypothetical operation had a potential yield per thousand tons as follows:

SILVER	1600	ounces
LEAD	50	tons
ZINC	70	tons
IRON	190	tons
SULPHUR	168	tons
CADMIUM	680	pounds
BISMUTH	48	pounds

The paper then examined the actual yield that would have been realized from this amount and quality of ore during each decade of the century. During the first decade the yield per thousand tons would have been 29 tons of lead and 985 pounds of silver. The rest, well over half the value of the ore, would have been rejected as tailings.

During the second decade of the century a differential flotation process was worked out for recovery of lead and zinc from the ore. The process called for extremely fine grinding of the ore, which was then put in water with certain oils and reagents and stirred and bubbled to bring the lead to the surface. The lead was floated off; then, by use of different reagents, the zinc was floated off. The residue, consisting mainly of rock and iron sulphides, was discarded. A second process recovered still more zinc by use of sulphuric acid and electrolysis. These processes increased the yield of lead to 37 tons of the potential 50, realized 47 tons of zinc where none had been recovered before, increased the yield of silver to 1020 ounces and also yielded 237 pounds of cadmium.

The next development was recovery of zinc from lead slag and lead from the zinc residue. This was achieved by slag fuming, which left the lead but fumed off the zinc. The fumes were collected in the form of zinc oxide dust and the zinc itself was recovered from this by leaching with sulphuric acid. At this point the mine was realizing 44 tons of lead from the possible 50, 60 tons of zinc out of 70, 1270 ounces of silver and 475 pounds of cadmium. Its capitalization had increased from $4,300,000 to $11,600,000; its use of labour from 260 man-shifts per day to 479, its use of power from 900 kw. to 11,380 kw.

In burning off the sulphur to recover the iron and zinc, the mine was not only wasting a resource but was damaging vegetation in the surrounding area. The next two stages saw the development of a complicated series of processes which recovered sulphur dioxide, not only from the lead and zinc but from the iron ore as well. The yield from this is some 346 tons of fertilizer a day, plus complete recovery of the lead and zinc.

The final stage of development is recovery of iron from the iron calcine residue and the manufacture of pig-iron and steel. There are problems in this that were still unsolved at the time Mr. Morris presented his paper, but research has been continued and eventual recovery of the iron is now certain. When this stage is reached the mine's one thousand tons of ore will be employing 7½ times as much capital, three times as much labour, nearly 50 times as much electrical energy; and it will be yielding a little over six times the original cash return, a daily total of $54,000.

This account gives a clear idea of what has been and can be achieved by way of extracting maximum value from a suitable ore body. The ores involved in this particular achievement were highly complex and the metals extremely difficult to realize, but they were sufficiently abundant to justify the long and painstaking research that led to their complete recovery. Other ores present other problems, not all of which are yet solved, but it can be safely said that the province is well advanced in the second stage of development as a mineral-producing area.

The third stage, that of secondary industries producing finished metal products, cannot possibly be supported in a large metal-producing area with a population of only one and a half million people; but the province is making some advances and others are expected in the fairly near future. One matter of recurrent concern, which has been discussed at several Resources Conferences, is that of developing a steel industry. Steel is the most likely development because it is a low-cost product that must carry heavy freight charges to reach the province from large and efficient production units in the east. This gives an important advantage to small local producers and there are already small steel-producing units in Vancouver, as well as in Edmonton and Winnipeg. The amount of rolled iron and steel used in the province fluctuates considerably and can be noticeably affected in any year by a single major construction project. It has not so far exceeded a quarter of a million tons in any one year. This market could be well served by a small plant producing two or three hundred tons a day and it is considered probable that a plant of about this size will be built in the near future.

A local concern of this type is, of course, on a scale altogether different from major steel industry and unless protected in some way – in this case, by high freight rates – cannot possibly compete with large coke-fired blast furnaces, whose smallest economic size is about a thousand tons a day. Nor do the province's known iron ore reserves suggest that it is ever likely to become a major exporter of steel. Favourably located ore is estimated at about twelve million tons, with possibly a further twenty million tons that is either low-grade or remote from economic transportation routes. No doubt other deposits will be found, but there is nothing so far known that is comparable to the great iron ore deposits of eastern Canada and there is no geological evidence to suggest that any discovery of this order will be made. Establishment of a steel industry on the coast, where most of the suitable deposits occur, may well be delayed by a new steel plant at Kimberley.

There is a market for about 2000 tons a year of copper bars and tubing in the province, which might be filled by a local plant. But copper products are worth about 1200-1400 dollars a ton compared to a value of about a hundred dollars a ton for rolled-steel products, so the freight costs do not give anything like the same advantage in proportion. A copper extrusion and drawing plant has been planned for the province, but must depend on copper refined elsewhere and must be able to command a considerable outside market, since local demand is not sufficient to put the plant on an economic basis.

The primary aluminum produced at Kitimat is not usually considered as part of the province's mineral resource, since it is made entirely from imported bauxite; there is no possibility of bauxite discovery within the province, since the necessary tropical or semi-tropical climates, with resulting deep weathering of alkaline rocks, have never existed here. To date, the whole Kitimat production has been shipped to markets outside the province, but it is probably significant that the consumption of aluminum within the province has increased at a considerably faster rate than in the rest of Canada since the establishment of the plant. This has stimulated secondary fabricators of aluminum products, though the aluminum alloys used are brought into the province from elsewhere. It is reasonable to suppose that in time the local market will be large enough to justify production of alloys at Kitimat and so lead to more direct consumption of the local output.

These very small ventures give a clear idea of the province's tentative advances into the third stage of a mineral area's development, and some idea of the inhibiting factors. Practically all the lead and zinc produced in the province is shipped elsewhere and from 70-75 per cent of both metals is exported from Canada. The province's total consumption of these two metals would make only a tiny fraction of the total produced. Similarly, it has been estimated that the province could not use more than five per cent of the aluminum produced at Kitimat. This is a natural situation and not one that should be deplored; if areas of high population could not import raw materials to be manufactured for export, trade would be negligible and the province's minerals would stay in the ground.

This principle also extends back into the second stage of development. In the light of the tremendous technological advances that have been made in extracting minerals from ore during the past forty or fifty years, it is sometimes argued that no ores should be mined until a maximum yield can be extracted from them. At first glance, this idea seems to carry a sound burden of common-sense conservation, but it does not stand up to examination. It is essentially the same as saying that not a

Ultimate conservation: re-working old mine tailing for gold on Spruce Creek near Atlin. The shovel feed the portable washing plant and the drag-line shove in the foreground stocks the tailings on the side.
Colour photographs taken by the
B.C. Department of Mines and Petroleum Resource

One method of prospecting is to look for outcrops which are indicative of mineral deposits. The mountainside shown here is composed of iron oxide, which is characteristic of a mineralized rock—in this case molybdenum. It is located 40 miles west of Telegraph Creek on a tributary of the Stikeen River, and is quite an outstanding example of an outcrop.

stick of timber should have been logged until pulp mills, plywood plants and all the machinery of the great modern lumber industry had been developed; in which case, of course, none of it would have been developed and the timber would still be standing. If no lead had been mined in the province until the metallurgists had learned to extract zinc as well, both lead and zinc would still be in the rock. These are extremes of argument, perhaps dangerous in their simplicity. But Professor L. G. R. Crouch put the matter quite clearly at the Ninth Resources Conference. Discussing the possibility of leaving ore deposits "until a fairly complete recovery of the useful mineral content could be obtained," he said: "If this were done without duly considering the economic and technical factors involved, base metals and some other valuable minerals would soon be in short supply, and the very disruption of industry that the conservational measures were designed to forestall could be precipitated. A further unforeseen consequence could be the loss of much of the value of the minerals so carefully guarded if research should yield substitutes that were even better."

This brings us full cycle on the question of conserving minerals, back to the original concept that the industry must constantly probe ahead in search of new deposits and as constantly re-examine known deposits to see if they will lead to new ore bodies. Efforts such as these will maintain research and yield technical improvements. Even slag heaps and tailings can become valuable with new discoveries, as the Consolidated Mining and Smelting Company will shortly demonstrate by producing steel from the Sullivan Mine tailings, which are estimated to contain about 15 million tons of iron, though it should not be assumed from this that recovery from slag heaps and tailings is a common possibility.

It is important to remember that mining, in the last analysis, is an industrial gamble. Logging is a gamble in that the logger bets his timber, his equipment and his skill against the market price. Fishing is a gamble of somewhat the same type, but with the added difficulty of estimating and finding a raw material that is mobile and hidden from the eye. Mining is a search for static material, but material hidden in rock, often beneath a cover of soil or forest or glacial drift. Even when signs of an ore body have been found, its bulk and mass and direction nearly always remain hidden, its quality remains uncertain. Only by drifting and drilling into the rock at high cost can the miner hope to determine the size and value of his find and his only guide in this expenditure is the expert, but still imperfect, understanding that geologists and mining engineers may have of the mechanics of ore deposition and the inferences they may be able to draw from surface geology. If the miner's drifting and drilling are wrongly directed, he may lose everything; at the same time, the ore body he hoped to find from its original showing at the surface may be there all the while, in another direction or at some other depth; it may be rich and extensive, it may be too small or too low in grade or it may not be there at all.

But in spite of all this the possible rewards are still enough to keep men searching and gambling, backing their skill and judgment and experience against the geological uncertainties. Direct search and exploration are for the most part under-taken by private interests. Each year many individual prospectors go out into the hills, a number of them grubstaked in a small way by the provincial government. Companies send out both individual prospectors or scouts and survey parties. Dis-coveries are made in this way and knowledge slowly increases.

On a different scale is the systematic work done in the province by the Geologi-cal Survey of Canada and the more special and detailed survey work of the B.C. Department of Mines. The purpose of geological survey is to delineate broad geo-logical features and structures and to progress from this to more detailed work in areas that reconnaissance has suggested may be particularly favourable – in other words, to provide information that will constantly narrow the actual search for minerals and direct it or concentrate it in localities where it is most likely to be profitable. An example of the detailed work of the Provincial Department of Mines is the examination of a major gypsum deposit discovered near Windermere in 1947. Three seasons' work was needed to map all the known and possibly economic gyp-sum in the area; it yielded an estimate of five hundred million tons of gypsum, con-tributed much to the general knowledge of gypsum itself and incidentally provided information for petroleum exploration by its mapping and interpretation of Rocky Mountain structures.

Within survey and geological work of this kind there is always the effort towards better understanding of unsolved geological problems, the special problems of find-ing useful minerals and especially the factors which localize concentrations of metallic minerals. Essentially such work is both survey and research and it plays an important part in maintaining the rate of discovery that is needed to ensure the future of the industry.

The high cost of proving ore reserves is, perhaps, the greatest problem in the mining industry. It is difficult to see any possibility of sharp technological advance that will simplify this problem and as long as the problem remains as tough as it is, mining will always be a high-risk industry. It is also an industry of narrow mar-gins. A drop of a few cents in the market price of the base metals is enough to put some mines out of production; a period of high prices will bring many marginal mines into production. For these reasons taxation can readily affect mining produc-tion and perhaps delay discovery. New mines are helped by a certain number of tax-free years which encourage the proving of reserves. It has been suggested that development work might be exempted from sales tax on equipment and supplies, and there is no doubt that this would hasten the development of some prospects and it might also encourage exploration work in remote areas. But presumably the marginal farmer or logger or manufacturer might feel entitled to the same encour-agement and it is difficult to imagine that any government would care to risk such implications.

Export and import taxes on minerals are more direct and may have even more drastic effects. When a great metal-consuming country like the U.S.A. applies import duties to protect its own marginal or sub-marginal mines, it effectively inter-feres with the natural course of world prices and the natural progress of mining development. Smaller exporting nations can do nothing to protect themselves and the long-term result may well be an eventual critical shortage and unnecessarily high prices everywhere or else wholesale use of substitutes that leaves the higher-priced metals unused and useless in the ground. Taxes imposed by the domestic government to restrict export produce almost exactly the same hazards, and the risk of delaying exploration and development is particularly serious in a mineral area such as British Columbia.

While taxes may have restrictive effects and should be assessed with a careful regard to this, transportation is an even more important factor in mining develop-ment. A good showing of gold-copper or silver-lead-zinc within easy reach of a main transportation route will certainly justify exploration; proof of an ore body sufficient for three or four years' operation might well justify development and so facilitate further exploration, which might or might not reveal an extensive mine. The same showing at a considerable distance from a main transportation route would be unlikely to interest risk capital; if it did create interest it would be neces-sary to find ore in sufficient quantity to pay not only for the initial exploration and opening of the mine, but for a connecting link with the nearest transportation route and the cost of hauling over that link. From this it is easily seen that a railroad or major highway opening a new area may well create operating mines where there were none before. Miners have asked that consideration be given to this, where pos-sible, in planning the location of major routes; if it is possible to build a road or railroad through a geologically promising area rather than one less promising, the rewards for proper choice might well be very large.

Since mining activity is normally limited to quite small areas, conflicts with other resources are not serious. Mine tailings and effluents can be a problem and have at times caused pollution and obstruction in streams; this is easily controlled and should be controlled. Serious air pollution may be caused by smelting operations, but the experience of the Consolidated Mining and Smelting Company at Trail has shown that control is not only possible but directly profitable in increased recovery of minerals. Waste-disposal problems of these types are again likely to affect only marginal properties, since mechanical and technological solutions are always avail-able at some cost. Under modern conditions and in the light of experience in other areas, pollution must be considered bad resource management.

The removal of gravel from streams for various construction purposes is another abuse that seems to have little justification. Gravel is readily available in most parts of the province and streams simply offer an easier alternative to regular quarrying. Damage invariably results and is often progressive through later upstream shifts of the river bed. While it is possible that a closely controlled operation of this type might occasionally be justified, control is extremely difficult and would add considerably to cost.

These are fairly minor matters. The industry's most serious difficulties with other resource uses are probably those of access, and these are increasing. In the early days of the province the prospector was free to range at will and mining operations, then considered the most probable source of quick wealth and rapid development, commanded a general land-use priority. While this preferred position still exists, the miner sees himself limited by more intensive land use of every kind. Tree farm licences and public working circles complicate the use of timber for mining purposes. Private roads, replacing old trappers' and prospectors' trails destroyed by logging, often make access a matter of permission. Parks, almost by definition intolerant of other land uses, contain large acreages of alpine and subalpine lands that are favourable to prospecting. When and if development goes ahead, there may be problems of easement and compensation for right of way to be paid to other land users before necessary transportation links can be built. These are all signs of development and increasing population, and the problems they present are by no means insuperable. The old free miner is not quite so free as he once was, but his capacity to produce a high yield from a limited land area is still recognized and his priority, short of unnecessary damage to other resources, should remain high.

The province's mineral position, especially in regard to base metals, is good. It is already an important producer and exporter and geological indications suggest that new discoveries should be sufficiently rich and frequent to maintain this position for a long while to come. Since minerals are a non-renewable resource, they cannot be discussed in terms of sustained yield but the province is steadily advancing towards realization of maximum yield from what is available. It is bound to remain an exporter of metals for a very long while to come and any attempt to restrict export by taxation or other legislation in the hope of "conserving" metals until population growth justifies local fabrication is likely to be self-defeating. Such measures tend to restrict both exploration and development and could well leave the province eventually with smaller known reserves of ore than would have been the case under unlimited export.

The case for further exploration seems a strong one. While the province as a whole has not so far revealed major mineral belts to equal those of eastern Canada, it is an established mineral area. At present it must compete for exploration capital with such well-established areas as the great iron fields of Ontario, Quebec and Labrador and the nickel deposits of Sudbury, Ontario, and Thompson, Manitoba. Most of the province is known in some degree and most of its exposed rock has been examined and re-examined over a period of many years. Large areas of intrusive rock carry heavy cover of forest or glacial till or both and these have not been exhaustively examined. The remoteness of some areas, especially in the Coast Range batholith, has limited exploration to date. Further discoveries of importance are certain and the possibility of major discoveries cannot be ruled out. These factors, at least for the time being, must take the place of full-scale inventory and may be considered to justify continued production at whatever rates are made possible by world markets.

recreation: general CHAPTER 19

RECREATION FILLS A VERY LARGE part in the life of mankind and covers an almost infinite variety of activities and interests. A people's greatness is measured in its literature, music, painting, sculpture and philosophy, and in the development of the ephemeral arts. Unless it has used its natural resources to produce and record human advances through these means, it is nothing more than a biological incident, with about the same significance as a successful herd of elk or a well-adjusted run of salmon. In a modern civilization, film, radio and television provide additional means of expression for the same fundamental arts. Under most civilizations festivals, athletic games and other forms of mass entertainment also contribute to the means of expression and recreation, though they are often signs of climax and decadence. Ideal recreation implies participation, a great body of true amateurs who share everything except the genius of the master practitioners.

These forms of recreation are essentially artificial except in that they grow out of man himself, his needs and his spirit. They do not directly make use of any natural resource except man himself and so are more properly considered elsewhere.

The "natural" recreational resources are based on the land itself and their use is generally called "outdoor recreation" to distinguish it from the artificial kinds. They include all those natural aspects of his world in which man finds and takes enjoyment. Sunset and moonrise, start of leaf in spring, turn of leaf in fall, the glory of ocean surf and the shine of white mountains against blue sky, wind and rain and birdsong, the whole range of plant and animal life, the soil and the rocks themselves, are all resources within this meaning, universal things and simple things that lift the heart and touch the soul of man even in the midst of his most urgent preoccupations. Philosophers of recreation believe that such things are so much a part of man's being that he cannot live fully or even comfortably without them. The whole history of man, his art and his culture, suggests they are right.

Arising out of this is the proposition that to-day's intense and growing demand for outdoor recreation reflects the suppression of this aboriginal need in an increasingly urban civilization.

In considering this matter Canada, which is still a relatively underpopulated country, has an immense amount of guiding experience to draw upon in every highly developed country in the world, but the most pertinent experience is probably that of the United States. Here population growth, industrial growth, increase of leisure, increase of wealth and improvement of transportation facilities have all taken place at an almost inconceivable rate. What was a vast and sparsely settled country, full of superb and almost undeveloped recreational areas within the present century, is already faced with immensely serious difficulties in providing its citizens with satisfactory opportunities for outdoor recreation. Streams, lakes and hunting areas are generally crowded and have far too often been seriously damaged by badly calculated industrial or urban development. Beaches and waterfront lands have been too often and easily alienated from the public domain. Many parks, both state and national, are already feeling the pressures of excessive use. It may be that the country can and will solve these problems, at least in some measure. But it is a critical situation and likely to prove extremely costly. One expert has estimated that "perhaps $50 billion or more [will have to be spent] just for buying and improving [recreational] land between now and the year 2000."

Canadian and British Columbian outdoor administrators and enthusiasts have long watched the developing American situation with a keen awareness that the same factors which brought it about are operating with almost equal force on this side of the forty-ninth parallel. It is true that American experience is a guide and that the pattern and hazards of development are much clearer than they were a few years ago; but someone else's experience is never the best teacher and industrial ruthlessness, political short-sightedness and public apathy have been and still are problems here exactly as they were and are in the U.S., even though they may be less in degree.

The phenomenon of sudden and massive demand for outdoor recreation has been traced to many causes. Increased leisure through the 40-hour week and holidays with pay, high wages and easy mobility through almost universal use of the automobile obviously have had their effect and will continue to do so with progressively increasing force. But these things are not so much causes as facilities; they might have been used for quite different purposes. The real causes lie deeper and almost certainly reflect, as already suggested, the highly artificial nature of modern civilization and the monotonous, unexacting nature of much urban work. In other words, the demand reflects a real need, intimately connected with the general health and well-being of the community.

This is an extremely important concept. It is of a piece with the realization by many modern employers that a labour force is attracted not merely by wages and working conditions, but by general living conditions and recreational opportunities within reach of the plant. A plant must, of course, be placed in logical relation to its raw materials, markets, power sources and other requirements, but where these facilities are equal, and in some instances where they are not, the wise investor will choose the site with the better social and recreational facilities. Considered in this light, as well as in the light of physical and mental health, recreation becomes an important economic factor. The real importance of the recreational resources is not in the fact that their use helps to support a wide range of businesses and industries, from hotels and gas stations to sporting-goods manufacture and public transportation, nor in the tourist dollars attracted from other provinces or countries, but in the direct return of pleasure, relaxation and health to the citizen. What might be called the "exportable surplus" is available for the tourist and usefully balances the expenditures of citizens who seek recreation abroad; the partial support of many useful services is a valuable, though incidental, return. The extent, quality and proper use of the outdoor recreational resources should be considered primarily in terms of what they can do for the needs of the province's own residents.

The availability of outdoor recreational opportunity was pretty well taken for granted throughout North America until quite recently. Parks were set aside mainly with the idea of preserving perfect samples of primitive ecology and with the idea that public use would be protected for all time. The problem at first was to attract the public to the parks at all. This emphasis has long since changed in the United States and the problem now is how to protect the parks and maintain the values they were designed to preserve in the face of the immense public demand. Use of the great U.S. national parks has increased twenty to thirty times since 1920 and is expected to increase to thirty or forty times the present figure in the next forty years. At the same time, recreational use of lands outside park areas is already reaching the point of reducing returns – overcrowding and competition tend to inhibit exactly the sense of freedom and relaxation that the outdoors should provide.

In British Columbia, use of the major provincial and national parks is not yet nearly so intensive and in many instances only limited development of park areas has been undertaken. Use of smaller parks, especially those with camping and picnicking facilities, is very heavy indeed and annual additions to the provincial system have so far been unable to keep up with demand. Recreational use of land outside park areas is heavy enough to make restriction of access through other uses, such as forestry and ranching, a major issue. The demand on fish and wildlife stocks and hunting and fishing areas within easy reach of the main urban centres, especially on the Lower Mainland, is already excessive and is forcing intensive management policies.

British Columbia has an enormous potential for outdoor recreation and it could fairly be said that the total resource has so far been little used, little developed and little damaged. Because the potential is so large and has so far been taken for granted, recreation is the least understood and in many ways the least protected of the resources. Because the potential covers practically the whole province, it comes constantly into conflict with other resource uses. Because it covers so many facets of use, it is difficult to assess. Because its best and most important uses do not produce a direct cash return, it is difficult or impossible to evaluate.

Constant effort has been made, by surveys and systems and theories, to put a cash value on recreational resources. "Estimated expenditures" of non-resident tourists in British Columbia, for instance, are quoted at an annual figure of about a hundred million dollars. The State of Washington has calculated that anglers spend some 70 million dollars annually within its borders in pursuit of their sport and compares this with the average annual return of only 20 million from the commercial fisheries. Other experts have tried to estimate how much recreation seekers would pay for the rewards they seek if they had to pay for them. Still others have tried to get at the "value added" – that is to say, the difference between the cost of services rendered and the amount paid for them as a result of recreational attractions.

All of this, with the possible exception of the expenditure of the non-resident tourist, is largely meaningless. That figure has some bearing on the exportable surplus of recreational value in the province, and in most years it is more than matched by the expenditures of British Columbians who go elsewhere in search of recreation. In other words a perfectly natural international trade in recreation exists and the province usually ends up with an adverse balance.

What cannot be assessed is the value realized from recreational opportunity by the residents of the province in the form of physical and mental health and human happiness. It is impossible to assess the part played by recreational opportunities in attracting settlers and distributing the work force through the province. No one can measure the added value of the young doctor or lawyer or school-teacher who chooses service in a small community largely because of its recreational values. No one can assess the value of abundant outdoor recreational opportunity on the character and thinking of the people of the province as a whole.

The best indication of the value of the recreational resources is in the demand for them. It is clearly expressed by hunting and fishing pressures, in crowded highways and crowded campsites, in the constant and constantly increasing pressure for

Rockhounding

1. Travertine from Merritt.
2. Banded Agate from Monte Lake.
3. Conglomerate from Fraser River.
4. Agate from Queen Charlottes.
5. Hausmanite from Keremeos.
6. Thulite from Big Ben Creek in Cariboo.
7. Jade from Lilloett.
8. Porphyry from Fraser River.
9. Dumorturite from Fraser River.
10. Rhodonite from Vancouver Island.
11. Quartzite from Fraser River.
12. Nephrite from Bridge River.
13. Plume Agate from Robins Creek.
14. Petrified Wood from Kamloops.
15. Chrysoprase from Fraser River.
16. Banded Jasper from Bridge River.

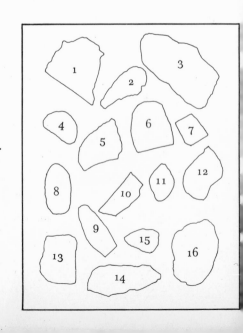

Wild Tiger Lily
LILIUM COLUMBIANUM

White Rhododendron
RHODODENDRON ALBIFLORUM

Arnica
ARNICA

Mock Orange
PHILADELPHUS GORDONIANUS

Calypso
CALYPSO BULBOSA

Poison Camas
ZIGADENUS VENENOSUS

Paint Brush
CASTILLEJA SP.

Shooting Star
DODECATHEON

Mountain Daisy
ERIGERON PEREGRINUS VAR. CALLIANTHEMUS

Tow-head Baby
ANEMONE OCCIDENTALIS

Stonecrop
SEDUM STENOPETALUM

Rabbitbush
CHRYSOTHAMNUS NAUSEOSUS

Spotted Knapweed
CENTAUREA MACULOSA

Common Cactus
OPUNTIA POLYACANTHA

Three-spot Lily
CALOCHORTUS APICULATUS

Columbine
AQUILEGIA FORMOSA

Mariposa Lily
CALOCHORTUS MACROCARPUS

Orange Honeysuckle
LONICERA CILIOSA

Rhododendron
RHODODENDRON MACROPHYLLUM

Milkweed
ASCLEPIAS SPECIOSA

Touch-me-not or Jewelweed
IMPATIENS NOLITANGERE

St. John's Wort
HYPERICUM SCOULERI

Trillium
TRILLIUM OVATUM

Large Sea Cucumber
STICHOPUS

Rubber Worm
NEMERTEAN

Lined Chiton
ISCHNOCHITON

Sandpaper Star
HENRICIA LEVIUSCULA

Pink Star
PISASTER BREVISPINUS

Anemone
CRIBRINA ELEGANTISSIMA

LEFT: *Bat Star or Sea Bat* PATIRIA MINIATA
CENTRE: *Sun Star* PYCNOPODIA HELIANTHOIDES

Leather Star
DERMASTERIAS IMBRICATA

Common Star
PISASTER OCHRAECEUS

Crab
CANCER PRODUCTUS

Kelp or Spider Crab
PUGETTIA PRODUCTA

Rough Piddock
ZIRFAEA PILSBRYI

access to lakes, streams, salt-water beaches, forest and range land and alpine slopes. It is expressed in the purchase of camping equipment, boats, diving equipment, skiing equipment, cameras, guns and ammunition, fishing tackle and all the other paraphernalia of outdoor recreation. Fashion or habit or choice may make changes within the demand, but no one doubts that the demand itself will go on increasing, rapidly and unfailingly, throughout the rest of this century and into the next. And no one seriously doubts that it must be met.

Given reasonable care, the outdoor recreational resources are self-renewing and perpetual. The actual demands on them by recreation seekers are seldom damaging provided the pressures can be reasonably well distributed. The most serious threats usually come from other forms of land and water use – industrial development of many kinds, residential settlement, hydro-electric flooding, water pollution, large-scale ranching, any uses that seriously modify the natural habitat of wild creatures, damage scenery or restrict access. In most instances, careful planning and sound management can largely compensate for or limit damage; sometimes, when an industrial use will cause major damage, an alternative recreational area may provide a satisfactory substitute for what is lost; when damage to recreation outweighs the probable industrial gain, industry must be turned to an alternative project.

It is unhappily true that the greatest industrial pressures and the greatest recreational pressures are all too likely to occur together. Recreational assets near cities and major settlements are of immense value because they permit residents to use them after work, on short holidays and at weekends. Expanding cities rarely plan soon enough to protect them and they disappear exactly when they are most needed. Vancouver's crippling loss of the Capilano and other North Shore streams and the wildfowl areas of the Fraser estuary are examples of unimaginative planning. Few cities anywhere can have have been developed with less regard for the protection of recreational values, and even the park and playground facilities within the city itself are well below normal standards in both quantity and distribution.

While some recovery of recreational facilities close to the city may be possible in the future and far more aggressive planning of city parks and playgrounds is inevitable, it remains true that the most important recreational areas will always be at some distance from main centres of population. Improvement of roads and other means of transportation will reduce travelling time to major parks such as Garibaldi, and extensive development will help to distribute the use of these to best advantage. Some recreational needs, such as winter sports and the summer enjoyment of alpine country, will be well served in this way; but the ready enjoyment of all forms of outdoor activity that British Columbians have long taken for granted is bound to become progressively more difficult for city dwellers.

Fishing and hunting are the obvious and probably the major forms of outdoor recreation in the province. Both have long histories of use and have contributed much by attracting settlers and making the province well known in other countries. Both are important factors in the tourist trade, but fishing is considerably the

The colour photographs of the wild flowers and
marine life were taken by David J. Martin of Vancouver.

more important of the two; it is estimated that visiting sports fishermen spend well over five million dollars a year in the province.

Boating, often combined with fishing, has become immensely popular during the past few years, since the introduction of reliable outboard motors and low-priced planing hulls. It is probably the fastest-growing form of recreation and will call for constantly increasing facilities such as marine parks and campsites. Other popular forms of activity that take people widely through the province are camping, hiking, skiing, swimming, photography, horseback riding, rock-hunting – a new, but fast-growing sport – and the search for historical sites. All these are desirable uses and entitled to every consideration. But it is important to remember that a very large proportion of recreation seekers, while they might tentatively identify themselves with one or other of these more or less active pursuits, are simply in search of rest and relaxation. They find these elements of restoration in scenery, in chance observations of nature and wildlife, in easy, unhurried travelling to new sights and simply in being away from the cares and routines of home and work. This last group may well be the largest and most important of all and it may also be the most demanding, if only because the success or failure of the holiday will be judged by its total impression.

Until. recently the recreational resources were administered in British Columbia by several different departments of government. Fish and wildlife were the care of the Attorney-General, parks were the responsibility of the Forest Service under the Minister of Lands and Forests and tourists were the care of the Department of Trade and Industry. This administrative weakness was examined in some detail at the 6th Resources Conference and establishment of a single ministry with responsibility for all the recreational resources was strongly recommended. Since that time the Ministry of Recreation and Conservation has been established and unified control is assured. The new department has made for greatly improved planning and a considerably more aggressive approach to management. While the recreational resources will probably always be at some disadvantage in competition with other resource uses, this consolidation of authority and responsibility has undoubtedly strengthened their position. As the experience of the department grows, much more closely integrated planning for both protection and development of the recreational resources will become possible and the province should have an excellent chance of keeping pace with the inevitably increasing demands.

While the true value of recreation, and even its total economic value to the state, will always be impossible to assess with anything approaching accuracy, its simple contribution to the economy as a whole by redistribution of wealth is roughly measurable. The travel and vacation business is ranked as the first industry in fifteen states of the Union and the second in nine others. In Canada as a whole, this business is rated at a billion dollars annually and in British Columbia at over a hundred million, which makes it the fourth largest resource-based industry. The prediction has been made that within ten years it will be second only to forestry.

parks and recreational land CHAPTER 20

PARKS ARE THE MOST tangible and in some ways the most valuable of outdoor recreational assets. Essentially a park is an area whose natural attractions are so strong that it has been permanently set aside for the use and enjoyment of the public. In resource use parlance, recreation is the prior and often the sole use compatible with sustained yield of the attractions that make the area desirable.

Parks may be of all sizes and serve many purposes, from untouched wilderness areas to highly used campsites and picnic grounds. On the North American continent they were originally conceived to preserve spectacular values for future generations, and it is unlikely that their earliest proponents dreamed of the intensive use they would be put to within so short a time. Most of the larger Provincial Parks in British Columbia are still fulfilling this function of preservation rather than use, not because they would not be used if developed and made accessible, but because the money for development has not so far been available.

It is axiomatic that park areas must be set aside long before they are needed, otherwise population growth and industrial development will inevitably alienate the land and destroy its values. But it has been shown again and again that land so set aside is far from inviolable, whatever protections the original legislators may attempt to provide. The very fact that it is not immediately put to use exposes it to attack; and the utter impossibility of setting cash values on recreational resources often makes park areas seem doubly attractive to other resource users. British Columbia has already suffered losses of this sort and some weaknesses in the present park system are attributable to them. But growing public conscience and more direct ministerial responsibility offer reasonable hope that existing park areas can be protected until they are developed for use. Once developed and in use, the risk of destructive encroachment is very much reduced.

The province has four National Parks, all in the eastern or south-eastern part.

All four are mountainous, with superb scenery, and three of them, Yoho, Glacier and Kootenay, are more than 300,000 acres in area. The smallest, Mount Revelstoke Park, is 64,000 acres. Yoho and Kootenay are on the western slopes of the Rockies, Glacier and Mount Revelstoke are in the Selkirks. Three of the four are accessible by road and railroad. The fourth, Glacier, is accessible only by railroad, but will soon be opened also by the Trans-Canada Highway, probably in 1961.

These parks were first conceived as railroad parks – the railroad opened beautiful country that plainly needed protection. Together with Banff and Jasper National Parks on the Alberta side, and Hamber and Mount Robson, two large British Columbia Provincial Parks, they protect a tremendous segment of the Eastern Cordillera. In keeping with the idea of protection rather than use, the National Parks are remote from main centres of population – about 500 miles distant, for instance, from Vancouver and the Lower Mainland – but in spite of this their use has increased enormously in the years since World War II. Visitors to Kootenay Park increased from 28,000 in 1945 to over a quarter of a million in 1955. Use of overnight campgrounds also increased about ten times in the same period.

The National Parks are well managed and quite highly developed. Facilities of all kinds are being constantly increased. Plant life and wildlife are rigidly protected, no hunting is allowed and every effort is made to preserve a natural state. A low scale of fees is charged for various services and uses. These parks are administered by the National Parks Service of the federal Department of Northern Affairs and National Resources.

In spite of their all-round excellence and magnificent scenery, it is obvious that the National Parks do not in themselves represent anything approaching an adequate park system for the province as a whole. While most residents of the province will probably visit them sooner or later they are too remote, even under conditions of modern highway travel, for short holiday visits or for regularly repeated visits. Concentrated in the south-east corner, they present only one facet of the immense variety the province has to offer.

Presumably the federal government is well aware of this. From time to time there have been indications that federal authorities would be willing to consider taking over other park areas provided these were offered to it by the provincial government free of encumbrances – timber berths, mineral claims and other private holdings. It has been estimated that it would cost something in excess of one million dollars to free Garibaldi Provincial Park of all encumbrances and offer it to the federal government for development; but this might well be a very good bargain, since full development of the park would certainly cost very much more than a million dollars. It would probably cost almost as much to free any other major park of private holdings, and provincial governments have shown a reluctance to take action not only because of this, but because assignment of an area to National Park status would permanently restrict its development for any use except recreation. The reluctance is natural at this early stage of the province's development, but it is unfortunate if it means that parks which could be developed remain un-developed, and still more unfortunate if it means, as it has in the past, that any possibility of major industrial development in a provincial park area may take priority over recreational use.

The Provincial Parks have gradually grown into a system, still far from complete and with serious weaknesses, but one that is flexible, adaptable and open to further growth. This system is made up of seven major parks, ranging from about 180,000 to 2½ million acres, a few intermediate parks varying from three or four thousand acres up to about sixty thousand and about 140 small parks more or less strategi-cally located to provide campsites, picnic grounds or protection for single outstand-ing recreational attractions. The rapid and constructive increase in these smaller parks is shown in the total figures for the provincial system. In 1956 there were 75 parks with a land area of almost 8 million acres; in 1958, 132 parks with an area of 8,418,000 acres; in 1959, 149 parks with an increase in total area of less than three thousand acres. About ten more small parks will be added to the system during 1960.

The three largest parks in the province are Hamber, Tweedsmuir and Wells Gray, with areas of 2.43, 2.3 and 1.3 million acres respectively. All three are Class B parks and Tweedsmuir, until recently, was one of the largest wilderness areas in North America. Boundary revisions since the construction of the Nechako Dam have reduced its area by over a million acres. A Class B rating permits other re-source uses such as logging and mining provided they are not "detrimental to the recreational value of the area", and its primary purpose is to protect extensive wil-derness areas for which no early development is planned. The degree of protection provided by this rather vague classification is highly questionable since Tweeds-muir has not only lost a million acres, but has had its most important recreational values completely destroyed by industrial development. The intention to protect them is clearly stated in the legislation, but so far has been honoured as much in the breach as in the observance.

Class A parks are the backbone of the provincial system and are protected from the cutting or sale of timber "except as such cutting and incidental sale may, in the opinion of the Deputy Minister, be necessary or advantageous in developing or improving the parks or protecting and preserving the major forest values of the park for the enjoyment of the public." They are considered to be areas highly suit-able for immediate development.

Three of these parks, Garibaldi, Strathcona and Mount Robson, have areas of half a million acres or more; Manning Park has 180,000 acres. Garibaldi, almost at Vancouver's back door, Manning on the Hope-Princeton highway and Strath-cona on Vancouver Island, are all well placed to serve large centres of population. Mount Robson is most remote, but makes a valuable link between Jasper National Park in Alberta and Hamber Provincial Park, and protects a splendid scenic area on the British Columbia slope of the Rockies. Kokanee Glacier, 64,000 acres, Mount

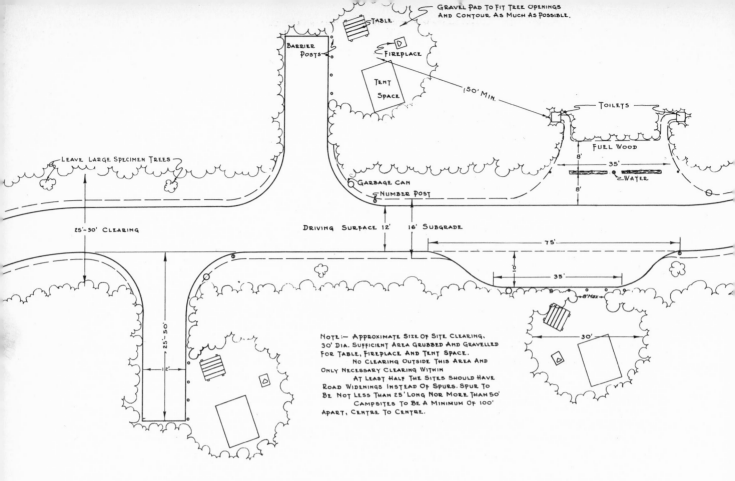

Assiniboine, 13,000 acres and Mount Seymour, 9000 acres, are valuable Class A parks of intermediate size; Seymour, near Vancouver, and the large (22,000-acre) Class C park, Silver Star, near Vernon, are both well placed to meet the demands of existing populations.

The remaining Class A parks, varying in size from 2½ to 3500 acres, serve a wide range of recreational purposes. Many are ideal camp and picnic sites, with fishing, swimming or other recreational opportunities. Many are centred on single outstanding assets, such as the three hundred acres of virgin rain-forest in MacMillan Park, the sand beach of Kokanee Creek near Nelson, the famous rock in Sir Alexander Mackenzie Park near Ocean Falls, the ancient rock carvings of tiny Petroglyph Park near Nanaimo. Nearly all are accessible and highly used and it is to be expected that many others will be added to the system as communications improve; some will be created from government reserves as demand develops while other desirable areas, at present in private hands, are likely to be recovered by gift or purchase.

A third group of Class C Provincial Parks is designed to provide the rough equivalent of city parks in unorganized territory. Most are picnic grounds, community play areas or small beach areas and vary from two to twenty or thirty acres, though a few are considerably larger. They are administered by local park boards, but have the same statutory protections as Class A parks.

The very large increase in boating during the past few years has led to the devel-

Although the Provincial Government camp-sites are disarmingly rustic in appearance, a great deal of planning goes into each of them. The plan on the opposite page shows the basic detailing involved in several camping units and the photograph alongside shows one of the occupied units.

opment of marine parks at Sidney Spit on Sidney Island, Tent Island near Chemainus, Montague Harbour on Galiano Island, Rebecca Spit on Quadra Island and at Harwood Point on Texada Island. Additional sites have been acquired at Keats Island and other points, and many early developments are planned.

All government lands fronting on fresh or salt water are reserved from alienation until their recreational possibilities have been assessed by the Department of Recreation and Conservation. This should ensure that no further losses of public access to good recreational areas will occur. At the same time the department is steadily surveying lands so reserved and selecting from them additional parks and campsites.

Campsites, whether marine or inland, are the most pressing need at present, as demand far exceeds supply. Four hundred and thirty-seven family-size camp units were developed in 1959, and five hundred more are planned for 1960, bringing the total to 2755; but even with this total the province has only half as many units in relation to population as are available in the neighbouring states of Oregon and Washington and the neighbouring province of Alberta. Near large centres of population the proportion is even worse – in 1957, for instance, Seattle had within a 75-mile radius of the city one campsite to every two hundred people, while Vancouver had one campsite to every 3200 people in the same radius. The comparison is not strictly fair, since Vancouver is bounded by the Strait of Georgia on the west and the highly developed agricultural lands of the Fraser Valley in the east while the

forty-ninth parallel cuts off the southern radius, and it can be considerably modified within a few years by wise planning and judicious land purchase; but it is a
good example of how swiftly recreational needs can become a problem even in
what is apparently a sparsely populated country. Millions of acres under reserve in
areas remote from population centres are not the answer to everything, even though
they may be important to the future. Small but desirable sites near centres of population are of tremendous importance in any over-all plan. Once these have been
alienated from the Crown their recovery is slow and costly or sometimes impossible.

While the shortage of public campsites is immediate and pressing, it is by no
means the only weakness in the Provincial Parks system. Considering its enormous
length of coastline the province has, as yet, very little sea frontage specifically set
aside for park use. The shoreline is generally steep and rocky, often with mud flats
off the river mouths and only a few stretches of shingle or sand beaches. The
Crown owns some six thousand miles of the seven-thousand-mile total shoreline,
and all this is now held under reserve from alienation until its recreational potential has been assessed. But it is unfortunately true that much of the most useful and
strategically placed shoreline is already in private hands. The finest beach in the
province is Long Beach, between Ucluelet and Tofino on the west coast of Vancouver Island; here and at Florencia Bay, just to the south, the Crown has only
four miles of frontage backed by about 320 acres, but there is some hope of acquir-
ing a much larger area with several miles of frontage. Along the east coast of Vancouver Island and on the mainland and island shores of the Strait of Georgia,
where the greatest demand is bound to be felt because of population pressures and
climate, most of the good beaches are already privately held.

The states of Washington, Oregon and California together have more than 560
miles of publicly owned sea frontage on a coastline only half as long as British
Columbia's and this is already considered inadequate. British Columbia has about
fifty miles of sea frontage set aside for park purposes and some two or three miles
in developed parks. The situation is not really a close parallel to that of the Pacific
states because enormous lengths of the province's coastline are not accessible by
land and will not become so in the foreseeable future. But increasing marine use
emphasizes the need to reserve beaches and anchorages for the public while it is
still possible to do so. Wherever there is a possibility that roads will come through
to the coast or travel along it, public sea frontage will certainly be needed. Along
both coasts of Vancouver Island some recovery of alienated lands is essential. Present surveys of Crown-owned waterfront should turn up many desirable park sites
to be reserved for future development, and it is not unreasonable to believe that
British Columbians will always enjoy a proper share of public sea frontage.

The present shortage of waterfront parks is essentially a part of the other great
weakness in the system – excessive concentration of parklands in alpine areas. The
truth is that the province is extremely short of valley lands or lands at low altitude,
and competition for such lands among the various resource uses and for residential

purposes is very great. Since spectacular scenery is usually associated with mountainous areas, it has been the most natural thing in the world to push the parks back into the alpine country where hundreds of thousands of unneeded acres can act as "conscience-savers" – great green blotches on the map, haloed by vague plans for a distant future, that lull everybody into supposing that recreational needs are well provided for, exactly as the noble mass of Stanley Park has lulled the citizens and councillors of Vancouver into believing there was little need for local community parks properly spaced throughout the city.

Even where valley land at relatively low altitude has been set aside within the parks, it has often been subject to attrition by industrial claims long before the time had come for recreational development. Tweedsmuir Park and Strathcona Park are excellent examples of this. The most important single value of Tweedsmuir Park was in its great circle of lakes – Ootsa, Whitesail, Eutsuk and Tetachuk – which could readily be travelled by boat or canoe. The level of this wilderness waterway was raised by the Nechako Dam in 1954 without any prior clearing of timber or any attempt to preserve lakeshore values. As a result the main way into the park and most of its potential high-use area has been completely lost. Subsequent southward extension of its boundaries has brought some new values into the area, but nothing to compensate for the loss. No new plan of development has yet been attempted.

The main value of Strathcona, the only large-scale park on Vancouver Island, was in Buttle Lake, the long, narrow, mountain-bordered lake that stretched back into its heart at an elevation of only 700 feet. Here also was a high-use waterway and, under the dense rain-forest conditions of the coast, the area of highest value for wildlife of all kinds, as well as the only relief from coniferous timber. Although most careful clearing was undertaken at considerable cost and although the lake was raised only nine feet above natural high water, the loss in scenic, recreational and wildlife values has been very great; on all but the brightest days the lake has the gloomy appearance of a reservoir and the normal draw-down of storage slows and limits shoreline regrowth that would be of value to the original wildlife. The new lake, with its extension in Upper Campbell Lake, can still provide a good deal of recreation, if only because no similar area is available. An access road has been provided from the foot of Upper Campbell to the foot of what was formerly Buttle Lake, but from a management point of view this is a liability rather than an asset. Extensive boundary revisions are necessary and it will be some while before a satisfactory plan of development can be worked out; premature access will make proper controls much more difficult to establish when the time comes.

Wells Gray is still another of the large parks that is threatened by hydro development. A system of five dams, varying from 140 to 500 feet in height, has been planned for the main watershed, necessitating the clearing of more than ten thousand acres of timber and brush. There can be no doubt that these undertakings would make extreme changes in the character of much of the park area and would adversely affect wildlife and other values. They form an important part of the Fraser River Basin development plans.

These examples emphasize the extreme competition for use of the province's limited valley lands and the very precarious nature of the protection afforded to Provincial Parks. While it is true that reservoirs do offer some recreational values, these represent gain only in arid or semi-arid country. In country that is mountainous and heavily forested, losses far outweigh any possible gains and all projects should be weighed in this light. It may be that the province cannot afford to assign any valley lands for recreational use; if so, the decision should be reached with open eyes and some sort of constructive effort should be made to compensate for losses. At the present rate of attrition none of the major Provincial Parks will have much to offer except alpine areas within a few years.

The present distribution of Provincial Parks also leaves much to be desired. The mainland coast has only one park, a historic monument of thirteen acres, between Howe Sound in the south and Prince Rupert in the north. The Chilcotin and Cariboo countries are without major parks, though both have special features worthy of preservation. The Chilcotin is fine saddle-horse country and was the scene of British Columbia's only official Indian War. In the Cariboo the acquisition of much of the town of Barkerville as a historic site and restoration of its buildings has proved a step of great importance. The nearby circle of Bowron, Spectacle, Long and Isaac lakes, though much smaller than the Oosta-Whitesail-Eutsuk chain now lost to Tweedsmuir Park, has similar possibilities. It is now under reserve, but has not yet been gazetted as a park. Its potential can hardly be over-emphasized, because it is the only first-class canoe country left in the province and canoe travel is the ideal wilderness use, as has been clearly demonstrated in the success and popularity of the Quetico-Superior Wilderness.

Over half of the province lies north of Prince George and while two Class B parks, at Muncho Lake (218,000 acres) and Stone Mountain (64,000 acres), both on the Alaska Highway, were established in 1957, it is time to consider other suitable areas. While development of ground transportation will influence some of the final decisions, strong representations have already been made in favour of the Spatsizi Plateau at the headwaters of the Stikine River in the Cassiar Country, as a park, game reserve and hunting area. Extensive open areas, favourable summer climate and important concentrations of thinhorn sheep, mountain caribou, moose and other big game species make the choice a logical one.

Selection of smaller parks, campsites and other recreational reserves in the north and in many other parts of the province must await the penetration of roads or other means of communication. The present policy of selecting and reserving such areas as soon as the location of road or railroad is decided, and before construction begins, should ensure that newly accessible lands are adequately served in these respects.

It is important to realize that parks alone can never begin to satisfy the need for outdoor recreation. Many outdoor enthusiasts never go near a park and the non-park lands of the province must always bear the burden of supplying the major demands. This means that most recreation is available as a secondary rather than a priority land use. This is sound and desirable because secondary recreational uses such as hunting, fishing, observation of wildlife, enjoyment of the countryside and similar pursuits make almost no direct physical demands on the land itself. Where-ever a priority resource use, such as forestry or farming or ranching, is properly conducted, these other uses are automatically provided for; where multiple use is practised, special care must be given to watershed management and consideration must be given to wildlife habitat and aesthetic values, but these precautions are at least as beneficial to the priority use as to the secondary. Good land use never damages recreational potential.

This is not to suggest that conflicts do not arise between recreational interests and those of priority operations such as logging, farming, mining and ranching. Economic pressures always have and probably always will encourage industrial practices that are harmful to land and water and so to recreational resources; only government control can weigh such pressures accurately and determine whether economic need really justifies even short-term damage. But the main conflicts arise in the simple mechanics of use. The forester, for instance, is afraid of fire if the public has summer access to his holdings; he wants to reserve his main roads for high-speed, heavy traffic; he wants to protect his secondary roads from the damage of traffic of any sort under bad winter conditions. The rancher is concerned for his gates and fences and livestock. The farmer doesn't want shot-gun pellets splattering around his farmhouse or around his ears if he is working in the fields. At his worst, the recreation seeker can be a callous and damaging nuisance; he sets fires, steals equipment, kills or wounds livestock, cuts fences, leaves gates open, steers his objectionable family in to picnic on the farmer's front lawn, leaves litter where it is most unsightly and broken bottles where they can do most harm.

Most of these are sins of ignorance rather than of deliberate malice and there is no doubt that the public is steadily becoming better educated in its responsibilities to the priority users of the land, just as loggers and ranchers are beginning to realize that they have responsibilities to secondary users. Access to forest, farm and ranch lands is still a matter of constant negotiation, but relations between the two sides are steadily improving and many successful working agreements have been reached. While this is an advance, it is not satisfactory. Without full access to forest lands and range lands, the recreational resources cannot be realized and simply go to waste. Farm lands, being smaller holdings and more intensively used, present a more difficult problem but even here the principle of multiple use can usually be recognized with gain to both sides.

The province's land-use policy in these matters has not yet been clearly stated. The public generally feels that it has legitimate right to full claim in the recreational resources of the country. While this claim is somewhat doubtful in regard to

Crown-granted lands, it seems clear enough in such holdings as timber licences and leases, tree farm licences, public working circles and leased range lands. It is a strong right that must be recognized and protected in fact as well as in theory.

Comparison with United States practice is difficult because of differing systems of land tenure, but it must be emphasized that the U.S. National Forests, as distinct from the National Parks, play a very important part in providing recreational areas. In British Columbia a tentative start was made some years ago towards the establishment of Provincial Forests, with clear planning and provision for recreational uses. Several such forests were in fact established and at least one was briefly operated for the encouragement of recreational use. But there the matter has rested. Nothing is now heard of the Provincial Forests and many changes in forest holdings have been brought about since they were first conceived.

British Columbia has plenty of recreational land, but not so much that it will serve the needs of a rapidly growing population without good planning and aggressive management. So far "protected" areas in which recreation is nominally considered the priority resource use have provided very little protection. Privately held lands are steadily reducing the available areas where recreation should be a secondary resource use and no land-use policy to reverse this trend has yet been established. Planning and development of recreational facilities is sounder and more aggressive under the new department, but funds are far from adequate to ensure the future. Within 20 years British Columbians will be feeling the pinch they only think they feel now and within forty years there will be very serious shortages unless far more aggressive and imaginative policies are developed and adopted. The time is too short for the only other alternative, development of a new species of citizen, *Homo urbanus urbanus*, who would be adapted solely to city streets.

wildlife CHAPTER 21

WILDLIFE IS RATHER a vague term. There is a tendency to think of it as including only the game birds and mammals and the fur-bearing mammals; but this hardly bears examination in any full discussion of recreation, for many creatures, birds especially, that the hunter or trapper never considers, are highly important to those who simply like to watch and listen. In considering use of the land, all created life is important. Even in considering game animals and fur-bearers, nearly all other creatures play significant parts in the total that is a healthy working balance of interdependent species.

Generally the fishes are excluded from the term "wildlife" – if they were not, the familiar term "fish and wildlife" would be redundant. Obviously the word is meant to exclude man and his domestic animals, however doubtful the grounds; and it seems sensible, even though completely illogical, to exclude the insect world. The range between these extremes, then, is wildlife.

Even within these limits any inventory of the province's wildlife resources is clearly out of the question here. They are abundant, varied and exciting enough to interest almost any hunter, naturalist or observer. They include, for North America, a wide range of big game animals, several upland game birds, waterfowl in fair quantity, a number of important fur-bearers, some splendid predators and all that lovely host of creatures, especially migrant birds, that have given pleasure to mankind since the beginning of time or the beginning of man's conscious appreciation of his world.

Although the wildlife of the province is abundant for most present needs, the province generally is not a highly productive wildlife area. Abundance of wildlife, apart from human interferences, roughly reflects the richness of the soils available to it. British Columbia, then, has its wildlife populations rather widely scattered over very large areas and some of these populations, such as mountain goats and

MARTEN

mountain caribou, are quite highly specialized to particular forms of terrain. Heavily forested country, contrary to popular belief, is not highly productive of wildlife – wherever the sun cannot penetrate to the forest floor for significant periods, there is little for most forms of wildlife to live on. Very large areas of mountainous terrain are important to wildlife and are likely to ensure the survival of some species against the most drastic encroachments of industrial civilization, but they do not and cannot maintain a high abundance per acre. For most species mountain areas are only summer feeding grounds; in the winter months the herds must concentrate on feeding grounds at low elevation, usually along rather narrow river valleys. So the absolute abundance of many stocks is dependent upon competition with other uses for the province's limited valley lands.

FUR-BEARERS

The fur-bearing animals of the province are the base of its oldest industry and earliest settlement. Their value in recreation is indirect, though of considerable importance, since many are carnivores which act as controls on other species and at least one of the rodents, the beaver, is an important agent in conserving water and in modifying habitat. All add interest to the countryside and give pleasure and satisfaction to the casual observer as well as the naturalist. This is a value that inevitably increases with the increasing use of other recreational resources, though it is certainly not a measurable value.

The early fur trade was concerned chiefly with two species, the sea otter and the beaver. The first of these was hunted almost to extinction and has never been able to recover in B.C.; beaver were overtrapped and seriously reduced, but have recovered well and are now abundant in many parts of the province. Some eighteen other fur-bearers make up the annual catch, which has a normal value of about two million dollars, though it is extremely sensitive to price fluctuations and has been reduced to a fraction of this in recent years by extensive fur farming and the introduction of synthetic furs.

The chief value of the fur industry is perhaps more in its provision of an independent means of livelihood in remote areas than in its simple cash return. Trappers reach the most distant valleys and into headwater country where few others go; their trails simplify travel for engineers, cruisers, surveyors, prospectors and others who come after and their cabins make shelter that is often welcome. Traplines are outposts of ownership in wilderness country that is not otherwise used and trapping continues to be an important factor in the livelihood of many of the native Indian groups. About half of the five thousand registered traplines in the province are owned by native Indians, mainly in the northern parts.

Three rodents are among the most important fur-bearers of the province: muskrat, beaver and red squirrel. The others are carnivores: mink, marten, fisher, wolverine, otter, skunks, weasels, raccoon, fox, wolf, coyote, lynx and bobcat. Four of these, the otter, wolverine, fisher and lynx, are primarily wilderness creatures and reach their greatest abundance in forests of little or no commercial value, where their habitat is likely to remain undisturbed. Beaver, wolf, fox, skunks, and squirrel are considered to be "forest edge" animals. Marten are abundant both in wilderness and in commercial forest. All these species are likely to feel the effects of extensive logging and local abundances may be expected to fluctuate accordingly. Coyote, mink, weasel and muskrat are most abundant outside heavily forested areas, but the coyote is considered a pest around livestock or poultry and the muskrat is a nuisance in dyked areas, such as the Lower Fraser Valley, which are particularly favourable to their increase.

The balance of these factors is favourable rather than unfavourable and there is good reason to believe that the present yield of fur-bearers can be maintained or even increased if world prices improve. Management legislation has been particularly sound. Catch statistics are accurately recorded by the royalty system that was introduced in the province in 1920. In 1925 and 1926 British Columbia instituted a system of trapline registration, the first of its kind anywhere, that ensures intelligent harvesting rather than careless exploitation. By registration of his line, the

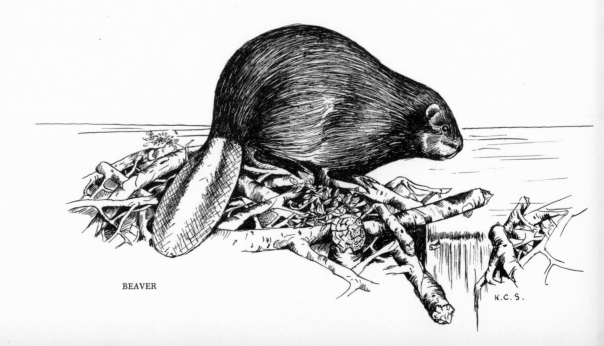

BEAVER

K.C.S.

WOLVERINE

trapper is protected from competition and guaranteed continuity of tenure; but he knows that he must harvest his furs with close regard for the future because no other line will be registered for him if he exhausts the first one.

Trappers in the more settled parts of the province have begun to feel restriction of access to privately owned non-forest land, but this is inevitable and not too significant. A more serious problem is restriction of access to Crown-granted forest land and to land held for special purposes, such as logging or grazing, where the problem concerns the use of roads rather than use of land. Quite clearly trapping is a legitimate subsidiary land use under such circumstances and proper harvesting of the annual crop should be beneficial to the priority user as well as to the trapper himself.

After the trapping of fur-bearers, which brings a direct commercial return, hunting is the most obvious and measurable use that is made of the province's wildlife resources. In the early years there was some market hunting, as there was throughout North America, but those days are long past. Trappers, prospectors and survey parties in remote areas may still at times kill meat for their own use and native Indians do so on their own reserve lands without restriction. But hunting is now primarily a matter of sport and recreation everywhere in the province. It has been estimated that some hundred thousand hunters in the province spend about six million dollars annually to harvest about three million dollars' worth of meat. Those estimates are probably conservative as to the amount spent and generous as to the value of meat that actually reaches the table in good condition. It is perfectly

British Columbia's big game animals as painted by Keith C. Smith.

GRIZZLY BEAR

BIGHORN SHEEP, WHITETAIL DEER, ELK OR WAPITI

MOUNTAIN GOAT, OSBORN CARIBOU, AMERICAN MOOSE

INTERIOR BLUE GROUSE   SHARP-TAILED GROUSE

FRANKLIN GROUSE   RUFFED GROUSE

WILLOW PTARMIGAN   ROCK PTARMIGAN

clear that the average hunter expects considerably more from his hunting than help with the family meat bill. And since he goes back to hunting year after year he undoubtedly finds it.

The animals hunted fall naturally into three main classes: big game, upland birds and waterfowl. The majority of hunters probably follow more than one type of hunting during a season, but this is not particularly significant. Most aspects of management and land use fall naturally within the groupings suggested.

BIG GAME

The most important big game animals of the province are: deer, moose, elk, mountain sheep, caribou, mountain goats, grizzly bear and black bear. Deer and moose are the most widely hunted and, with the black bear, the most widely distributed. Owing to the great size of the province and its varying climate and terrain, the big game animals all occur in two or more species or subspecies, some of which are important to hunters. Even in areas where the animals are identical, the population breaks down into separate herds, dependent on specific winter ranges though their summer ranges may overlap. This is an important factor in management.

The mule deer is the most widely distributed of the deer, ranging from the eastern boundary of the province to the summit of the Coast Range and from the southern boundary into the far north, though abundance varies greatly. Its close relative, the Columbia blacktail deer, is found on the western slopes of the Coast Range and on most of the islands, including Vancouver Island and the Queen Charlottes. The whitetail deer is limited to the south-eastern corner of the province. The annual deer kill of the province is about 60,000 animals of all species, which is considered to be well within the sustained-yield limit. In most, if not all, areas, deer are probably under-hunted, a situation which carries with it risk of damage to the range and deterioration of the herds. Distribution of hunting pressure over such a vast area is impossible with the present population and communi-

NATIVE UPLAND GAME BIRDS

These paintings by the B.C. wildlife artist, Hugh Monahan, illustrate two types of upland game birds – *the grouse* and *the ptarmigan*. Both are members of a group known as "gallinaceous" or scratching birds, and are related to the common barnyard chicken, having many characteristics in common with it. They spend most of their time on the ground, are excellent runners, seldom make prolonged flights and are adept at hiding. Because they are both palatable and beautiful, they are among the favourite game birds of North America. Although the ptarmigan is also a grouse, it is differentiated because it is an alpine and arctic species that changes to white plumage in the winter months.

LYNX

cations, but efforts have been made to bring about more rapid turnover and improved conditions in some areas by encouraging the taking of antlerless deer.

About twelve thousand moose are killed each year from a total population estimated at almost seventy-five thousand animals. Moose are widely distributed through most of the province east of the Coast Mountains. Because of its great size and strength, the moose is able to winter over wider areas than are the other browsing animals and has spread gradually southward from the fifty-fourth parallel to the U.S. border during the past fifty or sixty years, as more and more country has been opened up by fires and logging operations. This greatly increased range is now being curtailed by forest regrowth and some ranges are known to be carrying a heavy overstock which must inevitably lead to a decline. Here also the taking of a proportion of cows and calves is encouraged in an attempt to protect the ranges and maintain the herds in good health.

The bighorn sheep of the more southern parts of the province and the thinhorn sheep of the northern parts are found in remote and mountainous areas. The California bighorns of the interior total perhaps a thousand animals, the Rocky Mountain bighorns probably no more than twice this number. There has been some decline. The abundance of thinhorn or Dall sheep is not known, though they are believed to be holding their own. Mountain sheep are a quality big game animal and can never support heavy hunting, though they are of great value in attracting trophy hunters and will always be of high interest to naturalists and other observers. Winter ranges are limited and crucial, so some form of protection is essential if the herds are to survive. Excessive grazing of sheep ranges by domestic stock would lead to rapid decline.

In prehistoric times elk were abundant throughout most of the southern part of the province. The main herds are now found in the East Kootenay District and on Vancouver Island; a few small herds, founded by introduced stock, are established in the southern interior. The herds of the Rocky Mountain Trench have been roughly estimated at a total of 20,000 individuals; those of Vancouver Island do not exceed fifteen hundred individuals and are considered to be relics of a previously greater abundance that have found narrowly suitable conditions in the climax rain-forest. Elk are not merely of value to hunters; they are superb animals, easily seen by the casual tourist as well as the more determined observer, and their perpetuation is of great importance. Some loss of winter range has occurred on Vancouver Island from hydro-electric flooding and damage is also done by clear logging, though the small deciduous growth of newly opened areas should provide at least partial compensation for this. In the interior of the province, hydro-electric flooding will create a problem in some areas, but excessive grazing by domestic livestock could become an even more serious threat unless proper allowance is made for the needs of the elk herds.

Mountain goats are distributed throughout the length of the Rockies and the Coast Range and have so far been little hunted and little disturbed by the activities of man. Mountain caribou are intermittently distributed in all the major mountain systems, thriving wherever old and decadent forest promotes growth of lichens. Fires or logging in old growth of this type have caused local fluctuations in abundance, but herds in many parts of the province, including Wells Gray Park and the Monashee Mountains, are believed to be increasing at present. Both mountain goat and mountain caribou are likely to play an increasing part in the game harvest of the province as hunting pressures increase.

MINK

K.C.S.

Black bears are distributed throughout the province and are abundant. They are little hunted and sometimes a nuisance near settlements, but in the wild they are attractive and harmless except for minor predation upon spawning salmon and, more rarely, fawns. Grizzly bear populations are thought to be gradually continuing their continental northward retreat before the protective measures of sheep and cattle herders. Many are believed to fall victims to poison baits set out for wolves. Though not found on Vancouver Island or in the Queen Charlottes, the grizzly is widely distributed through most alpine and subalpine areas and in the Coast Range is found in good numbers down to tidewater.

The modern conception of big game management is that populations should be cropped annually to ensure that uncontrolled increase does not lead to drastic decline through destruction of feeding areas. The first step in management of browsing animals such as deer and elk and moose is to bring their numbers within the safe carrying capacity of their winter ranges, so that does and cows winter well, produce early and to capacity, with a minimum of early mortality in the young. Given good wintering conditions, blacktail deer, for instance, reproduce for the first time at ten months instead of two or three years of age, and the older animals are likely to bear two fawns and raise them both. On an overstocked range reproduction is delayed, single fawns are common and heavy early die-off is not unusual. From this it is clear that a small winter carry-over can be expected to produce a larger stock of animals in the ensuing hunting seasons than one that strains the capacity of the winter range, and will do so with much less risk of permanent damage to the range itself.

Most game management must accept and work within the large and often abrupt changes of habitat that are brought about by necessary industrial uses of land and

MUSKRAT

K.C.S.

water. These changes may be damaging or beneficial, so the purpose of management will either be to keep damage at a minimum or to ensure that full advantage is taken of the benefits. Where clear logging and burning are practised in the coastal forests, deer populations are abruptly and enormously increased. Wise management attempts to realize heavy annual crops of deer from the very start of this era of abundance, so that both range and stock are kept in good order and will yield maximum results while it lasts; as soon as dense second growth again takes over the ground, decline is inevitable and hunting pressures will turn elsewhere. This, of course, is management by expediency, a sort of opportunism to compensate for bad forest practice which is also bad land management for wildlife purposes. Under sounder logging practice, such as controlled patch logging and selective logging, management can be planned on a long-term basis and something approaching a permanently sustained yield may be hoped for.

More positive management practices than these will certainly be necessary in the future and some may well be practicable even on land that is under priority use. In coastal forests, the deer thrive where openings are plentiful; good forest management tends to ensure that this condition exists, but positive planning with both uses in mind would lead to better rotation and distribution of openings for wildlife purposes without adversely affecting either logging or forest regrowth.

Lightning strikes and other chance agents have always caused fires in wild land, sometimes to the detriment of both forests and wildlife, sometimes to the benefit of either or both. Deliberate burning of ground-cover has not so far been used as a tool of wildlife management in the province, yet it offers great possibilities on deer, moose and probably also elk ranges. Properly controlled burning destroys debris, as well as unthrifty old-growth plants and trees, without damage to soil. It cleans

TIMBER WOLF

INTRODUCED GAME BIRDS

European Grey Partridge (Hungarian Partridge)

the ground, encourages both annual and perennial plant growth and may greatly increase the carrying capacity of a range. In the interior of the province, where many ranges support little or nothing but wildlife, controlled experiments in burning are long overdue. Where wildlife yields are not the priority use, burning presents more difficulties; but in many areas, especially in the poorly restocked forest areas of the coast, properly controlled burning programmes would benefit both forest regrowth and wildlife.

UPLAND GAME BIRDS

The important native upland game birds of the province are all of the grouse family. Of these the ruffed grouse and the blue grouse are the most widely distributed and the most heavily hunted. Sharptail grouse are found in some abundance on the Interior Plateau, in the Peace River country and the East Kootenay. The spruce grouse is widely distributed east of the coast range, but is not so highly regarded. Three species of ptarmigan, willow, rock and whitetailed, are distributed through the alpine areas but are as yet little hunted. The sage grouse was once native near Osoyoos and efforts have recently been made to re-introduce it by importing stock.

Some grouse populations are considered to be cyclic – that is, they increase over a more or less predictable number of years to relatively high abundance, decline and then climb back towards maximum level again. Since these fluctuations cannot be related to hunting pressure it is concluded that hunting has little significant effect and populations are usually under- rather than over-hunted, especially at peak periods.

Little is known of the nature of these cycles and some biologists even question their existence. Certainly they are far more apparent in the interior of the province than on the coast. The blue grouse of the coastal forest, for instance, is a fairly scarce bird, but increases to spectacular abundance behind clear logging and burn-

California or Valley Quail   Chukar Partridge (Chikor)   Ring-necked Pheasant

ing at low elevations, and declines again as dense second growth becomes well established. Several of the factors influencing or controlling these fluctuations are quite well understood. Continuing observation will determine the nature and extent of grouse fluctuations in other parts of the province, where habitat conditions are more stable, and in time the underlying causes should become apparent. It is conceivable that this knowledge may suggest management practices that would maintain more stable populations.

Both the ruffed and the sharptail do quite well on or near cultivated lands, but grouse are essentially wilderness birds. Three non-indigenous species, ring-necked pheasant, Hungarian partridge and California quail, have been introduced at various times to take advantage of areas opened up by agricultural settlement. The pheasant has proved the most successful. It was first introduced in 1882 and since then has been established in all farming districts, except possibly the Peace River and the Bulkley Valley, where it has not yet shown that it can survive and increase under the severe climatic conditions. On south-eastern Vancouver Island, in the Fraser, Thompson and Okanagan valleys and near Grand Forks and Creston it has provided a lot of sport, though numbers now appear to be declining in the face of changing agricultural practices. Original releases were followed by many subsequent plantings in most areas, but there is a good deal to suggest that these were ineffective in increasing total kill or total abundance.

Quail and partridges have been less successful and are not so widely distributed, but all three are important in that they provide hunting in settled areas and make good use of agricultural land without damage to crops.

The chukar partridge was first introduced in the Thompson Valley in 1950. This bird was considered more likely than any other to make use of the dry interior valleys and survive hard winters, and it seems to be doing so. There have been open seasons since 1955, with increasing kills; both Thompson Valley and South Okanagan populations are considered to be still increasing.

WATERFOWL

British Columbia is not a highly productive waterfowl breeding area in comparison with the prairie provinces, but ducks breed in considerable numbers throughout the interior parklands and grasslands. There is also a heavy migration along the Pacific coastline. The Cariboo, Chilcotin and Peace River parklands and the upper Columbia Valley are among the most important breeding areas, though there are significant concentrations of nesting birds near Kamloops, Vanderhoof, Vernon and Cranbrook. Drainage and overgrazing have done some damage to water-holding capacities, especially in the parklands, and production has been reduced over the past 25 years.

Migratory birds are a federal government responsibility and provincial governments do very little for them. The Canadian Wildlife Service has neither staff nor funds for positive management on any significant scale and the country as a whole has shown no greater awareness of its responsibilities than have the provinces. So far as British Columbia is concerned, any reduction of breeding or nesting grounds represents serious loss and is entirely unnecessary. Good range management and good farm management go hand in hand with good wildfowl management; proper use of water is fundamental to all three.

Good waterfowl management goes far beyond any simple responsibility for species that are hunted. The province has the largest concentration of trumpeter swans left in the world; whistling swans pass through in great numbers; many wading and diving species that are of no significance to the hunter nest in the province or pass through it. Together these represent a tremendous asset, yet there is not a single public sanctuary for nesting or transient birds and only limited study has so far been made of their needs or of the possibilities of improving existing conditions.

No brief treatment of this most intricate resource can hope to cover more than general principles. The most important concept of wildlife management to-day is that habitat – the conditions and circumstances of a creature's living space – is far more important to its survival than anything else. Only in a few instances – mountain sheep are one – is hunting under normal controls likely to have anything but beneficial effect on breeding stocks. When stocks are up, hunting is a necessary control to maintain the quality of both stock and range; when stocks are low, the law of diminishing returns makes hunting pressure largely ineffective. This is not an argument for wholesale slaughter, but it is a general guide to management policy.

Predators are detrimental only when numerical relationships of prey and predator reach certain specific proportions, and then only for rather brief periods. Necessary predator control is undertaken by the provincial game department, but recent legislation has placed all predatory birds, including bald eagles and the long-tailed hawks, on the protected list. This is an important advance which recognizes at last that these birds are beneficial rather than harmful in the balance. Cougars, which are abundant in many parts of the province, were hunted for many years on a bounty system with little effect. They do no harm except when they come down to areas of human settlement, but they offer one of the most interesting and challenging forms of hunting in the province – at present very little used.

Unfortunately, detrimental modification of habitat is all too frequently, though unnecessarily, a concomitant of settlement and industrial use. Abuses of land and water by overgrazing, poorly conceived drainage of swamplands, clear cutting of timber, encouragement of pure stands of regrowth, excessive spraying of timber and agricultural crops, failure to provide adequate parks and green belts, pollution of watersheds and ill-considered flooding of valley lands all contribute to the destruction of wildlife. Many of these activities are justified by expediency, but all contribute ultimately to the reduction of the country as a whole.

The native fauna of a country is an important part of its character. It has survived and multiplied because it is adapted to the land and, in lesser degree, the land is adapted to it. The activities of modern man inevitably interfere to some extent with these balances and some degree of compensation is desirable and necessary. Occasionally major adjustment may be necessary; it is clear, for instance, that the great agricultural development of the prairies could not have taken place without great reduction of the buffalo herds. But the ideal of management should be to preserve wildlife balances, controlling where necessary, preserving and protecting where necessary, because wildlife forms and wildlife habitat, including plant life and water tables and drainage systems, all play some part, and very often a critical part, in maintaining the land that man ultimately depends on.

Against these considerations, the recreational values of wildlife are scarcely more than a fortunate by-product. But their importance has increased steadily from the very first settlement of the province and it will continue to increase with every population increase, every industrial development and every advance of settlement. In other words, the very factors that are likely to damage habitat and destroy wildlife are those which make preservation and protection through proper use most urgent.

CHAPTER 22 *game-fish*

FISHING FOR SPORT is by all standards the most popular form of outdoor recreation in British Columbia, as it is in many other parts of the continent. About 180,000 freshwater licences are sold each year to residents and more than 25,000 to non-residents; in addition to these, thousands of children under eighteen, who are not required to buy licences, also fish in fresh water. No licences at all are needed in salt water, but it is estimated that at least 25,000 residents and several thousand non-residents fish there. While most of these also fish in fresh water and so appear in the licence figures, a considerable proportion does not. A partial survey among licensed anglers in 1959 indicated that they spent over thirty million dollars on their sport, so the total annual expenditure on all forms of angling in the province cannot be much less than 35 or 40 million dollars.

The most important game-fish of the province are three of the five Pacific salmons—the spring or king, the pink or humpback and the coho—and two trouts, the rainbow and the cutthroat. The rainbow trout is well distributed throughout the province, except in the Arctic watershed, and while geographical separation has produced only minor, intergrading biological differences, it has led to differences of habit that demand recognition. The seagoing rainbow of coastal streams, which grows to large size and has habits roughly similar to those of Atlantic salmon, is known as the steelhead; resident fish in coastal waters are usually called rainbows; resident fish of interior waters are called Kamloops trout. A small alpine subspecies of minor importance is also recognized. Cutthroat trout are found on the western slopes of the Coast Range and in parts of the Columbia watershed, but not in the central part of the province. This wider geographical separation has established clearer biological differences between the coastal cutthroat and the Yellowstone cutthroat of eastern parts. Coastal cutthroats are both sea-running and resident and the cutthroat also has an alpine subspecies. European brown trout have been successfully introduced to one or two streams on Vancouver Island and more recently to the Kettle River.

The Dolly Varden or Arctic char is distributed pretty well throughout the province and, though a handsome fish of fair game quality, is not highly regarded. Great Lakes char, often called lake trout, is found in the upper reaches of the Skeena, Fraser and Yukon watersheds, but otherwise is limited to the Arctic watershed. Eastern brook trout have been successfully introduced in the southern interior and on southern Vancouver Island.

The Arctic grayling, a game and handsome fish, takes the place of the trouts in the Arctic watershed and the Montana grayling is native in the extreme south east of the province, whence it has been transplanted to some lakes in the Kootenay area. Rocky Mountain whitefish are distributed through most of the mainland except in the Yukon watershed. Northern pike and walleye are native to the Peace River proper and the Liard and Yukon watersheds. Large- and small-mouth bass have been introduced in certain southern waters considered favourable to them.

With a few other species of limited importance, such as the ling, the white sturgeon and the introduced yellow perch, these fish represent the existing game-fish resources of the province. So far, British Columbia anglers can afford to be particular and intensive fishing is pretty well limited to the salmons, steelhead, Kamloops and cutthroat trout. As communications and settlement spread into the north, grayling, northern pike and walleyes will be increasingly sought and as fishing pressures increase throughout the province the Dolly Varden char will probably become more popular.

As with other forms of wildlife, habitat is crucial in the protection and management of fisheries. It is true that habitat is nothing without breeding stocks, but given the right breeding, feeding and living conditions stocks can be introduced from elsewhere, as trout were brought to the lakes and rivers of South America and New Zealand and red deer were established in the New Zealand mountains—or, for that matter, as Kamloops trout were transferred to many lakes in British Columbia, once fishless but now producing some of the best fishing in the province. But fish are important in their own right and the province is particularly fortunate in

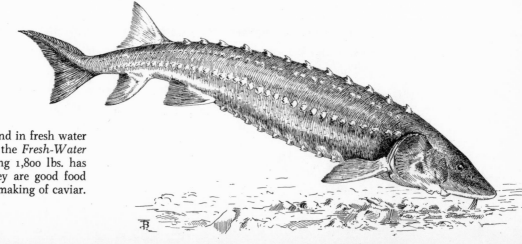

HITE STURGEON. The largest fish found in fresh water B.C. Carl, Clemens & Lindsey in the *Fresh-Water* shes of B.C. state that one weighing 1,800 lbs. has en taken in the Fraser River. They are good food h and their roe is valuable for the making of caviar.

the quality of its native stocks; they are at least equal in quality to those of any other part of the world, superbly designed to use the true resource which is in the lakes and streams and the salt water, in the mountain storage areas of ice and snow and headwater timber.

Until recently it could be argued that salmon angling was a by-product of the commercial fishery; so long as the commercial fishery was well maintained there would be plenty of fish for the sportsman and his take would make little difference to the spawning escapement. Even to-day the rod-caught spring and coho salmon amount to little more than 400,000 fish, less than ten per cent of the total catch of the same species throughout the province. But most of these fish are caught in the Strait of Georgia and nearby waters and here the angler's percentage, steadily rising over the past few years, reached the significant figure of 45.6 in 1959. It will undoubtedly continue to increase and before very long anglers will be catching more than half the spring and coho salmon that are taken in the Strait. A further point of importance is that over half the angler's catch is taken in the form of immature fish weighing 3 pounds or less – usually very much less. Fish of that size caught by the usual salt-water methods afford very little sport in the real sense of the word and they represent a real loss to both sport and commercial catch later in the year. The argument so far put forward in favour of this catch is that the fish are available then but might not be later. It is wearing very thin. One might almost as well argue for the harvesting of Douglas firs at 30 years instead of 100 years, on the grounds that it is easier then to cut them down and transport them to the mills. Control by seasons and by fishing boundaries rather than by size limits may become necessary, since mortality is heavy in the return of these small fish to the water.

The whole management of the salt-water sport fishery is due for early re-examination. Its growth calls for more research, more control, much more positive planning and greater recognition in the use and development of the salmon fishery as a whole. Licensing of salt-water anglers is long overdue; it is necessary for control, for statistical record, for financial reasons and, not least, to make the angler more fully aware of his responsibilities.

There is no doubt that the Gulf of Georgia will provide the bulk of the angling catch for many years to come. The streams supplying it come from the most settled and highly developed parts of the province and many of them have been adversely affected by obstructions, pollutions, diversions and, above all, by reduction of summer flows through clear logging. Coho salmon runs have been particularly affected, because these fish use even the smallest streams and, since they spend a full year in fresh water before migrating, are highly dependent upon adequate summer flows.

This is an instance of resource damage that was little felt at the time, but which now demands positive rehabilitation work. Some of the smaller streams, left completely dry by logging damage to their watersheds, have lost their runs altogether; with the regrowth of ground-cover flows are restored, but the runs can only be reestablished with any certainty by planting. Others, whose summer flows have only been reduced, have runs proportionately reduced; much could be done to restore them by small storage dams, like the one at Horne Lake on Big Qualicum River, from which water can be released at times of low flow. On some streams obstructions should be removed and on others access to new spawning areas can be opened by building salmon ladders over falls. Broad measures of this kind would show results very quickly, but the time will come when more detailed stream improvement and protection will be economically sound.

In the past, artificial hatchery techniques have never proved successful in increasing salmon runs and even the new techniques of hatching and release now being tested promise best results with pink and chum salmon, which migrate to sea almost immediately after hatching. Similarly, the artificial spawning areas that have produced such wonderful returns of pink salmon can do nothing for spring and coho salmon without equivalent stream improvement. Apart from the sockeye, whose very high commercial value justifies heavy expenditure in both research and improvement work, spring and coho salmon are the most difficult species to build up. The commercial returns of these fish have not justified extensive expenditure while simpler problems remain to be solved, but the combined return from the commercial fishery and the rapidly increasing sports fishery will soon change this perspective, if it has not already done so.

While the coho makes up the bulk of the sporting catch in most areas, the spring salmon is of great importance because of its much larger size. Coho salmon average about eight pounds and rarely exceed 20; the spring salmon commonly averages 20 pounds and attains weights of 70 pounds or more – the present rod-caught record is a fish of 92 pounds taken from the Skeena River in 1959. Most spring salmon runs return after four years sea-feeding and the individuals rarely exceed weights of 20-30 pounds. But several rivers in the province have runs preponderantly made up of older fish which average thirty pounds or more and produce the really large fish that attract anglers from all over the continent. These runs – those homing in the Campbell, Phillips, Nimpkish, Gold, Somass, Nahmint, Kildalla and Skeena rivers are among the better known – demand special attention and protection. Not all are used extensively by anglers at the present time, but all will be sooner or later. The mouths of three of these rivers, the Gold, Phillips and Kildalla (Rivers Inlet), are classed as "special permit areas" and close record is kept of fishing effort and catch. But the runs generally have not been investigated and very little is known of their composition and needs.

Pink salmon play an increasing part in angler's catches and probably will continue to do so as commercial runs are built up. Though less spectacular than the coho or spring and considerably smaller than either, the pink salmon is a perfectly adequate game fish.

Most Pacific salmon, unlike steelhead and Atlantic salmon, run into the rivers so late in the year and so near their spawning time that they deteriorate rapidly and

PACIFIC LAMPREY AND STEELHEAD
The lamprey has a life cycle not unlike the Pacific salmon; laying its eggs
in fresh water, spending two or more years in the stream and then migrating to sea until mature when it returns to tne stream to spawn. It is often
referred to as an eel, but this it is not, it does not have any paired fins like
the eels, and the mouth does not have jaws but is a sucking disc with rasp-
ing teeth; with this it attaches itself to a fish, both salmon and steelhead
being popular, then lives on the body juices extracted. The drawing shows
one attached to a steelhead.

provide sport in fresh water for only a limited time. Some rivers, such as the Puntledge on Vancouver Island and the Kitimat on the northern coast, have early runs
of spring salmon that enter the rivers in April or May and provide outstanding
sport. These runs also call for special investigation and at some future time interchange of runs between rivers by transplanting may become a practical possibility.

In addition to the sea-running species, a form of land-locked sockeye salmon,
usually called the Kokanee, is found in many lakes of the province. These fish mature at from eight to sixteen inches in length and make some fresh water angling.
They also provide important forage for big Kamloops trout in some of the larger
lakes.

The most highly used and productive freshwater fishing in the province is in the
lakes of the southern interior, mainly on the Thompson and Okanagan watersheds.
Most of these lakes are at elevations of from two to five or six thousand feet, with
good average depth and reasonable temperature ranges. They tend to be neutral or
slightly alkaline and, in comparison with lakes elsewhere in the province, very high
in the dissolved minerals that supply the necessary nourishment for plant growth
and so are the base of the food chain from plant to plankton and insects to fish. A
few of these lakes carried native stocks of Kamloops trout, many were without fish
of any kind but have been successfully planted, others are still fishless but will be
planted and brought into production as they are needed.

Such lakes are an important resource. Generally they are capable of producing
ten or more pounds of fish to the acre each year, which is enough to make excellent
trout fishing. They are situated in attractive country with an excellent summer
climate and their conformation supports all the popular forms of fishing – nearly
all provide excellent fly fishing except in the full heat of summer. The chief problem of management is in maintaining adequate stocks of fish of the desired size.
Some lakes have satisfactory spawning areas and maintain fairly level stocks from
year to year; some have too much good spawning area and soon produce an overstock of small fish; some have inadequate spawning areas and need annual supplementary planting. This is a relatively simple problem, but it does call for very exact

knowledge of the lake conditions as well as the spawning and rearing conditions. Even when such knowledge is available, the number of lakes involved would call for considerable staff and expenditure if full management were to be undertaken.

The lakes of this central interior area, centred approximately around Kamloops, Kelowna, Princeton and Merritt, support over twenty-five per cent of the fishing effort of licensed anglers in the province; the Kootenays support a little under twenty per cent, the Cariboo country about fifteen per cent, Vancouver Island thirteen per cent, the Lower Mainland eleven per cent, the north country ten per cent and the northern coast five per cent. These figures do not include the salt-water fishery, where no licence is required, and they tend to reflect population concentrations as well as the quality of the fishing.

With certain exceptions, notably in the southern Rocky Mountain Trench, the trout lakes of British Columbia generally are less productive than those of the southern interior. Heavy precipitation and low evaporation rates, with generally poorer soil and more thoroughly leached rock formations, reduce the total dissolved solids in the water, making for limited weed growth and proportionately poorer food resources. Lakes on Vancouver Island and the western slope of the Coast Range are likely to produce only two or three pounds of trout annually per acre. At present there is no economic means of increasing the yield of these waters, but since fish tend to concentrate on shoals and other favourite places, anglers do find satisfactory sport at certain seasons. In some lakes coarse fish compete for food supplies, to the detriment of trout. Near travelled highways or large centres of population it is considered economically sound to poison out all fish, including trout, and restock with trout alone, thus obtaining a higher yield in the absence of competition. About a hundred lakes in the province have been treated in this way.

Most streams in the province produce only limited numbers of resident trout, but this weakness is more than made up for in coastal streams by the sea-run fish: steelhead and migratory cutthroats and to a lesser extent coho and spring salmon and precocious males of both species called "jacks". Attempts have been made to establish resident stocks of trout by introducing European brown trout; after many years these fish appear to be well established in the Cowichan River and provide good sport there. It is possible that they may compete undesirably with the pre-migrant stage of native game-fish such as steelheads, cutthroats and the Pacific salmons. But casual observation suggests that there is a good deal of unused insect life in many streams, especially sedge and mayfly larvae, and the brown trout may, in the balance, prove a welcome import.

The steelhead runs are an outstanding feature of nearly all streams open to salt water and support an intense fishery wherever these are accessible by road. Good winter runs, from December to March, are far more common than good summer runs and the fish of the winter runs tend to be larger, averaging nearly ten pounds and occasionally weighing as much as twenty or thirty pounds. Winter fish are somewhat unwilling takers and are fished for by crude and unsatisfactory methods, including the use of salmon roe, though these are not really necessary. Summer-run fish are much more readily taken and are, in fact, fully the equal of Atlantic salmon in this respect. Most streams have at least vestigial summer runs and it is conceivable that ways may be found to increase them.

Most interior streams are scarcely more productive of fully resident fish than are the coastal streams, but many have seasonal runs that come up from the lakes and make excellent fishing. Parts of the Skeena watershed, which is gradually becoming more accessible, provide stream fishing for both local and sea-run species that is of a very high order.

While the lakes and streams of the province, like its lands, are not highly productive, they are extensive, varied and exciting. Their own quality and the quality of the fish that frequent them make a game fishery that is the equal of any in the world and which so far has suffered only limited damage. Management to date is simple rather than intensive and should probably remain so for many years to come, designed to protect habitat where possible and to restore it if damage is done. Limited "put and take" stocking may be justifiable in a few areas near large centres of population, but in the province as a whole every effort should be made to protect breeding stocks and habitat so that such management may never become necessary.

Some effort has been made to take advantage of environment not adequately used by native species by the introduction of exotics, as farmland has been put to use by the introduction of pheasants, partridges and quail. The brown trout may fill a useful purpose, though his status remains in some doubt, as has already been suggested. The Eastern brook trout has been introduced with some success, but can never be considered a desirable fish where the natives are doing well. The introduction of large- and small-mouth bass, though it has been successful in producing good fishing in some of the warmer waters of the southern areas, is unquestionably a mistake. The risk that these fish may be transferred, either deliberately or by chance, to good trout and salmon waters is so great that it would be perfectly sound to clean out all waters that now hold stocks. In a province so well served by native fish, there is very little to be said for the introduction of exotics; since most of the

Introduced fresh-water game fish
TOP TO BOTTOM: BROWN TROUT RISING TO A MAYFLY; EASTERN BROOK TROUT; SMALLMOUTH BLACK BASS.

Native fresh-water game fish
TOP TO BOTTOM: COASTAL CUTTHROAT TROUT; RAINBOW TROUT; STEELHEAD TROUT; ARCTIC GRAYLING;
DOLLY VARDEN CHAR; GREAT LAKES CHAR.

Native salt-water game fish
TOP: COHO OR SILVER SALMON; BOTTOM: SPRING SALMON OR TYEE.

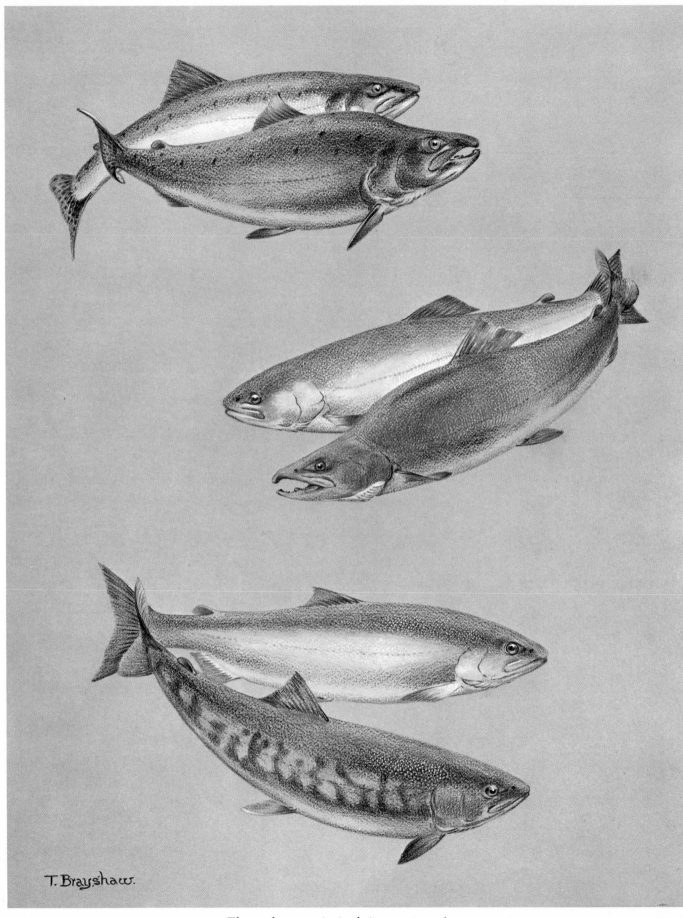

Three salmon species in their spawning colours
TOP TO BOTTOM: HUMPBACK OR PINK SALMON; SOCKEYE SALMON; DOG OR CHUM SALMON.

present distribution has been brought about by accidents of glaciation, it is far safer and probably far more profitable to test possibilities of extending the range of native species and specialized runs or populations.

It is difficult to emphasize the values of the native species adequately without seeming chauvinistic or sentimental. Yet these values are real and highly important to proper maintenance of the resource. The Kamloops trout is a fine fish because he is a rainbow ideally adapted to the area in which he is found. So it is also with the other distinctive native stocks such as the cutthroats and steelheads. Just as the forester reseeds or replants with stock from equivalent elevation and climate, so the fisheries man must select his stock according to environment if he is to achieve good results. Moving Kamloops trout to coastal waters, for instance, is a waste of time and money. Bringing rainbow stock from California hatcheries to British Columbia, as had been done recently, is certainly wasteful and may even be harmful to native stocks when interbreeding occurs. Preservation of pure, wild, native strains should be one of the most urgent cares of management and only when these have been manipulated to the fullest possible extent should the introduction of exotics be considered.

The greatest present need is for research; close investigation of life histories and detailed examination of the conditions that make the various fisheries. While research of this type is seldom popular, because it does not produce immediate and obvious results, nothing else is so likely to produce the right kind of results and nothing will provide surer safeguards for the future.

The game-fish resource depends in large measure upon waters in unspoiled, primitive condition and so, inevitably, finds itself in conflict with other resource uses. Improper logging and agricultural practices are most likely to cause damage, as are pollutions from many sources. Dams may obstruct migratory runs and cause serious losses, though they may in some instances benefit fisheries by stabilizing stream flows; some dams may spoil lake fisheries by uncleared shorelines and excessive draw-down, others may benefit them by slowing the flushing period and promoting the growth of plankton. Careless abuse of small spawning creeks by badly planned settlement and construction has caused cumulative losses of considerable magnitude in the province as a whole. Most of these conflicts can be reduced in effect by better land and water use, by intelligent planning and some measure of compromise. It is important to realize that each conflict is a separate issue of its own, to be solved only by individual study and carefully tailored compensations.

The broad rules of game-fish management are exactly the same as those for sound management of all wildlife. The first and most important is to protect and, where possible, improve habitat. The second is to make the fullest use of surpluses by proper distribution of the hunting or fishing effort. Rule three is to develop new range where possible and to make the best use of range modifications created by other resource uses. One further point sets the recreational resources, including fish and wildlife, sharply apart from all other resource uses, and that is the *true nature*

All the salmon shown in this picture are males, the ones in the background being the silvery sea colouration and the ones in front showing the spawning colours.

of the yield. In most resource uses the main objective is to realize a maximum production within the capacity of the resource's sustained yield. In the use of recreational resources the desired yield is not measured in pounds of dead meat, nor in numbers of wildlife seen and observed, nor in the quantity of scenery that passes before the eye; it is in direct human happiness and satisfaction and therefore is a matter of quality, not quantity.

In some respects this may conflict with good management. The naturalist and the observer and the photographer harvest their full yields without affecting the resource in any concrete way. The sportsman, if he is a sportsman, is little concerned with "harvesting the crop" but very much concerned with the manner in which he realizes his yield – the quality of his sport. In the recent past management policies have tended to overlook this point and measure sport in terms of kill and bag limits. This view is self-defeating because the sportsman will co-operate with it only to a limited extent and because its logical outcome is not sport or satisfaction but merely a quantity of dead creatures. Proper use of the recreational resources entails a constant respect for quality and once this point is understood recognition and maintenance of quality become both ends and means of management. A summer steelhead run, for instance, has higher value in terms of sport than a winter run; a lake producing its yield of Kamloops trout at an average of one pound or more comes much closer to a fisherman's ideal of his sport than one producing twice as many fish at half the average weight; two or three mature coho salmon make a day's sport when a dozen small "grilse" will not; a few trout caught on the fly give a satisfaction that many times their number caught on gang trolls cannot. These are values to be preserved where they occur most naturally and conveniently. At the same time there is room in the province for a great diversity of fishing – there are ideal small-fish lakes, ideal big-fish lakes, lakes where trolling must be encouraged, lakes and streams that could well be limited to fly fishing only, lakes and streams where all types of fishing fit together equally well. The province is large enough and rich enough in the resource to offer all these alternatives without prejudice to any. Possibilities of this sort must be examined and understood if the true values of fish and wildlife in recreation are to be preserved.

Standards can be debased almost as easily as they can be maintained – large numbers of sportsmen can be persuaded to accept inferior quality if they have known nothing else, at least for a while. But it is far better long-term management to direct their attention to quality and to emphasize their obligation to get the fullest satisfaction out of their sport. The naturalist and the observer, because they do not kill, have a personal rather than a communal obligation. But the sportsman, who does kill, must constantly seek to give more meaning to the sport he follows and less to the catch or kill, if the recreational resources are to maintain their true yield of human satisfaction indefinitely into the future.

the pollution story   CHAPTER 23

SOME THINKERS BELIEVE that man, like any other successful biological entity, is fated to multiply to the point at which his success either controls itself or destroys him. This natural law has operated in the past again and again to destroy civilizations at the height of their flowering through what biologists would call loss of habitat – the destruction of soil and water resources by excessive populations and bad management. But although individual colonies have disappeared or been reduced to minor significance, man as a species has so far persisted, mainly by use of his outstanding characteristic – a highly developed power of reasoning.

This same power has now given the human race its first means of total self-destruction – atomic radiation. Already, under limited peacetime uses, some first highly dangerous steps towards radiation pollution of land, air and water have been taken. In addition, all the necessary preparations have been made to ensure that, the moment man's fear or aggressive instincts overcome his reason, total pollution of the earth's surface, and consequently total destruction of life, can almost certainly be achieved.

This is pollution in its most spectacular form – senseless, meaningless and menacing. There are other less obvious forms, such as the wholesale use of non-selective insect sprays, that may in the end do just as much harm to man by upsetting the natural balances on which his survival depends; and still others which go all the way down the scale to the point at which benefits may outweigh damage. But all pollutions are, as the name suggests, in some degree harmful, and it is a reasonable principle of wise resource management that no pollution should be allowed unless its benefits can be clearly shown to outweigh the harm done in both the long- and the short-term view.

No principle of this sort has yet been observed in any human society. Ignorance or expediency or both have always outweighed sound reasoning and sense of re-

sponsibility. British Columbia already has pollution problems and many others undoubtedly will come up in the very near future; but because of the province's great
size and relatively small population, by far the greater part of its land, air and
water is still in clean condition. Modern understanding of the evils of pollution and
modern developments in the handling of wastes, backed by positive prevention of
dangerous abuses and rigid control of all waste disposal, can still achieve ideal
management.

The various forms of pollution are not rigidly separable. Air pollution, for instance, may affect land and water as well when the pollutants settle out of the air.
Land pollution is likely to affect water as most pollutants usually find their way
into the natural drainage of the area; misuse of land may lead to dust storms and
so to air pollution and to further land pollution when the dust is deposited elsewhere. Water pollution is likely to be self-contained, since evaporation would not
carry the pollutants with it; but where water is used for irrigation, pollution may
be carried to the land and taken up by the crops. In many countries where irrigation is extensively used and sanitation is inadequate, dysentery is spread by the
high bacteria content of the irrigation water.

Land pollution is an immense subject and the question immediately arises as to
whether or not damage to land by ordinary mismanagement constitutes pollution.
All the factors leading to soil damage – improper selection of crops, whether forest
or agricultural, inadequate manuring and fertilizing, fire damage, overgrazing,
poorly planned roads and drainage – change the soil and may cause air, soil and
water pollution, as already noted. But it should also be noted that all these forms
of damage are brought about by removal of substances from the soil rather than by
adding some damaging material to it. It is reasonable to exclude them from the
present consideration.

Land pollution is not yet a major problem in British Columbia and has not been
thoroughly studied. Sprays and dusts used for weed and insect control have complicated effects on soil, some of them apparently not always bad. Steadily increasing
use of these controls and the constant development of new chemicals makes research essential. It is known that excessive use of some chemicals causes damage
not only to plant life, but to beneficial bird, mammal and insect life and to essential
soil bacteria. D.D.T., which is commonly used in pest-control sprays and dusts, is
itself relatively indestructible and therefore cumulative in effect. It is definitely
harmful to humans and other mammals and to birds, fish and insects. Much of it
is washed away from soil and plant foliage by rain and, being highly resistant to
oxidation, eventually finds its way into streams and lakes where it attacks all
forms of aquatic life.

Deposit of mine tailings and dredging wastes are forms of land pollution, and
while they have not yet reached serious proportions in B.C., control and prevention
would be more easily effected now than later. An apparently trivial form of land
pollution, rural garbage disposal, has already assumed serious proportions in nearly

all the settled parts of the province. No effective form of control or regulation exists, and limited educational attempts have so far been totally ineffective. Haphazard disposal as practised at present is a health menace and a costly aesthetic nuisance. Since it occurs in unorganized areas, it is a direct responsibility of the provincial government; and since modern packaging of food and other goods creates most of the nuisance, it is clear that funds for a satisfactory system of rural garbage disposal could readily be found. It was pointed out at the 10th Resources Conference that the province's meat-packing industry alone uses a million dollars' worth of paper, board folders and board boxes a year, to say nothing of cellophane and other packing materials; the nuisance, then, clearly provides the necessary funds, in the form of taxes paid at many points, for its own abatement.

Air pollution may be said to have begun with the first smoke of the first wood fire, and it was before that in the shattering explosions and immense conflagrations of volcanic action. But the earth and its creatures have survived the most formidable of natural air pollutions and man has been able to live on some sort of terms, if not always happily, with his own air pollutions until recently. Modern industrial civilization has been changing all this through the past 150 years and air pollutions are no longer to be disregarded.

The thickness of the earth's atmosphere is 18½ vertical miles, a windy, turbulent immensity that might well be expected to take care of enormous quantities of waste. Unfortunately many of the wastes do not disperse well and few of them remain indefinitely in suspension. Instead, they return to the earth and distribute their poisons. The most deadly and terrifying instance of this, if only because its full effects are still unknown, is radio-active fall-out. Dramatic localized examples of injury and death to human beings through industrial air pollution have occurred during the past thirty years – at Liege in Belgium during 1930, at Donora, Pennsylvania in 1948 and in London, England during the winter of 1952. These serve to emphasize the air pollution problems of crowded cities like Los Angeles, Vancouver and many others, where inhabitants are already inconvenienced and made uncomfortable by the wastes of rapidly growing industry and steadily increasing automobile traffic.

Vancouver and the Lower Fraser Valley are unquestionably the area of the province most seriously threatened by air pollution at present and there is no doubt that harmful effects are already felt by the population, though their precise nature and degree are not yet well understood. Since onshore winds, with fog and heavy atmosphere, are common and the high mountains along the north side of the valley make a natural trap, intensive research is essential. Strongly enforced controls will certainly become necessary, if they are not already overdue.

Elsewhere in the province air pollution, though frequently offensive, is not so threatening as in the Vancouver area. Victoria is well protected by open water on three sides and low ground on the fourth, with almost constant winds. The city of Alberni is badly trapped at the head of a long inlet and already suffers from its pulp mills and sawmills. Kraft pulp mills all along the south-east coast of Vancouver Island are extremely offensive at times, though better recovery and careful handling have materially reduced the nuisance. Most air pollutions of this type are a matter of economics rather than of necessity and it is reasonable to expect that control or complete elimination will become economically possible in the fairly near future.

All pollutions can, in fact, be controlled to the point where their effects are harmless and inoffensive. Whether they are or not is simply a matter of economic convenience. The view has been expressed that pollution in any degree is not *necessarily* an evil; it may be sound use of a natural resource. Effluents, gases and other wastes have to be disposed of in some way and the logical course is to make use of the readiest and cheapest means available – streams and watercourses, the air or the land. This practice has, in fact, been largely followed throughout western civilization, with effects that are sufficiently depressing to warn any country with clean rivers, clean air and clean land that the only reasonable and provident course is to keep all three as clean as possible for all time. In spite of every possible effort at prevention, some pollution is going to occur; this is in the nature of man's way of living, especially man's newly developed industrial way of living. Without the most rigid controls, domestic and industrial pollutions rapidly become intolerable under modern conditions and destroy many valuable things that can be restored, if at all, only at great cost in time and money; it will, for instance, take 40 years to restore the cleanliness of the United States' historic Potomac River if the present aggressive rehabilitation programme is followed through. Most pollutions are caused by poor utilization – inefficient combustion of fuels, inadequate recovery of useful chemicals, wasteful production methods in the manufacture of wood and other raw materials – and rigid control has the highly beneficial side-effect of forcing better utilization.

By far the most interesting example of air pollution in British Columbia was that of the great lead and zinc smelter at Trail. From its beginning in 1896 this plant was pouring about a thousand tons of sulphur a month into the atmosphere and this amount had steadily increased to over ten thousand tons a month by 1928. Besides being extremely unpleasant for nearby residents the sulphur fumes, in the form of sulphur dioxide, caused extensive damage to agricultural crops, timber and other vegetation. Since the plant is only ten miles from the international border, complaints soon came from United States residents and in 1928 an International Joint Commission was set up to look into the matter and set a cash value on the damage.

The company acted promptly and began to reduce the escape of sulphur at once. By 1935 the recovery was about fifty per cent of the eleven thousand tons processed in the plant each month. By 1942, the recovery had increased to over 65 per cent. By the 1950's only about a thousand tons a month were being wasted in the atmosphere while some fourteen thousand tons were being recovered. This recovery was costly in terms of research and the installation of equipment, but for many years has shown a handsome profit in the sale of ammonium sulphate and ammonium phosphate fertilizers. At the present time the quantities of sulphur coming into the plant are insufficient to keep up with the demand for these products.

Several points are worth noticing about this incident. The complaint had to come from another country to be effective. Significant damages assessed against the company by the International Commission provided a strong incentive. Something approaching complete elimination of pollution was achieved – a reduction of waste from a hundred per cent to less than seven per cent. And the recovery proved profitable, thus making better use of a resource and providing a new industry in the area.

Though air pollution is an increasingly serious threat to human health and comfort, water pollution has had the longest history of injury to mankind and still presents the most serious problems. Every phase of human activity is placing increasing demands on freshwater supplies and most of these demands are for water uncontaminated by human or industrial wastes; water that has been used must eventually be released again to find its way back into the natural drainage of the land, and unless it has first been cleaned of the impurities of use, it will inevitably spread contamination to water that is still clean.

Most water pollution results in reduction of the oxygen content which is essential to all aquatic life. Thus a large stream or a large body of water can carry a good deal of pollution before its free oxygen is exhausted or too drastically reduced, especially if turbulence of flow or wind action distribute the pollution and provide more oxygen. But the capacity of any stream or freshwater body to absorb pollution is limited. Comparatively minor pollutions may produce a modification of conditions that leads to gradual elimination of the original plant and animal life and its replacement by less desirable and more tolerant "weed" species. The deposition of solids, a characteristic of most pollutions, has a cumulative effect which, besides being offensive and unsightly, is more than likely to affect the carrying capacity of the drainage. The argument that streams and rivers should be used to carry off untreated domestic and industrial wastes can, therefore, have only limited validity in the very early stages of a country's development. As soon as population builds and water is needed for more important purposes, waste disposal must be controlled. If pollution has been carried too far and vested interests in the disposal of untreated wastes have been allowed to develop, control may be very difficult to establish. Most authorities on the use of water agree that prevention is a more practical and a more desirable objective than control and that no country can really afford to pollute its watersheds with untreated wastes. It is arguable that any community in Canada that cannot "afford" to treat its domestic wastes properly has been spending its money on the wrong things first. Any industry that cannot afford to treat its wastes properly is likely to be more of a liability than an asset.

The most important uses of water are usually listed as follows, in the order of

Brunette Creek near New Westminster is an example of a stream polluted from various sources.

their demand for water of high quality:

1. Domestic supply
2. Fisheries
3. Recreation
4. Industrial supply
5. Agriculture
6. Power
7. Navigation
8. Waste disposal

Waste disposal that limits or damages any of the first seven uses is bound to prove uneconomic in the long run. Since all water will be needed sooner or later for priority purposes, if it is not already so needed, it seems clear that waste discharges should be limited to fully treated wastes that will not cause offensive or damaging deposits.

This is an ideal policy, not one that has been followed anywhere on the North American continent. The practice is rather to permit discharge of effluents, both domestic and industrial, where these cause only slight or negligible damage, but to require treatment where and when pollution becomes intolerable. In effect, this often puts a heavy burden upon an established industry or a community that has not allowed for it, with the result that installation of the necessary treatment facilities is delayed for many years while the situation grows steadily worse.

Pollution from domestic sewage has not yet reached serious proportions except in the Vancouver and Lower Mainland areas. Here such cities as Vancouver, Burnaby, North Vancouver, New Westminster, Chilliwack and many others are discharging untreated sewage. Six cities or towns in the province provide primary treatment of sewage: Kamloops, Dawson Creek, Cranbrook, Fernie, McBride and Lake Cowichan. Only five cities, Vernon, Kelowna, Penticton, White Rock and Duncan, provide secondary or complete treatment; of these, only Kelowna reclaims sewage as fertilizer.

Sewage pollution has already destroyed shellfish resources in the harbours of Vancouver, Victoria, Nanaimo and in parts of Ladysmith harbour. Swimming areas in Victoria and Nanaimo harbours have been contaminated. Most of the beaches in the Greater Vancouver area present a constant problem and some have been closed for shorter or longer periods; it is obvious that these problems must increase and all beaches will become unusable in time unless treatment facilities are installed. Similar problems are developing in the neighbourhood of other smaller cities and towns in the province.

In the lower reaches of the Fraser River, industrial wastes combined with raw sewage have already created an oxygen demand that makes the North Arm of the river unsuitable for nearly all purposes, including the maintenance of fish life, while the coliform bacteria counts are far in excess of proper standards. While the great volume of the river still allows passage to migratory fish, it is obvious (a) that safe tolerances are already being approached, (b) that further increases of both population and industrial development are bound to occur, (c) that present use of the river for waste disposal allows for absolutely no increase, (d) that under unfavourable conditions, such as prolonged low water during the sockeye migration, serious damage might be caused by pollution already existing.

This is exactly the sort of situation that all too commonly develops when "harmless" pollutions are permitted and which leads in the end to serious difficulties that can only be solved at high cost. The problems of the Lower Fraser must be solved quite soon, not only for protection of the most valuable salmon runs in the world, but to permit the continued growth and development of the city of Vancouver. The logical policy would be to enforce treatment of all effluents, both domestic and industrial, since the eventual development of the area will probably strain the capacity of the river with incidental pollutions that cannot be readily controlled.

There have been many damaging local pollutions in the history of the province, usually affecting fish runs. Sawmill wastes, mine tailings, oil wastes, cannery discharges, toxic industrial wastes or oxygen-demanding organic wastes have all done damage from time to time, some of it unrepaired to this day. Better understanding of the problems and a closer watch by both federal and provincial authorities has materially reduced such incidents, but it remains true that a single irresponsible discharge can do harm that will take years to repair. The establishment of new pulp mills throughout the interior of the province, especially on the Fraser watershed, will present serious difficulties of waste disposal and anything short of complete treatment of all such effluents before release is likely to prove disastrous. While the physical responses of homing salmon are not yet fully understood, it is known that the olfactory senses play some part in guiding them; there is a real risk that insidious pollution by relatively minor chemical releases might lose the Fraser its runs by misdirection. Even the release of large quantities of non-toxic and otherwise clean effluents could have adverse effect on temperature conditions except at times of high flow.

The Lower Fraser and Vancouver city pollutions affect both fresh and salt water. Several pulp mills in the province have threatened marine pollutions and have led to important investigations. One of the most important of these was in relation to the proposed establishment of a sulphite pulp mill at Port Alberni. It was found that release of the sulphite effluent would reduce the oxygen content of the waters of Alberni Inlet below the tolerance of the fish during several months each year, unless it could be stored for release at periods of high flow from the Somass River, or unless the river itself could be controlled to yield a flow of 1600 cubic feet a second throughout the year. Since either alternative seemed too costly at that time, the company decided to construct a sulphate pulp mill, which discharges less than one-tenth as much effluent. This mill came into production in 1948. Its effluent is discharged through a retaining pond which settles out the waste fibres, and the oxygen content of water in the inlet has been maintained at a satisfactory level even during periods of minimum river flow.

Investigations at Alberni and elsewhere have shown clearly that the safety and efficiency of marine waste disposals vary from place to place in accordance with many complicated factors, such as tidal currents and turbulence, freshwater flow, salinity stability, natural oxygen content of the water and, of course, the quantity and quality of the effluent itself. The correct pattern of investigation is now well established and results are predictable with considerable accuracy. Proper provision for waste disposal is an essential prerequisite to the establishment of pulp mills everywhere; it seems likely that the steadily increasing efficiency of the mills themselves and better recovery of wastes will materially reduce both the cost and the difficulties of providing proper treatment of the effluents before discharge.

Freshwater pollution from herbicides and insecticides, such as D.D.T., 2-4-D, heptachlor, aldrin and other compounds, is pollution of a somewhat different nature in that it is a deliberate use of toxic substances to protect or enhance the yield of one resource use at grave risk to the biological balances that protect all resources, including the one being served.

It has been estimated that one billion pounds a year of pest-control chemicals are used on United States farms, with great damage to wildlife, especially aquatic creatures. British Columbia's relatively limited agricultural acreage makes it unlikely that farm spraying and dusting will become a major threat to other resource uses, except locally. Orchard spraying is known to have caused damage to bird life

The model built to study pulp mill pollution in Alberni Inlet – by the Fisheries Research Board of Canada at the Nanaimo Biological Station. Another model is currently being used to study halibut in Hecate Strait.

and all such spraying or dusting affects beneficial insects as well as pests and may also cause soil modifications – in other words, they represent a grave long-term risk for an immediate benefit. One large U.S. chemical firm, in announcing it had stopped manufacture of non-selective sprays, expressed itself in this way: "A twelve-year study has convinced us that currently known and used broad spectrum insecticides and their wide-scale application to agricultural crops – although giving temporary control and temporarily increased yields – is at best palliative and perhaps will prove dangerous and uneconomic in the long run. The growing number of insect pests of economic importance that are becoming resistant to presently used insecticides demonstrates a serious inherent danger in wide-scale use. The imbalance of the fauna population caused by the destruction of natural predators and parasites is further proof to us of the unsoundness of the current chemical insecticides." A statement such as this, supported by deliberate withdrawal from a profitable business, represents a high degree of informed conviction as well as an unusual sense of responsibility.

If agricultural sprays represent only a limited threat in the province, forest spraying could become very much more serious. Spraying of 155,000 acres on northern Vancouver Island in 1957, carefully planned and calculated to cause minimum damage to stream life, proved extremely destructive: "In the four major salmon streams affected by spraying, the progeny of an estimated 1956 escapement of 43,000 coho adults, and the juvenile stages of several thousand steelhead and trout was almost eliminated." The Keogh River escapement of 40,000 fish in 1956 brought back only 200 fish in 1959 and the losses of aquatic insects are expected to reduce the returns of subsequent years materially. In other words, complete recovery of streams in this area will probably take a dozen years or more. This particular spraying programme was effective in controlling the spruce bud-worm, against which it was directed – temporarily. But it undoubtedly damaged other natural controls in the form of birds, insect predators and parasites, frogs and snakes at the same time and may well contribute to further infestation at some later date. It is a balance of loss that plainly cannot be sustained.

Further experiments are to be undertaken in the Queen Charlotte Islands during 1960, using only ¼ lb. of D.D.T. to the acre instead of 1 lb. to the acre. This is expected to give satisfactory bud-worm control with only negligible damage to fish life, but even if this proves to be the case, the other questions remain unanswered.*

The disadvantages of D.D.T. and other known chemical sprays is that they are non-selective – that is, they affect birds, mammals, fish, reptiles and insects of all types; and they are relatively indestructible – their residues may accumulate and cause damage for many years. In other words, they are not in any way a safe or proper answer to the problems involved. Better forestry, especially the avoidance of pure timber stands, is probably the basic answer. But many authorities believe that selective biological controls can be achieved and the use of a bacterial insecticide for bud-worm control is already in the experimental stage.

British Columbians at present are all too vaguely aware of the dangers of pollution and all too ready to accept it as one of the necessary evils of development. It is a highly complex subject involving many aspects of resource use, and was examined in some detail at the Resources Conferences of 1953 and 1954, under a continuing pollution panel. In its final summary the panel directed itself chiefly to the problem of freshwater pollution and was able to state certain principles which, if adopted by both government and public, would ensure satisfactory control. The most important are as follows:

1. "The pollution control legislation in force in British Columbia to-day has had some effect in controlling pollution. . . . However, it has not dealt with the pollution problem as a whole. It is felt that the control of pollution is still in a preventative stage in British Columbia, and there is still time for effective measures to be taken to avoid having pollution become a major problem."

2. "There should come a day, if we plan properly, when it is accepted that no pollution will exist without the permission of a responsible authority and that such permission has been given in the public interest in accordance with sound principles of resource use planning."

3. "One agency should have authority to control all aspects of freshwater pollution."

With the guiding experience of a continent to draw upon and all the resources of modern technology at hand, it is difficult to believe that the ideal of clean waters is too great a luxury for the province to afford. No other area has had waters more worth guarding or more compelling economic reasons for guarding them.

*Preliminary reports indicate that effective bud-worm control was achieved with little or no serious damage to fish life.

TRANSPORTATION IS A NATURAL RESOURCE only in the sense that the natural features of the land and its situation in relation to other trading areas are more or less favourable. But transportation is the ultimate key to almost all the resources and so calls for some brief examination in a book of this sort.

Every natural feature of the province, including its situation, has worked to delay development. The coastline, distant from Europe and eastern North America by the long sea voyages around Cape Horn or the Cape of Good Hope, was one of the last in the world to be fully examined. In the east the Rocky Mountains were a barrier to early travel and in the west the Coast Range prevented easy inroad from the coast. All through the interior of the province mountain ranges and rapid, broken rivers limited travel and slowed exploration.

The earliest development of travel and transportation was by sea routes along the coast, by trail and canoe along the rivers and through the mountain passes of the interior – the fur-traders' routes. Early gold miners used the same trails and inland waterways; the first access roads, still following the waterways, were built in the 1860's. Nearly 25 years later the first railroad came through from the east to join the province to the rest of Canada by one of the passes that David Thompson, the geographer and fur-trader, had discovered and used some 75 years earlier.

To this day, there are few main routes of travel, except the airlines, that were not used by the earliest travellers and traders. Road and railroad and pipeline have replaced trail and canoe and river steamboat, but the lines they follow by twisting, steep-sided river valleys and difficult mountain passes must be the same; and they remain both difficult and costly in spite of the formidable means of modern construction and travel.

From the completion of the transcontinental railroad, the province's favourable geographic situation was recognized by increasing Oriental trade. While this trade has been seriously interrupted by two world wars and is now curtailed by political considerations and the disorganization of early Communist development in China, it is certain to increase in time and become a tremendous factor in the economy of the province. Trade with Japan has increased steadily since the Second World War and is already the major factor in iron ore development. Important future developments in the trade of coal, lumber, pulp and fishery products in exchange for manufactured goods are logically certain unless political considerations interfere again.

The opening of the Panama Canal in 1914 shortened the main sea routes to eastern Canada and Europe immensely and gave added meaning to the Pacific ports as outlets for bulk shipping to occidental markets. Over 4 million long tons were loaded for shipment through the Canal from these ports in 1955, compared to about 1½ million tons in 1927; figures for 1956 and 1957 were 3.6 and 3.5 million tons respectively. All of this has the added value of making a standard of competition for other transportation rates between east and west.

As recently as thirty years ago the province's main transportation facilities were the railroads and the coastwise tugs and steamships. Tug and barge transportation has largely superseded the coastal steamships and self-dumping barge transportation is replacing the log rafts on longer tows. Small float planes are becoming increasingly important in transporting passengers, fresh food and urgently needed equipment to outlying camps all along the coast. In other words, the transportation value of the coastal waters is as important as ever, though the means of using them are slowly changing.

The two transcontinental railroads, the Canadian National with terminals at Prince Rupert and Vancouver and the Canadian Pacific with its terminal at Vancouver, have increased their efficiency by substitution of diesel power for steam and still carry the main freight traffic eastward from the province. Truck traffic has already cut into the high-grade traffic of the railroads and will become increasingly competitive as highways are completed and improved, although the total volume of freight carried by the railroads has been and still is steadily increasing. The breakdown of railway monopoly has resulted in an undue burden of freight costs on the "captive traffic", mainly bulky primary products. The railways face the alternatives of further increasing freight rates on this non-competitive traffic, asking relief in government subsidy or abandoning costly passenger services and unremunerative branch lines. But on the longer hauls over bad terrain, especially under adverse weather conditions, it would seem that road and railroad should be complementary rather than competitive for a long while to come, with truck trailers loaded on flat cars playing a large part.

It is within the province that the greatest recent changes in transportation have come about. The Pacific Great Eastern Railroad, now completed from North Vancouver by way of Prince George to Fort St. John and Dawson Creek in the Peace River country, makes the first north-south rail line in the history of the province.

Another railroad, still in the planning stage, may eventually lead northward from a point just south of Summit Lake on the P.G.E. above Prince George, to the Yukon boundary, providing the first major transportation route into and out of the great northern section of the province lying between the Rockies and the Alaska Panhandle; ultimately it should connect with rail facilities in Alaska, to provide the first rail link between Alaska and the United States. Major transportation routes of this type, as has already been pointed out, are among the most important factors in resource development. They not only bring known timber stands and mineral deposits into economic production, but open the country to more intensive exploration. There should, of course, be sufficient freight to meet operating costs from the start, though depreciation and other costs may not be met for some time; in this way though conventionally uneconomic, they can probably be considered a most valuable and constructive form of subsidization, if government run. Private capital, because of the great economic risk, can usually be attracted only by large land grants which later prove costly to the country as a whole. Accurate appraisal of just what concessions and grants may safely and usefully be made to private railroad companies has proved one of the most difficult and treacherous problems in resource management.

By far the most significant advances in transportation within the past fifteen or twenty years have been brought about by the steady development of the commercial motor vehicle. Roads are not easily or cheaply built in most parts of British Columbia, but in the ten years from 1949 to 1959 the mileage of gravel highways increased from about 8000 to 10,200 and that of paved highways doubled, from 1900 to 4000. In the same period the number of commercial vehicles in operation increased from 60,000 to 122,000.

The fabulous Cariboo Road through the Fraser Canyon was started by the Royal Engineers in 1861. It has been improved over the years and used continuously as a major transportation route to the interior, but its most frightening parts have recently been eliminated.

This by no means tells the whole story. Freight vehicles steadily become more flexible and adaptable in operation, load capacities have increased to 80,000 pounds or more and in the case of logging vehicles to as much as 200 tons; speeds have increased to the point where sixty miles an hour on good paved highways is standard for even the largest vehicles. These are among the factors that have brought about the revolutionary change from steam to internal combustion motors in nearly all logging operations and so rendered accessible much timber that could not have been reached by the older methods. Fast trucks now handle practically all the haulage of general farm products, including milk, to local markets. Most of the fruit from the Okanagan and the Kootenays is carried by truck to Vancouver for shipment. Even grain and livestock are commonly transported by road within the province. Mining products, including coal and iron ore, have been carried successfully over relatively short hauls to tidewater.

All these changes tend to offset the difficulties of terrain, make resources more accessible and allow for a better distribution of the productive effort, which in turn makes for a larger return within the limits of sustained yield or a better opportunity for redirecting pressures where sustained yield has been exceeded. Assorted modern vehicles such as the jeep and the power wagon, half-track snow and muskeg vehicles, the airplane and the helicopter, play major parts in exploration, in the early stages of construction and in later maintenance, permitting safe and even rapid travel and transportation where either would have been next to impossible a few years ago.

In larger-scale construction, bull-dozers, earth movers, giant shovels and other machines have improved highway construction, dam-building and land-clearing techniques and helped to bring many resources into service. Carelessly used, some of them have proved a mixed blessing. Thousands of acres have been cleared of trees and stumps for house construction without the slightest regard for anything except realizing a quick return in real estate, with the result that householders have to replace soil as they can and start on the slow process of growing themselves a little shade where hundred-year-old trees grew only a few months earlier. Roads and power lines, hastily forced through by formidable machinery, often expose the land to soil erosion; speculative land clearing and drainage projects are too easily undertaken and when poorly planned can do great harm. Unquestionably the heavy bull-dozer and other great machines are beneficial in the balance; but their power and effects make them tools that should never be used lightly or without proper regard for the land.

Pipeline transportation is another development of major importance in overcoming difficulties of terrain and distance. The Transmountain pipeline brings oil from Alberta to refineries at Kamloops and in the Vancouver area, while the natural gas line runs from the Peace River fields right down the centre of the province to reach Burrard Inlet and as far south of the border as Portland. The steady increase of proven gas reserves has already established the need for a second line

Booms – the first and still important method of transporting logs by water. As long as the logs are in the water, however, Teredos, a mollusc wood borer, are a great problem.

onverted sailing ships are utilized as one means of getting the logs out of the water.

The self-dumping log barge is a major innovation.

The experimental fibre-glass "bubble" for transporting wood chips.

from Taylor Flats on the Peace, while the yield of new gas fields in the Fort Nelson area will be brought down by a feeder line. The capacity of the double main line is expected to be about one billion cubic feet a day. While pipelines are costly to build and each carries only a single material, they are among the simplest of transportation means and suggest interesting possibilities of transporting other raw materials from source to central manufacturing plants. Pulp, for instance, can be transported by pipeline, a fact that may well be used to open up northern timber stands that are now remote from any main transportation route.

The mountainous nature of the province makes flying more difficult and dangerous than in most other parts of the country and certainly restricts the use of small private airplanes. At the same time scattered population, circuitous land routes and widespread commercial interests, especially in the natural resources, make flying essential and have contributed to the rapid growth of airlines offering charter and local scheduled flights. Sheltered water along the coastline and the abundance of suitable lakes in most parts of the province make for effective use of float planes nearly everywhere, but airports and airfields now number well over a hundred and are increasing every year. In some instances airlines are able to compete successfully with ground or water transport on freight hauls.

Most of the larger centres in the province are served by multiple daily flights to and from Vancouver, and regular flights leave Vancouver for Japan, Australia, Central and South America, and for Europe by way of the Pole. But unquestionably the greatest benefit that air transportation has brought to the province is in the multiple daily flights that cross the mountains to the rest of Canada. With Toronto, Ottawa and Montreal only four or five hours away, instead of four or five days, ready interchange of ideas between east and west is immensely simplified and the people of the Pacific slope can develop with the rest of the nation as never before in their history.

In a discussion of transportation facilities at the 11th Resources Conference in 1958 it was concluded that "viewed quantitatively, the development of transportation facilities essential to our economic development has been more than sufficient. The basic problem . . . is to become more efficient." Anyone who has suffered with the loading and unloading of the C.P.R. ferries between Nanaimo and Vancouver will confirm this suggestion, as will the airline passengers who travel from Vancouver to Victoria, spending thirty minutes in the air and two hours in ground travel. Road transportation in and near all large North American cities is notoriously inefficient and Vancouver is no exception, though the Deas Island tunnel has greatly improved access from the south. Railroad efficiency is considered to have increased 25 per cent with the substitution of diesel for steam as motive power. Barge transportation and use of specialized equipment such as self-dumping log barges and the pulp carrier *Duncan Bay* have increased the efficiency of water transport of bulk commodities. But loading and unloading are still the main factors reducing efficiency in nearly all forms of transportation. Special containers carrying large loads directly from warehouse to wharf or railhead to be loaded directly are one of the few recent improvements in freight handling.

Broadly it can be said that the province is making good use of all the natural lines of surface transportation except the Rocky Mountain Trench and possibly the coastal waters. The present stage of development in the Trench does not call for a continuous north-south link and the probability of flooding by the Peace River Power development will preclude land transportation in the northern section, though permitting a certain amount of barge and other water transportation in the storage lake. On the coast some limited highway development is planned and ferry links from Port Hardy on northern Vancouver Island to Kitimat, and from Prince Rupert to Haines on the Alaska Highway system, are under consideration.

The present pattern of transportation use centres on the line of the Fraser River, running eastward from Vancouver to Hope, then northward to Prince George, leaving the watershed at the Arctic divide just beyond Prince George, then swinging eastward through Pine Pass to the Peace River and the Alaska Highway. Two main branches turn westward to reach the Pacific coast at Bella Coola and Prince Rupert. Easterly branches lead off by the Hope-Princeton route to the southern interior, by the Thompson to Kamloops and the Trans-Canada Highway and from Prince George along the Upper Fraser to Yellowhead Pass. Main or secondary highways have been completed along all except the last of these routes and Yellowhead can now be reached in summer by the North Thompson River. Branch roads from these main arteries and the roads or railroads that follow them, together with water transportation, can tap most of the resources in the southern half of the province. In the north the Pine Pass and Alaska Highways serve the Transmontane section of the province, as does the Pacific Great Eastern. Only the massive northwestern section of the province remains to be opened by a major transportation route and there is good reason to expect that both road and railroad will find ways into it within the next decade.

aboriginal stock CHAPTER 25

THE PRACTICE OF the Resources Conferences has been to consider people as a resource – "the human resource". Occasionally this has been questioned, though on what grounds I am not quite sure; perhaps because of a reluctance to classify humans with fish, wildlife and trees. People are the catalytic resource; without them, none of the other resources would have any of the meanings I have tried to express in this book. They have somewhat the same relationship to all the resources that fish, wildlife, domestic stock, crops, trees and other plant life bear to soil and water. They put them to use, give them meaning.

In this process people serve each other and use each other; individually and in groups they do both of these things well or less well, depending on their manifold qualities. If people are to perform soundly and usefully, they need understanding and consideration, proper habitat and living conditions and all the other things that natural resources need; only if these are available will the human resource reproduce and maintain itself at a proper yield of sustained performance.

It is here, in the matter of performance, that the one essential difference lies. The highest and most useful qualities of man are not physical but mental. They are extremely complicated and unpredictable and the grandest qualities of man can be revealed in the most unlikely physical shells. Man himself has generally been quick to realize this and, realizing it, has always been properly reluctant to interfere with or reduce the multiplicity of natural chances of breeding and environment that produce the different shades and qualities of creative human thought. Efforts to improve the human race by selective breeding and other types of management have generally been short-lived and invariably self-destructive. Man does not know enough to manage men on this level and probably never will; but within that limitation man can do a lot to help mankind and, naturally enough, himself in the process.

Once this point of difference is clearly stated, it is wholly proper to consider people as a resource and examine their performance and deficiencies as thoroughly as may be. The real purpose of using any of the resources must be to advance the happiness and development of mankind; it is a purpose that cannot be achieved blindly, without close examination of man, his needs and desires and the nature of his growth.

The explorers and fur-traders used the native peoples directly as a resource. Without them the country would have been meaningless and useless. The explorers would have searched many years longer to find the ways into the country and most would not have survived their searching; without the Indian peoples the fur-traders could never have gathered the beaver and sea-otter skins for profitable sale in distant markets.

The explorers and early fur-traders were generally fair and humane in their dealings with the native peoples; in effect, they had to be, because they were tiny groups of visitors in a populated land where any strongly concerted action against them by the natives could have wiped them out. But they often went beyond this and showed themselves as men of sensitivity and understanding, with a real sympathy for the qualities they found in the Indian peoples; in their records are to be found the only clear accounts of what the Indians were like under primitive conditions.

Alexander Mackenzie, writing of the Bella Coola Indians, gives a clear idea of the wealth of the coastal peoples: "These people had salmon by thousands with roots and berries of all kinds in abundance. My people were well cared for. And the chief lent us his great canoe with four men and his son to guide us. The river proved swift, almost an unbroken succession of rapids. I had imagined my Canadians were the most expert Canoemen in the world, but they are very inferior to these people, as they themselves acknowledged." Twenty years later David Thompson wrote of the Kootenay Indians: "The Indians on the west side of the mountains pride themselves on their industry and their skill in doing anything; they are as neat and cleanly in their persons as circumstances will allow. I found them a fine race of moral Indians, the finest I have seen, and they set a high value on the chastity of their women." And Simon Fraser, writing of the Lillooets and Shuswaps: "These people have many chiefs and great men and are good orators, with extremely handsome delivery. They showed us every possible attention and supplied our wants as much as they could."

Accounts such as these are important, because they show prosperous, sufficiently industrious, often cultured peoples, behaving with civility and decency. The later fur-traders exploited them, just as any natural resource is exploited in a new country, taking much and giving little but they remained essentially visitors in the land, dependent upon the good will of the native peoples.

Many of the early miners were helped by the Indians and the first coarse-gold strike in the Cariboo country was shown to Dunlevy and Sellars by Tomaah the

Shuswap and Long Baptiste, the great Déné hunter. The early settlers and cattle-
men were similarly dependent. Kathleen Ellis said of her father's great ranch at
Penticton: "The Indians became our greatest friends. They were the best helpers
we had with the cattle." Mrs. Hester White of Osoyoos said: "The Indians were
very wonderful people. They were magnificent campers and packers." The Corn-
walls of Ashcroft found them "good people; we couldn't have got along without
them."

   This, then, was how the Indians of the Pacific slope appeared to those who first
saw them and had dealings with them; they were friendly, co-operative people, well
settled in the land, well adapted to it and making good use of it within the limits of
their needs and technical development. There was much that did not appear, or
appeared less clearly. These Indians, even the Kootenays of the Upper Columbia
to some extent, were the salmon peoples. They enjoyed a seasonal abundance that
controlled their lives. The peoples of the coast were best served by the salmon runs
and other yields of the sea, and also by a more moderate climate than anywhere
else in Canada. They were, within their needs, a wealthy people, with time to
think, time for entertainment, time for development. They were carvers and singers
and orators, inventors of dances, builders of houses, tellers of stories. They had
complicated religious concepts, an advanced system of morality and a developed
philosophy that allowed for relatively peaceful relationships between individuals,
between tribe and tribe and, in considerable degree, between the dozen or so civilizations that flourished in the area. It may well be that they produced more creative
development for the human spirit than has been produced in the hundred years of
white civilization that have followed upon the time of their greatest flowering.

   Little of this was apparent to the miners and other white settlers who moved in
in such numbers after 1858. Where the Indians could help, they were used; but the
earlier shortages of labour and local knowledge soon ceased to be a factor, and the

Carvings by British Columbia coastal Indians,
from the collection of the Marquis of Lorne.

Indians became an inconvenience rather than anything else. By 1862 the smallpox epidemic was raging northward and inland from Victoria. Tuberculosis and other white diseases began their steady inroads and liquor was doing its damage among a people completely unused to it and unprepared for it. By 1885 a total population of over 70,000 had declined to 28,000 or less. Whole villages and in some cases entire language groups had been wiped out. Little was left of the great civilizations that had flourished on the salmon runs and nothing had been given to replace them. The Indian peoples had become, in every sense, a depleted resource, used, misused and finally pushed out of the way. The decline in population continued to a low point in 1929 of 22,600.

Within the past thirty years the quality of the Indian peoples and the strength of their old civilizations has begun to reassert itself. Tuberculosis has been controlled; living conditions have improved and the Indians themselves have found more and more ways of working successfully within the frame of white civilization. By 1954 the Indian population had increased to more than 31,000 and since that time the increase has continued at a rate more than double that of the population as a whole.

The greatest and most highly developed of the primitive Indian civilizations were along the coast – the Tsimshian in the Nass and Skeena River areas, Haida of the Queen Charlotte Islands, Kwakiutl and Bella Coola of the central coast and northern Vancouver Island, Nootka on the west coast of Vancouver Island and Salish on the lower mainland coast and the south-eastern part of Vancouver Island. The southern interior groups are the Salishan and the Kootenays, while the whole northern part of the province from Alexandria on the Fraser and including the Chilcotin country was occupied by the Athapaskan group. Each of these major groupings represents a language relationship, but is broken down again into separate languages – the Sekani, Carrier and Chilcotin of the Athapaskan group, for instance, and the Shuswap, Thompson and Lillooet of the Salishan group – and again into dialects and finally into regional groupings of individual tribes. Altogether 28 languages have been recognized in the province, of which 24 are still surviving in some degree. This high complexity suggests the long-term establishment of the groups and the difficulties of travel that separated them, though the early explorers found that, by taking an interpreter forward with them from each group they met, they were able to establish satisfactory communication with the next group.

The wealth of the coastal Indians came to them easily from the salmon and eulachon fisheries, from the shellfish beds and even from the offshore waters in the form of halibut, sea mammals and whales. On the lower reaches of the great river systems, the people met the salmon as they came and also travelled out to the salt water itself; on the upper reaches they depended mainly on the salmon, but in other seasons vigorously hunted the land animals, elk, moose, deer, mountain goat, beaver and others. In the far north and in the east, against the Rocky Mountains, the people were primarily hunters, even crossing the mountains to hunt buffalo.

To a considerable extent these patterns of activity still hold to-day. The coast Indians are still fishermen; some of them are outstandingly successful, though others have not yet adjusted to the work as a livelihood rather than a subsistence. A number have turned to logging where they are usually valued workers and some few are successful small operators. In the interior, logging, farming and ranching are the main occupations, while in the north trapping, logging and sawmill work are the most important. In the Kootenay area, on the Interior Plateau and in the far north there is still much hunting for food and Indians are successful as guides and packers.

Between seven and eight thousand Indians in the province are considered to be gainfully employed. Of these, nearly 3500 work in the fishing industry, about two-thirds of them actually fishing and one-third in the processing industry. About 1500 work in the logging and sawmill industry, perhaps 1250 in agriculture or stock farming. Four hundred or more earn their main living as trappers and another four or five hundred combine trapping with other activities. Five or six hundred are "casual" workers, chiefly in agriculture or logging. About 250 are in other trades of various types. A fair proportion of those in the fishing industry own boats, nets and other equipment of considerable value and some of the ranchers, especially in the Okanagan, are also men of substance.

For a people demoralized by disease, dispossession and misunderstanding through nearly a hundred years, this is an impressive record, and it is by no means a static one. In many areas the Indian peoples are just beginning to take full advantage of the educational opportunities offered by the public schools of the province. In spite of some language and cultural handicaps and a rather casual attitude towards school attendance, they often do extremely well. Both language and cultural handicaps are disappearing fast except in remote areas, and in some of the more developed tribes there is a rapidly increasing understanding of the benefits of education. Within the next twenty years a considerable number of Indian children will be completing their high school education as a matter of course and a fair proportion of them will go on to university. Unfortunately, this will not happen equally throughout the province, but wherever it does it will have a sharply cumulative effect.

The Indian peoples still suffer from many disadvantages, and not the least of these is the discriminatory legislation that both protects and inhibits them. Discriminatory liquor laws, an anachronism that has been allowed to persist far too long, are a good example of this; originally conceived as a protection, they have long been an insult and a challenge that has trapped many young Indians into conflict with the law and a persisting sense of inferiority that sometimes leads to further troubles and, not infrequently, to alcoholism. The over-protective and often dictatorial attitude of the Department of Indian Affairs has been another great handicap, although there are now signs of more enlightened federal policies. Aris-

An Indian salmon cache, engraved from a photograph
taken by the Marquis of Lorne in 1882.

ing out of these is the greatest handicap of all, a narrow suspicion of white men and all their dealings. While far too often justified by past experience, this suspicion is unselective and has frequently deprived the Indian peoples of advice and assistance that could have made a great deal of difference in their affairs.

Still another handicap to direct competition in white society is the primitive sense of proportion that applies itself vigorously to work when necessary – that is, in the seasons when game is abundant or fish are running – and turns readily to other things, such as talk, thought or entertainment when immediate needs are supplied. Western man, hag-ridden by a culture that finds virtue in work for its own sake, has difficulty in understanding this attitude or fitting it into the treadmill of his own affairs. He is all too likely to consider the Indian unreliable and to employ workers who more nearly fit his own attitudes. He can hardly be blamed for this, but it works to the disadvantage of Indians who are adapting to the work habits of white people, just as the Indian's constant suspicion in business dealings with whites too often loses him sound opportunities of profit.

The Indian peoples as a whole do not want assimilation and loss of identity, and it is difficult to believe that they should want either of these things. Their own civilizations had many values that are worth preserving and which, properly interpreted and adapted to meet modern conditions, can continue to enrich the general development of mankind. Further, the Indian peoples are in a strong position to preserve their identity and many of their ways of thought. The reserve system may have its disadvantages and certainly has contributed to delay in development. But under the present conditions of steadily increasing land use many reserve lands are assuming important values that can be turned to the advantage of the bands that own them. Many Indian peoples have special skills and knowledge that might be put to far better economic use than has so far been the case. Fur trapping is at present depressed by low market prices, but the ownership of a good proportion of registered traplines is of importance and the native skills in woodcraft could well be developed by education to provide a better yield from the lines themselves and a better financial return through more sophisticated business attitudes. Some interior groups have special skill in handling cattle and here again there is room for significant development by better use of reserve lands, intelligent employment of capital and, in some instances, soundly planned co-operative effort.

On the coast, Indian seamanship and fishing skills are already well used and many Indian families have achieved a high degree of prosperity, especially since the return of the Fraser River sockeye runs. Though many Indians own valuable boats and equipment, the full potential of their special skills and knowledge has by no means been realized. Education and the wise use of capital could make immense differences. Educational advances are likely to be quite rapid over the next twenty years, and capital will certainly become available as the rehabilitation of the salmon runs continues. It is probably significant that the Indian peoples are better equipped both psychologically and economically to withstand the difficulties of the "off-years" than are the white fishermen.

Very few adult Indians to-day have a full high school education, but in many areas this will change markedly within the next generation. Though Indian attitudes towards school attendance are still too casual and there is also a continuing fear that children who take advanced education may be lost to families and reserves, there is little doubt that the effect will be progressive. The more reflective adult Indians already realize that a generally increased educational level will open many possibilities.

Most Indian groups could use people of their own race in nearly all the professional fields – doctors, lawyers, teachers and civil servants are perhaps especially needed, but people trained in business, agriculture, biology, engineering and most forms of land management could also contribute greatly. Perhaps the greatest need of all is for fully literate individuals who would be able to give leadership within groups and bands by developing and reinterpreting the old cultures to give them meaning and life renewed under modern conditions. The sooner the Indian groups become able to handle their property and affairs safely and effectively, the greater their contribution to the life and character of the province will become.

It should be emphasized that this account, as must be the case with any brief examination of so complex a subject, is essentially oversimplified. There are tremendous variations in degree of adaptation and development, in economic circumstances and acceptance of responsibility between group and group, tribe and tribe and often enough between individuals within the same tribe. This should not be surprising; there are similar differences between white groups and differences at least equally significant between white individuals within groups, though attention is not called to them in the same way because the groups are less formal. There are also wide variations from locality to locality in the educational facilities and other forms of outside assistance available to the Indian peoples.

Indians, no less than whites, are individuals, with exactly the same wide ranges of mental and physical capacity and character variation. They are grouped by force of circumstances; general habit, way of life and property considerations make it very difficult to break away from the groups or the localities in which the groups live, even though there is legal provision for any individuals who wish to make such a move. The remoteness of some groups will unquestionably delay their advancement, just as ideal situation will hasten that of others. There is no possibility of equal and steady advancement, though a good deal more could be done to hasten it in remote areas. Within the more advanced groups, the most important future moves must certainly come from the Indians themselves, as there is good evidence that they will. White acceptance and understanding of these moves will be important to their success, and white assistance can make some contribution. Increasing population, together with increasing sophistication and a genuine awareness of their own identity as the original inhabitants of the land, make it quite certain that the Indian peoples will play a powerful part in the future of the province.

CHAPTER 26 *immigrant stock*

ACCORDING TO A rather inaccurate census taken by the British Columbia government just before Confederation, the non-Indian population of the province in 1871
was about 15,000. The great majority of these people had come into the country in
the years after 1857. By the census of 1901 the non-Indian population had increased to more than 150,000; about 70,000 of these were Canadian-born, more
than 32,000 had come from the British Islands or other parts of the Commonwealth
and over 17,000 were born in the United States. Chinese and Japanese made up
the next largest groups, with 14,500 and 4,500 respectively, while immigrants from
all other countries combined were less than 10,000.

By the census of 1951, the population of the province had increased to about
1,200,000, 71 per cent of whom had been born in Canada, 16 per cent in the United
Kingdom, seven and a half per cent in Europe, 3½ per cent in the United States,
1.2 per cent in Asia, less than one per cent elsewhere.

The fifty-year trend between the two census years has increased the proportion
of Canadian-born residents from less than fifty per cent to over seventy per cent; it
has reduced the proportion of residents born in the British Isles from about twenty
per cent to sixteen per cent (the proportions in 1931 and 1941 were 26 per cent and
21.5 per cent respectively), reduced the proportion of U.S.-born from over ten per
cent to 3.5 per cent and the proportion of Oriental-born from over twelve per cent
to less than two per cent. The proportion of European-born is slightly increased,
but is less than the 1931 figure of 8.4 per cent. It should be noted that the reduction
of Oriental population was brought about partly by discriminatory immigration
laws, partly by forced emigration to other provinces.

Considered in another way, by ethnic origin rather than by place of birth, the
proportions in 1951 were as follows: British 65.7 per cent, Scandinavian 5.6, Ger-
man 4.7, French 3.6, Netherlands 2.8, native Indian 2.4. All other origins, includ-

ing Asiatic, were less than two per cent and made up a total of fifteen per cent.

The picture that emerges from these figures is of a population preponderantly Canadian-born and preponderantly British in origin. The proportion of those of British origin is slowly declining – it was almost seventy per cent in 1941 – while the proportion of Canadian-born population has rather rapidly increased, from fifty-four per cent in 1931 to sixty-three per cent in 1941 to seventy-one per cent in 1951. Both trends may be expected to continue, but the second should have by far the greater influence. It means that a steadily increasing proportion of the population shares a Canadian up-bringing and education and, presumably, a better understanding of Canadian ideals and institutions. It means also that the people of the province will become increasingly dependent upon the quality of Canadian education and the influence of Canadian environment for their ideas and progress and for development of the philosophies by which they live and use their resources. The broadening and enlivening effects of immigration will certainly continue for many years to come, but they can hardly be expected to make the massive contributions they have in the past.

At the same time it must be emphasized that immigration, from other parts of Canada as well as from abroad, rather than births within the province, continues to be the most important factor in population increase. From 1921-31 immigration made up seventy-one per cent of the total increase; it has remained at about sixty-four per cent of total increase through the years from 1931 to 1956. British Columbia has the lowest rate of natural increase of any province in Canada, with an average family size, including parents, of 3.4, compared to 4.6 in Newfoundland, 4.2 in Quebec, 3.5 in Ontario, and a national average of 3.8. It has been pointed out that immigration, depending as it does upon economic factors and upon specific population shortages, is a less reliable source of population increase than natural births. During the ten or twelve years after World War II immigration was greatly stimulated by a number of large construction projects and by population shortage in the 20-35 year age groups, accounted for by the low birth rate of the depression years. A majority of immigrants was within these age limits and fitted naturally into the jobs made by the various projects. In the event of another major construction boom, this situation will be considerably modified, because increasing numbers of native-born British Columbians are growing up to fill the population gap; it may well happen that conditions will never again be quite so favourable to massive immigration.

Another notable disproportion is in the number of older immigrants to the province, men of 65 or more, women of 60 or over. This is accounted for by the retirement of older people, especially from the prairie provinces, to the milder climate of the coast and southern interior. It is likely to be a continuing factor and has the effect of giving the province a higher proportion of older people and a higher death rate than most parts of Canada.

The conditions that make British Columbia attractive to immigrants from other parts of Canada, especially the prairie provinces, are higher wages, a shorter working week, climate and recreational opportunities. The first two factors may be modified in time, but the other two will always give the province some advantage in attracting population. There is also a fairly constant movement of people out of the province – in 1950, an exceptional year, 117 more families moved out than moved in – and it is believed that this is due largely to the seasonal nature of much of the work; frequent labour disputes may also be a factor.

There is some indication, mainly economic, that both birth rate and immigration will continue to decline during the next few years from the high peaks of the post-war construction years. But an annual birth rate of 30,000-33,000 is to be expected unless there is a severe recession. This natural increase, together with the large number of native British Columbians who will be growing through the 20-35 year age group, will reduce the province's excessive dependence on immigration and help to ensure a more stable population growth. This will have important sociological advantages since it will permit much more orderly and efficient development of housing, schools, local and provincial administration and other essential services. It is scarcely necessary to add that spectacularly large construction projects, occurring together, could change this prospect; but with every year of natural increase the province's resident population is better able to absorb such uncertainties of immigration.

In the years from 1931 to 1956 the total population of the province almost exactly doubled itself, from just under 700,000 to almost 1,400,000. Within the same period there has been a sharp change in the occupations of the working population. In 1931 about 25 per cent of the labour force was employed in the primary industries; by 1951 this figure had fallen to 13 per cent. Employment in manufacturing industries increased from 11½ per cent to fifteen per cent and in the service industries from 63½ per cent to 72 per cent. At the same time the percentage of population in the labour force dropped from 44 to 38.1, more closely approaching the over-all Canadian figure of about 37 per cent. This last change reflects development from a pioneer society with many single men working in more or less remote areas to a more normal pattern of marriage and family life. The occupational changes are not peculiar to British Columbia, but are part of a long-term development by which the productivity of primary workers has been steadily increased, to release more and more workers to serve the manufacturing and service industries. The rather dramatic figures in British Columbia, and throughout Canada as a whole, for the past twenty years simply reflect the very rapid recent advances in machinery and techniques that have reduced the manpower needed for primary production. Perhaps it should be emphasized that this does *not* mean that the population of the province as a whole is any the less dependent upon the natural resources that support the primary industries. All the major manufacturing industries, including sawmilling, pulp and paper production, fish and food production, metallurgical and chemical production, depend directly upon raw materials produced within the province by the primary industries. The dependence of the service industries is less direct, but just as essential.

This rather formidable assembly of facts and figures is a bald quantitative inventory of the people of the province, but it gives little idea of their qualities and peculiarities. As has often been noted, all Canadians are quite strongly regional or provincial and British Columbians are no exception. This is not a reproach. It is simply something that has to be in a country of great distances, sharp geographical divisions and sparse populations in large land areas. Prairie people are Prairie people, Maritimers are Maritimers, the peoples of Quebec and Ontario each have their own special viewpoints and peculiarities. British Columbians, behind their ramparts of mountains, facing westward to the Pacific and being the westernmost people of the nation, have been shaped into their own special ways not only by geography but by the rough selection of immigration.

For over a hundred years British Columbia has been a frontier province and essentially she still is one. It is true that immigrants can now move west from the great cities of the Old World and the East and find almost identical security on the sidewalks of Vancouver or Victoria or Prince George; but the province remains a place of uncertainty and endeavour, still reaching out to realize more of its potential and, in spite of the speed of modern travel, it is still remote enough to ensure that the immigrant is effectually cut off from all his former associations.

This means that the province has attracted, from the beginning, people who saw in their own countries little or no prospect of success or advancement and who had the initiative to do something about it – something, moreover, which took them out pretty well beyond the point of no return. A decision of this sort usually implies restlessness, dissatisfaction and a nice measure of instability; it often implies radical thinking, an adventurous spirit and considerable optimism. The people of British Columbia are all these things and others besides. In boom times, for instance, they forget radicalism and become avaricious, conservative in politics, pragmatic and destructive, careless of resource management if there is quick money to be made; in quieter times they ask questions again, fear for the future, consolidate their civilization and care for their resources.

People coming to British Columbia have expected the freedoms of a young country, the ready availability of land and opportunity, and a public sharing of the benefits of resource use that has never been realized under older societies. In addition, they have brought with them the powerful traditions of British trade-unionism. To some extent they have found what they were looking for. But they have found, too, that resources are not developed without capital in one form or another and that capital does not move into new countries without strong inducements. The result has been a long history of labour conflicts, occasionally violent, frequently protracted and often very costly to both sides.

The militancy of British Columbia labour has been supported by several factors besides the natural character of the people. The primary occupations, logging, min-

ARCHIBALD MENZIES, 1754 - 1842, was a Scottish doctor and botanist who visited British Columbia twice as a naturalist-collector for the Kew Gardens. He came first in 1790 with the fur trader Captain Colnett and again, two years later, with Captain George Vancouver on his famous voyage of discovery. He introduced many of our native plants into England, some of which were to be brought back later by colonists as English garden plants. Among those brought by the colonists was the Monkey-puzzle tree, which Menzies discovered by accident in Chile when he noticed a bowl full of odd-looking nuts and filched several of them for his green-house aboard Vancouver's ship.

ing, fishing, have always been particularly open to strike action. In similar industries across the border, aggressive American unions have set an example of determined action and the generally higher wages and lower prices of the American side are a ready source of dissatisfaction. The seasonal nature of much of the work in British Columbia has also made difficulties that are less felt elsewhere.

In general, it can be said that the militant nature of the province's labour organizations has been vindicated by establishment of the highest wage scales, shortest working hours and most advanced "fringe benefits" in the country. Unless these things were available they could not have been realized and they were available chiefly because of the quality of the natural resources – big timber, abundant fish, easily worked mines. There has been a great deal of "cream skimming" and both labour and capital have benefited. It is obvious that both wages and profits – and neither one can be taken without the other – must affect prices and from time to time British Columbia has priced herself out of the export markets on which she depends. In the future, with increasing world competition and natural resources with steadily less cream for the skimming, this is a problem to which both capital

DAVID DOUGLAS, 1798 - 1834, was another Scottish botanist who visited British Columbia in 1825 as a collector for the Royal Horticultural Society. He travelled overland to the East, and collected throughout the interior of the Province as well as along the coast, but he is primarily famous as the man who discovered and gave his name to the Douglas Fir, or Douglas Spruce as it is also known since it is not a true fir.

and labour will have to apply themselves with a considerably more mature approach than has so far been the case.

It can safely be said that the struggle between labour and capital in British Columbia is no longer a mismatch, an emotion-stirring affair of David and Goliath or the little guy against the big guy. Labour is powerful, well-informed and well-supported, with significant if still inadequate financial resources. Capital has organized itself accordingly, with strong public relations, well fostered political connections and the ability to deal on an industry-wide basis. Most negotiations start out amicably and are settled constructively, but too many still end in major dispute. The public finds itself looking on, usually with a sense of frustration and helplessness, while the giants fight, each claiming that it represents the public interest, though in many instances the general welfare is severely mauled.

To-day's disputes are no longer about equitable wages or adequate working conditions, though these are the matters put forward. The disputes are about profit sharing, the three-way split between labour, management and investment capital, and the sooner this is recognized the better it will be for all concerned. The diffi-

culties are large because this point is not recognized and because both sides, following their ancient traditions, propagandize, distort and obscure facts to the advantage of their own causes. Too often starting out in attitudes of hostility and hard
bargaining they are soon forced into uncompromising positions that make fuel for
later disputes. If the public interest is served at all by this sort of negotiation, it
can only be in the clumsiest sort of way.

The issues are difficult, only less difficult perhaps than those of international
human relationships, but they are not insuperable. Investment capital is entitled to
its return, commensurate with current money values and with risk, which is also
a changing factor. Money is needed for reasonable depreciation and for plant expansion – matters of no less importance to labour than to management, though the
second is a matter of judgment and by far the more difficult. Management is entitled to its return and a good one because it constantly accepts responsibilities
from which labour often tends to withdraw – the necessary learning of skills, long
hours of work, a dedication to production and realistic recognition of the exigencies
of foreign and domestic competition. These things are the realities of doing business, not figments of capitalist imagination, though some of the values assigned to
them may be. Accurately evaluated, they are just as important to labour as to management, though labour cannot be expected to recognize this without being given
far better means of assessing them. If this could be assured, the possibility of labour
participation in many management decisions should no longer be as remote as it
seems to-day.

Similarly, the real interests of labour are identical with those of management.
The closed plant, whether by lock-out or by strike, is to no one's advantage and
plants are going to be closing periodically just as long as there is no better basis for
negotiation than at present.

The health and well-being of the country as a whole directly reflects the health
and well-being of the labour force, and unless labour is receiving the largest share
of the gross income that can be realistically provided for it, it is not likely to be
either efficient or satisfied. It has been pointed out that the word "profits" is given
an evil connotation by many British Columbians. If this is so, it is because profits
have often been excessive and have too often been made out of the sheer quality of
natural resources available rather than through the skill of management or the
venturesome nature of capital, and the public is aware of this. There must be rewards sufficient to attract capital; there must be sufficient incentive to attract the
best minds and skills into the heavy responsibilities of management; expansion
may or may not be desirable, but if it is desirable it should be just as desirable and
just as rewarding to labour as to capital.

It is not suggested that profit-sharing is a magical solution to all labour problems, or that it would not create difficult problems of its own. But it is unquestionably the next step in labour-management relations, and its acceptance now would
put most problems in proper proportion, instead of leaving them to the distortions

and misrepresentations of both sides. It would bring out into the open many things that are now obscured and give the public a chance to make far more accurate judgments on matters that directly concern it – as all industry-wide disputes inevitably do. Most important of all, it would force both sides to reveal and examine real issues in realistic terms and so should lead to more predictable and more mature decisions and develop a clear pattern in every industry for future decisions.

The problems of seasonal employment have always been a factor in the lives of British Columbians. The early settlers solved them largely by means of the part-time farm, working when they could to raise cash for building, land clearing and the purchase of stock, developing their lands when other work was not available. Many workers shifted employment, from logging to fishing or mining or agriculture or trapping as opportunity offered. Both subsistence hunting and subsistence fishing were widely practised. Under modern conditions these things are not so easily done, nor are they so desirable as formerly. The modern worker has higher demands and is less adaptable. He is likely to be city-oriented and expects the stability of his employment to approach factory standards. This is reasonable and on the whole desirable, even though it probably represents some loss of individuality and independence. An economy based on instalment buying and heavy household expenditures makes little allowance for seasonal lay-offs, or for individuality and independence.

Logging operations are limited by heavy snows in winter and fire hazard in summer; they probably always will be. Fishing periods are controlled by the movements and seasonal quality of the fish involved, to an increasing extent by necessary conservation closures and to some extent by weather. Both mining and construction operations may be slowed or stopped by extremes of winter climate. Many forms of agricultural employment are seasonal.

Unemployment insurance is only a superficial and largely negative answer to these problems. Intelligent budgeting by individual families also has its place and has, of course, been successfully used by provident people from time immemorial; but this also is negative and little encouraged in a modern economy. The fishing industry offers at least some opportunity for seasonal adjustments which have always been used by some of the more skilful fishermen. The salmon season is the time of maximum operation, but salmon trollers and gill-netters can and do turn to cod fishing; seiners may be used effectively in the herring and halibut fisheries and even for ground-fish. Some modern boats are so constructed as to be readily convertible to almost any type of fishing. But at best these alternatives cannot as yet take care of all the salmon fleet nor of all those needed to harvest and process the peak of the salmon runs.

Seasonal difficulties of this kind are still further complicated by the province's dependence on world markets for sale of most of its primary products. Neither the province nor the nation plays a large enough part in such markets to be a controlling factor, so market fluctuations may be just as drastic in their effects on employ-

CAPTAIN EDWARD STAMP, D. 1872, was an English ship-master who first visited British Columbia in 1856 as a timber commission agent. He anticipated the lumbering potential of the Province's forests and returned in 1860 to set up B.C.'s first sawmill at what is now Port Alberni. Much of the lumber produced here was exported to China, Australia, New Zealand, South America and the Sandwich Islands. It is interesting that it was in this mill, some time later, that H. R. MacMillan, who was to become famous as a world-wide exporter of B.C. lumber, gained his first sawmill experience as salesman and assistant general manager. In 1865 Stamp established the Hastings mill, which became the nucleus of what is now Vancouver. It was one of the best-known mills in the Province and contributed in a large degree to the establishment of lumbering as an industry.

ment and even less predictable than the seasons themselves.

Some concerted approach to these problems by labour, industry and government is plainly needed in British Columbia, and more needed here than elsewhere. Some dovetailing of occupations is possible and some is practised, though a concerted effort and a sharper recognition of the problem would probably produce more useful results. Unemployment insurance can play a useful minor part, but only if the worker understands its purpose and uses it in good faith, which has not always been the case. Positive resource-management projects, initiated by both government and industry, could also be used to good effect and may well play a large part as more intensive use of resources develops. But it must be recognized that these possibilities do not contribute directly and immediately to available wealth and would have to be paid for largely through wealth realized in the productive seasons. In other words such efforts would mean a reduction in the seasonal returns to labour, capital and government, though the returns through a whole year would not be reduced and the returns of future years should be increased.

GEORGE MERCER DAWSON, 1849 - 1901, was the Director of the Geological Survey of Canada, but it is his own geological reports that make him important in British Columbia. This knowledge, labouriously collected many years ago under the physical disability of a hunched back, is still the main source of information on the basic geology of the Province. Dawson City, the centre of the 1898 Klondyke gold rush in the Yukon, is named after him.

These are not new thoughts, nor do they offer any complete solution to problems of seasonal unemployment and fluctuating world markets. But they deserve far more serious consideration than they have been given to date and a more co-operative approach by all sides.

The progressive shift of the labour force from primary industry to the manufacturing and service industries will tend to reduce and obscure the effects of seasonal unemployment in the province as a whole and should also make resource management and rehabilitation projects financially more practicable. But so long as seasonal unemployment exists at all, its impact upon individuals and individual families under modern conditions will always be serious. To some limited extent this is recognized by daily-wage scales in the primary industries, but more generous recognition is necessary and should become possible as technological progress continues, if it is not already. It will be of value only if the individual worker understands its purpose, that of providing for seasonal lay-offs, and contributes his share by producing effectively and budgeting intelligently.

CHAPTER 27 *resources – the end product*

THE END PRODUCT of resource use is or should be human happiness – which philosophers have long noted is a relative state. At some stage in the history of human development it is possible that a full belly and a warm place to sleep amounted to happiness. If so, it was a long while ago. Man needs food and shelter and clothing; once these needs are satisfied he turns to other things – religion, art, literature, procreation, sport, alcohol, drugs, charity, material wealth, their range is almost infinite – in search of satisfaction. The degrees of success are as varied as the means of search, but the aim is always much the same; to find happiness man must attain some measure of self-realization.

Any definition of self-realization is almost as elusive as a definition of happiness. It is one thing for the introvert, quite another for the extrovert; it may be in the self-immolation of a martyr or in the self-aggrandizement of a Napoleon. It is more likely to be in things spiritual and mental than in things physical and material. The only rule for legislators and planners is that men must be left free to search for it, so long as their freedom does not impede the search of others. Beyond this the only aids they can be given are education and upbringing, and abundant scope for search when the time comes. If a society does not direct the use of its resources to these ends, it cannot be using or serving the key resource, its people, as it should.

Though the distribution of economic rewards is still far from perfect under any social system, enough has been achieved to show clearly that even perfect distribution would not solve the problems of human happiness. Universal literacy, full employment, improved public health and long-term security are all desirable, in fact essential, objectives; but while these things may alleviate unhappiness, they do not reach very far into questions of positive happiness. Self-realization is not found in conformity or uniformity.

Perhaps there is some measure of how British Columbia is using its resources in the fact that the province has the highest drug-addiction rate in Canada and the highest rate of alcohol consumption. It has about 430 mental patients for every hundred thousand of population compared to the national average of just under 400, and 90-95 divorces per hundred thousand of population compared to the national average of 35. These figures argue a very high incidence of unhappiness in a province where wages and living standards are at least as high as those to be found anywhere in the country and very considerably higher than the national average.

Probably the commonest means of self-realization has been in the achievement of a satisfactory working life. Men and women have always taken pride and found satisfaction in the work of their hands and minds and in the recognition of this performance by themselves and their fellows. Generally these satisfactions have been incidental to needed production or to some form of human advancement, and self-realization has been the more complete in the sense of being necessary to others.

Under modern conditions of mass production there is comparatively little scope for craftsmanship or other satisfactions of skilled performance. The U.S.S.R. has attempted to compensate for this by such artificial means as setting work norms and providing special recognitions for high production, though it seems doubtful that these have achieved their purpose any more effectively than the piece-work of capitalist countries. A very large proportion of to-day's work, especially under factory conditions, does not provide the challenge or scope required for high satisfaction, and working hours tend less and less to fill men's lives. Paradoxically, it is also true that a modern economy has a very large number of jobs, in research, management, the arts, social services and various aspects of the human sciences, and even in the operation of some of the more complex machines, for which human beings of adequate training and ability simply are not available in sufficient numbers. So long as work of this sort, calling for constructive and creative thinking, is not carried on at the highest level of performance, the achievement of the whole society is impaired.

The answer to both problems would seem to be in education. The need of the man or woman who must fill the unsatisfying job is scope for fulfilment outside the job; this is most likely to come through power of appreciation, the ability to understand and enjoy and take part in the manifold forms of living and recreation and entertainment that are available or could be made available or would be created by a properly educated and developed people. Only education in the best sense, by instructors who are themselves well-informed and well-rounded people, is likely to develop this power of appreciation, which means the power to use and enjoy life.

If the more demanding jobs are to be filled by people who will accept the full measure of responsibility they impose and make the most of them, education must reach and search much more thoroughly into the whole population than it now does. It must offer much more to those who are able to make use of it. It must expect to influence and develop character as well as to provide learning.

Universal education is a fairly new development, but it has been carried far enough to establish two things: that universal literacy, in the most limited sense of that word, can be achieved, and that human beings do not make equal use of equal educational opportunity – a very large number fail because they lack mental ability and a smaller but extremely important number fail because they lack necessary character and discipline or because the opportunity is not well geared to their needs. Of the two failures, the second is more significant and costly to society.

Education in British Columbia is a provincial responsibility. The system is highly organized, quite firmly stereotyped and probably at least as successful as most other public education systems in North America. It has the weakness of all large systems in that it tends to disregard the individual, both pupil and teacher, in concern for itself. While it does many things well, it has not yet reconciled the ideal of universal education with the real needs of the individuals who make up a modern democratic society. To say that universal education has failed or is failing, in British Columbia or elsewhere on the continent, would be wrong; but it is true that it has not yet proved an inspiring success.

Most criticisms of North American education emphasize its permissiveness, its diffuse nature and its ready acceptance of mediocre standards. The remedies usually suggested are better teaching, an improved and far more intensive curriculum, more exacting standards of work both at home and in the classroom, and early separation of talented pupils. All of these things are desirable and necessary in British Columbia as elsewhere, but they would not of themselves solve the problems of universal education, nor are they likely to be achieved without radical thinking and radical changes of attitude.

Improved salaries in the province are unquestionably attracting more able teachers, but little has yet been done to assist the education of teachers. Far too many are left to struggle towards a university degree through year after year of summer school at severe cost to themselves and, too often, to their pupils. Teachers themselves are inclined to place too much emphasis on the mechanics of teaching rather than upon a richness of knowledge from which to teach, and the system tends to encourage this by providing a five-year educational course and by insisting that teachers be able to handle a multiplicity of subjects instead of specializing. No teacher can be expected to teach English, science, mathematics, history and languages with equal facility at high school level or, what is even more important, with equal powers of inspiration. It seems at least possible that a standard four-year degree, followed by no more than one year of specialized training, might produce better-rounded and better-developed teachers; and that encouragement of a good measure of specialization, by recognizing the interests and the aptitudes of the teachers themselves, should make for better teaching in high schools.

Another possibility that would bear close examination is that of giving far greater academic authority to school principals. It is true that central control of the curriculum ensures uniform standards, but there is a danger that it may also stifle creative endeavour and slow development to a pedestrian pace. While some sort of province-wide standards are essential, these could be maintained by regular government examinations calculated to test standards without rigidly governing the curriculum. It is important to give the fullest possible scope to originality and individuality in teaching, because strong principals and learned teachers can do more than anything else to stimulate intellectual curiosity and the powers of appreciation that are so desperately needed in a modern democratic society.

If people are considered the greatest and most valuable resource of the province, it follows that the greatest loss the province can suffer is in those who do not realize their full capacity. In Canada as a whole, one-third of the students leaves school before completing Grade 8, two-thirds before completing Grade 12, and only one-tenth goes on to university. While some of these "drop-outs" are caused by proportionately limited mentality, a great many are not. Children leave school because they are bored, because they are socially or academically unsuccessful, because they do not understand their duty to themselves or the community and, above all, because of the anti-intellectual climate that pervades not only British Columbia, but the whole of North America.

There is no single or simple solution. Better teaching, better school leadership and an improved curriculum will help. It goes without saying that outstanding students should be encouraged by more numerous scholarships, not merely at university level, but in the last two years of high school. But the outstanding student does not necessarily make the most valuable citizen; it is just as necessary to encourage the competent student and it is urgently important to find ways of holding and developing the incompetent student who has the mental capacity to complete high school or university.

In some cases it may be a real hardship for a family to keep a child in school when he could be out earning wages. It should not be difficult to find such cases and offer at least a measure of assistance and encouragement. Another possibility is to make provision for a wage-earning period, followed by easy resumption of whole-time education; a provision of this sort should benefit especially those children who drop out of school of their own accord and later regret it, and it would have the very real advantage of bringing back students who know not only that they want to learn, but what they want to learn and why they want to learn it. The principle of education or training divided by a period of practical work is one that has application at many stages and in most forms of education, and its possibilities should be much more closely examined than they have been, in spite of the obvious practical difficulties.

Co-education is often criticized for its distracting effects, for the false values it encourages and even as a financial burden on parents. It may have a more fundamental disadvantage than any of these. It is well known that girls develop earlier than boys, are more easily disciplined and apply themselves better to what is expected of them. Until very recently nearly all human societies have recognized this point and educated the two sexes separately and in somewhat different ways. When boys and girls enter the same classrooms at the same chronological age, the girls on the whole do much better than the boys and many boys become discouraged. It is all too easy for them to accept this and settle back into the comforting idea that learning is an effeminate occupation – an idea readily reinforced by the anti-intellectual level of so many influences around them. The inequality commonly persists right through school and levels off only at the university. But in the meanwhile it may have been a factor in causing a good many boys with the mental capacity for university training to drop out of school and find jobs. The point is by no means an easy one to assess and the co-educational system is so deeply entrenched that any change would be difficult and painful. But it is the sort of point that calls for examination and assessment in any radical approach to educational problems.

Many British Columbia schools are attempting to reduce anti-intellectualism not only by separating the more talented pupils and speeding their progress, but by establishing scholarship clubs and honour rolls for students who maintain high levels. Any effort of this kind is valuable, but possibly the greatest effect would be given by a measure of state recognition; this should be extended in some degree to competent students as well as brilliant ones and should emphasize the point that the individual owes the duty of satisfactory performance not merely to himself but to his fellow citizens.*

Education cannot and does not by itself make people of high quality in six hours a day for two-thirds of a year at a time. School is only a small part of character training, a supplement to the influence of home and family. If the family fails, education usually fails too and the cycle of failure is nicely set up for the next generation. If the divorce rate is any indication, family life in British Columbia is considerably less satisfactory than the Canadian average, and there are other reasons to believe that this is so. A modern frontier civilization is hard on families and even harder on children. Roots and stability are the prime factors in family life and among the prime needs of children; they are also important bases of happiness for most people, strong factors in the process of self-realization. Boom towns and grand-scale construction projects and the uncertainties of seasonal labour all work strongly against them, yet most British Columbians have been taught to be wholeheartedly in favour of the first two of these, if not the third.

It was pointed out at the 11th Resources Conference that development of resources can be too rapid and that, if this is permitted, a fluctuating economy of "boom and bust" is inevitable. In British Columbia this type of economy is not only permitted, it is encouraged. No government to date has shown concern about it, much less dared to suggest control. Yet there is no more cruel or evil thing for the welfare of a small community and the families that compose it than a really

---

*The Chant Commission Report, a detailed study of education in the province, was released in late December of 1960. It contains many recommendations for strengthening the system, some of which are likely to be implemented at an early date.

large construction project – except two or more such projects in operation at the same time. Services are strained far beyond capacity; values, both material and spiritual, are distorted and destroyed; more often than not a whole school-genera-tion of children is disturbed and harmed. Even when the tidal wave of destruction has passed, the settling-back period has to be faced and the immediate effects will be felt for another four or five years.

Construction projects have to be undertaken and completed. But any intelligent observer must wonder whether they need produce a frenzied orgy of waste and mis-spending and wholesale disorganization of community life. If the calamity of mul-tiple projects threatens a community, surely it is common sense to stagger them so as to confer maximum benefit and a minimum of disturbance. It is against provin-cial tradition to raise such questions as these, but it is time they were raised and thought given to them.

This is not to suggest that it is impossible to make a successful family life while following construction work. Many families do exactly this, by accepting and estab-lishing movement as normal and by setting up the necessary protections against the distorted values and other effects of boom conditions. It is the fringe families and the weaker community families that suffer chiefly, though all community families and services are affected in some degree. During the construction boom of the early fifties practically the whole social organization of the province was affected ad-versely and the effects will be felt for a very long while to come. Since any sudden and excessive influx of capital projects is inevitably followed by a period of let-down and unemployment and since capital cannot be permanently discouraged from sound investment in resources, the logic of controlling and staggering such projects is absolutely clear. The benefit to the future health and welfare of the people of the province, and so to their over-all happiness, would be incalculable.

Any family failure is costly to the state not only in its immediate effects, but in its future yield of inadequate citizens. Whether such failures are more numerous to-day or simply better observed and identified than they were some years ago is difficult to say. Certainly they are very frequent in British Columbia, far more fre-quent than divorce statistics suggest, because divorce is so costly and difficult that many people arrange or disarrange their affairs without it. The incidence and effect of family failure in the province is also a point for intensive research and intelli-gent thinking, though it is already evident that considerable strengthening of social services is overdue.

British Columbia's criminal statistics certainly reflect in some degree the insta-bility of families. Convictions for indictable offences consistently run well above the national average by population; in 1957 the rate per ten thousand of popula-tion was 45 in B.C. against a national average of 33. In the same year Alberta and Manitoba closely matched B.C. with 45 and 44 respectively but the fourth western province, Saskatchewan, had a figure of only 23. Rates for the industrialized prov-inces of Quebec and Ontario were 26 and 33. How much comparative significance should be given to these figures is doubtful, but it is worth noting that three of the four western "frontier" states have the highest figures in the nation while the fourth, Saskatchewan, has the lowest rate of any province except Prince Edward Island. Saskatchewan is generally considered poorer in natural resources than the other western provinces and has undergone less rapid development. It also has advanced social legislation.

British Columbia has made some important recent advances in penology and is strongly emphasizing the use of probation for both adult and juvenile offenders, though there has not yet been time for the probation service itself or its necessary auxiliary services to be built up to proper strength. There is no doubt that Canadian practice in the past has placed far too much reliance on imprisonment as a cure or control for criminal offences; more generous legislation and wider use of probation and other rehabilitative measures could well make an important difference.

Rehabilitation, whether of mental patients, retarded children, disturbed families, alcoholics, drug addicts, criminals or even the difficult minority groups like the Sons of Freedom Doukhobors, is the most interesting and disturbing test that can be found for any society. It has been well said that the surest measure of a civilization is in how well it cares for its weak and underprivileged members. Rehabilitation is slow, difficult and often disappointing in its results. It is costly in the short view, it calls for highly trained and dedicated personnel and it is quite unspectacular in its immediate effects; at best it can rarely hope to do more than return to society a citizen of low-average performance and quality. The machinery of rehabilitation must always be limited in some degree by regard for the liberty of the individual citizen.

But rehabilitation work is both positive and humane; nothing else, in the light of modern knowledge, can discharge the obligation of a modern society to care for its weak and underprivileged; and in the long run it is a paying proposition, in fact it may mean the difference between a declining society and a healthy one, between a balance of happiness or a balance of unhappiness.

British Columbians are not yet wholly convinced of the sort of values that are found in rehabilitation. There is so much to be done, so much to be spent in time and money on roads and railroads and power projects, on wharves and ferries and bridges and all the obvious forms of "progress" that little seems to be left for the hard and unspectacular work of rehabilitation. Yet there is no doubt that British Columbians individually are humane and sympathetic, perhaps more so than the average of people. It is only that they have not yet had time to understand the full possibilities of rehabilitation or its rightful place in the development of the province.

The present is not an easy stage at which to assess the people of British Columbia. It is an awkward stage, between that of a true frontier state and the later organization that reveals a people's real genius. A pioneer society denies itself much, finding its happiness largely in physical achievement and hope for the future. In compensation for the denial, its descendants become opportunist, pragmatic and materialistic, not quite knowing what to search for beyond material things. They find comfort and sometimes wealth and even shadows of happiness within a narrow frame. But man cannot stop there and be happy. What he needs are the "frills" the pioneers denied themselves and their descendants despised – the excitements of vision and abstract thought and self-recognition.

British Columbia has passed through the first stage and is struggling out of the second into a world whose values were never less certain. The pace of change under modern technology is so great that few material values are stable. The pressures of international disturbances and readjustments are constant and increasingly urgent. Ever since Lord Grey, the Colonial Secretary, warned James Douglas in the 1850's that undeveloped territory invites encroachment, fear of encroachment has influenced the affairs of the province in greater or less degree. It is in different form to-day, under the protection of established nationhood, but it still has its effect.

Can any people be free to develop its land and its resources in an ideal pattern of service and use and perpetual yield? Can it make an honest and proportionate contribution, not merely to its own people but to all humanity if it insists on doing so? And even if all these conditions are fulfilled to the last letter, will not some more aggressive conception, backed by force of arms and the drive of misery, come in to take possession and destroy?

One answer is clear. No people has a right to act against its knowledge and damage or destroy the face of the earth for short-term gain. Such a course must always do injury not merely to the people immediately involved, but to all peoples. The rest is not so clear. The eventual outcome is hidden in a maze of philosophical, political and economic questions whose answers will be the true testing of the quality of British Columbians and Canadians. If there is no answer but force or defence against force, the civilization will have failed, like others before it.

I have suggested that British Columbians are uncertain and often unhappy in spite of a degree of wealth and security that few peoples anywhere have known. To some extent this may be of their nature, in the selection of immigration and the conditioning of a new country. To a much greater extent it grows from political and social immaturity and the lack of common purpose, high vision and the sense of identity that comes from these things.

The grounds for optimism are broad and should be inspiring. From its earliest times the province has grown under a rule of law; the tradition of respect for the principles of law that must be the foundation of any healthy society is strong. Within the rule of law, the rebellious and dissatisfied spirit that turned people to a remote new place has proved itself both in the development of resources and in the resolute struggle to win a fair distribution of their yield; this in turn gives promise that a spring of radical thinking, forceful enough to break through into wholly new channels, is firmly in the people, needing only the release and stimulation of education and the direction that vision can give.

It is a good time for all this. There is a climate of question, a searching for intent and purpose, in the province itself, in the nation and throughout the world. In the province it is evident in the slightly precocious, still awkward development of the arts. It is stated in the growth of the great university at Point Grey, in Vancouver's courageous International Festival of the Arts, in the concern to uncover and protect details of the province's brief history and, not least, in the Natural Resources Conference itself, now thirteen years old and still not afraid to question its purpose, its effectiveness and its terms of reference. None of these things stands by itself; together they make a pattern of emergence into that third stage of civilization where mental and spiritual achievement takes precedence over things physical and practical.

Behind these signs of growth within the province is the stimulation of Canada's own increasing maturity, the slow development of a Canadian vision and ideal, and the sense of identity with it that is fostered by improving communications and solidified by outside pressures.

The provincialism of a British Columbian is no more than a part of his Canadianism and the well-worn political trick of trying to divide Ottawa from the rest of the country now rates nothing more than good-natured laughter. That British Columbians feel a love of their province and a possessive pride in it should be the best assurance that they will use it honourably and to good purpose.

bibliography

THIS BIBLIOGRAPHY is in no sense an attempt at full documentation. Its purpose is rather to suggest a few possibilities of further reading in the subjects discussed within the chapters.

CHAPTER 1

HOWAY, F. W., and SCHOLEFIELD, E. O. S., *British Columbia, from the Earliest Times to the Present.* 4 vols. Vancouver, B.C., 1914.
HOWAY, F. W., *The Early History of the Fraser River Mines.* Victoria, B.C., 1926.
ORMSBY, MARGARET A., *British Columbia, A History.* Toronto, 1958.
The British Columbia Historical Quarterly.

CHAPTER 2

OSBORN, FAIRFIELD, *Our Plundered Planet.* Boston, 1948.
STORER, JOHN H., *The Web of Life.* New York, 1954.

CHAPTER 3

STOCKWELL, C. H. (Editor), *Geology and Economic Minerals of Canada.* Ottawa, 1937.
The British Columbia Atlas of Resources. Vancouver, 1956.

CHAPTER 4

B.C. Natural Resources *Transactions,* Vol. IX, pp. 83-116. 1956.
The British Columbia Atlas of Resources.

CHAPTER 5

COLLIS, J. S., *The Moving Waters.* New York, 1955.
KIMBLE, GEORGE, and BUSH, RAYMOND, *The Weather.* New York, 1946.
PERSON, H. S., *Little Waters.* Washington, D.C., 1935.

CHAPTERS 6, 7, 8

ANDREWS, R. W., and KINSEY, D., *This Was Logging!* Seattle, 1954.
Continuous Forest Inventory of British Columbia. Victoria, B.C., 1957-1958 etc.
MULHOLLAND, F. D., *The Forest Resources of British Columbia.* Victoria, 1937.
Royal Commision *Report* on Timber and Forestry, 1909-10. Victoria, 1910.
SLOAN, HON. G. MCG., *Forest Resources of British Columbia.*

CHAPTERS 9, 10

B.C. Resources Conference *Transactions,* Vol. XI, pp. 131-9. 1958.

B.C. Resources Conference *Transactions*, Vol. IX, pp. 243-63. 1956.

HOLLIDAY, CHARLES W., *The Valley of Youth*. Caldwell, Idaho, 1948.

CHAPTER 11

Borden Royal Commission on Energy, *Report*. Ottawa, 1958.

DAVIS, JOHN, *Canadian Energy Prospects*. Royal Commission on Canada's Economic Prospects. Ottawa, 1957.

KOLDE, EDEL J., *Energy Base of the Pacific Northwest Economy*. University of Washington Press, 1954.

TEITELBAUM, P. D., *Nuclear Energy and the United States Fuel Economy 1955-80*.

THIRRING, HANS, *Energy for Man*. Indiana University Press, Bloomington, 1958.

CHAPTER 12

Fraser River Board, *Preliminary Report on Flood Control and Hydro-Electric Power in the Fraser River Basin*. Victoria, 1958.

KRUTILLA, JOHN V., *Sequence and Timing in River Basin Development, with special application to Canadian-United States Columbia River Basin planning*. Resources for the Future Inc., 1960.

KRUTILLA, J. V., and ECKSTEIN, O., *Multiple Purpose River Development*. Johns Hopkins Press, 1958.

United Nations, *Multiple Purpose River Basin Development*. New York, 1955.

CHAPTER 13

MIROLUIBOV, A. V., and ROKOTIAN, S. S., *Economic Characteristics of Long Distance Electrical Transmission in the U.S.S.R.* World Power Conference, Montreal, 1958.

PIERCE, R. E., and GEORGE, E. E., *Economics of Long Distance Transport of Energy*, Trans. A.I.E.E., Vol. 67, pp. 1089-94.

SPORN, PHILLIP, *Integrated Power System as the Basic Mechanism for Power Supply*. New York, 1950.

CHAPTER 14

B.C. Natural Resources *Transactions*, Vol. IX, pp. 131-88. 1956.

CLEMENS, W. A., and WILBY, G. V., *Fishes of the Pacific Coast of Canada*, Fish. Res. Board Bulletin LXVIII. Ottawa, 1946.

QUAYLE, D. B., *Edible Molluscs of British Columbia*. B.C. Fisheries Dept., 1941.

CHAPTER 15

COBB, JOHN N., *Pacific Salmon Fisheries*, U.S. Bureau of Fisheries Document 1092. Washington, 1930.

HAIG-BROWN, RODERICK, *Canada's Pacific Salmon*, Dept. of Fisheries. Ottawa, 1952.

CHAPTER 16

Summaries of Research on the Fish-Power Problem and Related Work, Dept. of Fisheries, Canada. Vancouver, B.C., 1960.

The Canadian Fish Culturist, Issue 27. August, 1960.

CHAPTERS 17, 18

B.C. Resources Conference *Transactions*, Vol. IX, pp. 383-427. 1956.

B.C. Resources Conference *Transactions*, Vol. VI, pp. 80-9. 1953.

GOSNELL, R. E., *Year Book of British Columbia*. Victoria, 1903.

STOCKWELL, C. H., *Geology and Economic Minerals of Canada*, Dept. of Mines and Technical Survey. Ottawa, 1957.

CHAPTERS 19, 20

B.C. Resources Conference *Transactions*, Vol. IX, pp. 297-381. 1956.

CLAWSON, MARION, *Statistics on Outdoor Recreation*, Resources for the Future Inc., 1958.

Department of Recreation and Conservation, *Annual Reports*.

LYONS, C. P., *Trees, Shrubs and Flowers to Know in British Columbia*. Vancouver, 1952.

LYONS, C. P., *Milestones on the Mighty Fraser*. Vancouver, 1956.

LYONS, C. P., *Milestones in Ogopogo Land*. Vancouver, 1957.

CHAPTER 21

COWAN, I. MCT., and GUIGET, C. J., *The Mammals of British Columbia*. B.C. Provincial Museum Handbook No. 11, 1956.

GABRIELSON, IRA N., *Wildlife Conservation.* New York, 1941.

KORTRIGHT, FRANCES H., *Ducks, Geese and Swans of North America.* American Wildlife Institute, Washington, 1943.

LEOPOLD, ALDO, *Game Management.* New York, 1948.

MUNRO, J. A., and COWAN, I. MCT., *Bird Fauna of British Columbia.* B.C. Provincial Museum, 1947.

TAVERNER, P. A., *Birds of Western Canada.* Museum Bulletin No. 41, Ottawa, 1926.

TAYLOR, WALTER (ed.), *Deer of North America.* Wildlife Management Inst., Washington, D.C.

CHAPTER 22

CARL, G. C., CLEMENS, W. A., and LINDSEY, C. C., *The Freshwater Fishes of British Columbia.* B.C. Provincial Museum Handbook No. 5, 1959.

DYMOND, J. R., *Trout and Other Game Fishes of British Columbia.* Ottawa, 1932.

HAIG-BROWN, RODERICK, *Western Angler.* New York, 1947.

WHITEHOUSE, F. C., *Sportfishes of Western Canada.* Vancouver, 1946.

CHAPTER 23

B.C. Resources Conference *Transactions,* Vol. VI, pp. 161-212. 1953.

BERRY, T. V., "Pollution Control in the Lower Mainland Communities of British Columbia." *Engineering Journal,* June, 1960.

CHAPTER 24

B.C. Resources Conference *Transactions,* Vol. XI, pp. 241-82. 1958.

Minutes, Alaska - Yukon - British Columbia Conference. 1960.

WADE, M. S., *Overlanders of '62.* Archives Memoir No. IX, Victoria, 1931.

CHAPTER 25

DRUCKER, PHILIP, *Indians of the Northwest Coast.* Washington, 1959.

FARMER, EDWARD M., *Native Arts of the Pacific Northwest.* Stanford U. Press, 1949.

HAWTHORN, H. B., BELSHAW, C. S., and JAMIESON, S. M., *The Indians of British Columbia.* University of British Columbia, 1958.

CHAPTER 26

B.C. Resources Conference *Transactions,* Vol. IX, pp. 17-81. 1956.

HAWTHORN, H. B. (ed.), *The Doukhobors of British Columbia.* U. of B.C., 1955.

CHAPTER 27

Report of the British Columbia Centennial Committee. Vancouver, 1959.

WATTERS, R. E., *British Columbia: A Centennial Anthology.* Toronto, 1958.

index